ENTERTA   OLOGY PRESS

In taking advan: .... digital printing techniques, Ente ...... ress is approaching book publishing in a very ...... y establishing a wide range of highly specific technical b..... .nat can be kept up-t date in a continuing publishing process, our plan is to cover the entertainment technology sector with a wide range of individual titles.

As will be seen by examining the back cover of this book, the ETP list is divided into various categories so as to allow sufficient room for generic growth and development of each title. To ensure the quality of the books and the success of the project the publishers are building up a team of authors who are practising in and well-respected by the industry. As specialists within a particular field of activity it is anticipated that each author will stay closely involved with 'their' title or titles for an extended period.

All Entertainment Technology Press titles have a dedicated area on the publisher's own website at www.etnow.com where latest information and up-dates can be accessed by purchasers of the books concerned. This additional service is included within the purchase price of all titles.

Readers and prospective authors are invited to submit any ideas and comments they may have on the Entertainment Technology Press series to the Series Editor by email to editor@etnow.com.

Entertainment Technology Press Ltd
The Stud High Green, Great Shelford, Cambridge CB2 5EG
Tel: 50806

LET THERE BE LIGHT

ENTERTAINMENT LIGHTING SOFTWARE PIONEERS IN CONVERSATION

Robert Bell

ENTERTAINMENT TECHNOLOGY PRESS

Biographical Series

To my boys Hudson and Rowan

LET THERE BE LIGHT
ENTERTAINMENT LIGHTING SOFTWARE PIONEERS IN CONVERSATION

Robert Bell
Foreword by Richard Pilbrow

Entertainment Technology Press

Let There Be Light
Entertainment Lighting Software Pioneers
in Conversation

© Robert Bell
Foreword ©Richard Pilbrow

First edition Published March 2004 by
Entertainment Technology Press Ltd
The Studio, High Green, Great Shelford, Cambridge, CB2 5EG
Internet: www.etnow.com

ISBN 1 904031 24 2

A title within the
Entertainment Technology Press Biographical Series
Series editor: John Offord

CONTENTS

FOREWORD

God said: "Let there be Light"

To achieve a world of stunning beauty he (or she) has ingeniously spun the stage through space ever since, somewhat aided by the atmosphere . . . and recently by man's own pollution.

On stage we — rather pathetically — waggle our little cones of light, change their distribution and colour and call it The Art of Stage Lighting.

Lighting the stage began with flickering firelight in a cave; centuries of candle and gas evolved into electric light and will continue to evolve using light sources we're not yet aware of.

I lit a show in 1957 with water dimmers (topping them up with a suitable solution could be hazardous!). Bracket handle controls manipulating resistance dimmers or transformers, tracker-wire or grand-master boards emerged in Europe. In the UK they had begun to be overtaken by motor-driven lighting consoles in the 1940's. In the US, the electronic preset board had begun in universities at the same time, but the ubiquitous manual piano boards dominated Broadway until *Chorus Line* in 1975. These early developments were led by a small band of pioneers, such as Frederick Bentham and George Izenour.

Robert Bell's book tells the stories of a new generation of trailblazers: those who are taking us into a new and computerized age - an age of computer-simulated visualization, multitasking timelines and movement manipulation. Where will it all end?

This book will be deeply satisfying to the expert; it contains enough computerese to glaze the mind of a casual reader, yet it also contains many wonderful stories of peoples' struggles to find new paths through fogs of complacency and the status quo. The personal stories are thrilling. Each individual has been through their own fiery place and made their own contribution to our profession. For myself the oft-repeated testament of not knowing what was impossible rings a powerful bell. I never knew I couldn't be a lighting designer, a producer, an author, or an international theatre consultant.

Soon after my foray with water dimmers, I lit a show in a small theatre in a country town in England. The electrician (with his dog named Sam) worked his small resistance bracket handle board on a perch[1] platform offstage right.

---

[1] Small platforms above either side of the stage from which side followspots (limelight) could be operated — often the board operating position.

I was using an unusually high number of channels — forty-eight! Sitting in the stalls (orchestra – US-speak) I called out for channels: "23 @ half, 32 @ full." Minutes later: "Where is 32?" "Half" came back the reply. "No, full," I repeated. This went on for some time. Finally I walked up to the stage, climbed to the perch and saw man and dog looking puzzled. I explained: "When I tell you a dimmer level, I expect it to stay there until I move it." "Sir," he said, "The handles are heavy — gravity you know!" I retreated. Back at the lighting desk I heard on the intercom: "Ah Sam, these people down from London must learn to modify their ideas a little!"

Fred Bentham, for decades technical head of Strand Lighting, pioneered the Light Console and evolved the entire principle of 'playable light'. His control was literally an organ console and he employed banks of keys, stopkeys, ten fingers and both feet[2] to play a light accompaniment to music with a fluidity hardly matched since. The motor-driven dimmer used by the light console added inertia. If a dimmer was not consciously moved in level it stayed where it had been put — gravity not being a factor! The 1940's emergence of electronic dimming added multiple dimmer level presets. Bentham was a man I admired tremendously, yet as an impatient youth, I fought strenuously. The first control system I specified was for the new National Theatre at the Old Vic: a three scene preset. Against Fred's wishes I utilized "inertia": group selection independantly on each preset.

In 1967/68 I lit Tom Stoppard's first play *Rosencrantz and Guildenstern Are Dead* on Broadway, followed by the new musical *Zorba*. It seemed to me about time for a memory control on the Great White Way. With the perhaps surprisingly encouraging support from David Merrick and Hal Prince I went to see Frank deVerna, head of Four Star, the top lighting rental house. He was less enthusiastic and led me into his shop that contained an apparently endless stock of piano boards. He said: "Richard, you own a rental business in London. If you had stocks like this would you allow memory boards into your territory?" It all turned out well — and I did experience my first 'memory' control on Broadway! The show was on six 14-plate 3kW piano boards with a shocking number of auxiliary dimmers. On opening night I went backstage to wish my crew (led by Donny Stern) well. To my surprise there were no 'books' in evidence (the loose leaf binders that contained the plots for each man). As the show had over a hundred cues this worried me. Donny said: "Relax, Richard.

---

[2] We drive vehicles with our feet and hands — why not lighting?

We know the plots by heart!" The whole thing was done by human memory! The advent of the computer brought Strand's fortunes low and led to its takeover by the Rank Organization. In the interim Thorn Lighting emerged with Q-file (designed by Tony Isaacs), built for the British Broadcasting Corporation. A memory system that worked! As a fledgling theatre consultant I had it modified to provide the first UK theatrical memory control using a keypad channel selector and multiple playbacks — no potentiometers!

Then I found myself the new National Theatre consultant for their long dreamt of South Bank home and a once-in-a-lifetime opportunity to design a new control system. Lightboard, as it became known, was designed in 1971-1973 by myself and partner Richard Brett. It combined a keypad and encoder wheel to allow equal access to any channel, cue or *group* of channels. No longer was the individual circuit to be necessarily all-important. A side wing allowed the simultaneous mixing and balancing (highest takes precedent) of any selection of lighting on six encoders and was called the 'Light Palette'. The playback section allowed up to twelve simultaneous fades, with partial moves (increase or decrease of chosen channel intensity) or complete crossfades on a latest takes precedent basis, all either automatically or manually. Monitors provided playback display of channel intensity of all channels or only channels in use; a separate remote wing capable of simultaneous operation for the designer was available (it even recorded the difference between recorded lighting memories and the designer's experimental modifications). A data-highway around the theatre allowed integrated remote control of colour or slide changers and remote control instruments. (In the 70's these were Ludwig Pani pan, tilt and focus 2kW Fresnels!). Finally, there was an effects controller allowing any channel to chase, or have sound to light modulation effects. The two most important principles were that lighting could be very *simply* operated, yet the expert had many other possibilities.

Lightboard, built by Strand led by their then Chief Engineer, Martin Moore, utilised a DEC PDP11 computer — and was expensive! Wally Russell (friend and then head of Rank Strand USA), telephoned me from California. He thought he could achieve a micro-processor control with American attributes. Kindly, he asked if I'd mind him naming it 'Light Palette'. The rest is indeed history.

One of the greatest highs in life is to stand at the production desk creating lighting as rehearsals unfold before you. Maybe skiing or surfing is better, but I doubt it! In those far-off days when only intensity was manipulable, a good memory system allowed 'light-surfing'. However, moving lights, albeit wonderfully liberating, brought a host of troubles. With so many more parameters to handle they were so complex to manipulate and the process took too long — and usually still does today. In my opinion stage time is for actors and performers, not for us lighting folk to endlessly masturbate our lighting (and our egos!).

Lightboard was fast. And I have yet to find for theatre an equivalently liberating control for the moving light era. Because for better — or worse — theatre needs subtlety. I'm envious, admiring and jealous of my compatriots in the music scene. Beautiful stunning images at the speed of light are what Bentham dreamt of fifty years ago. But legitimate theatre — drama, opera, ballet, musicals — is bound up by the needs of subtle change. Yet we can't waste onstage time.

In 1994, a group of friends carried out some experiments. Keny Whitright's Autopilot for 'instant' focusing, Robert Bell's emerging WYSIWYG, Fred Foster's Digitizer Tablet access and Flying Pig's Whole Hog touch screens all led me to a conceit for a future 'Lightboard 2000': an all-digital touch-sensitive working surface, three dimensional, manipulable visualization model, colour-picker straight from Photoshop, multiple timeline . . .

I used Wholehog and WYSIWYG on Broadway's *The Life* for both 'smart' and 'steam' lights together for the first time and, at a guess, saved twenty percent of onstage time. Before the lighting process formally began we focused 40 instruments each to 36 preset positions (for me a normal six to eight hour process) without the lights even turned on — and with only house head electrician and board operator – in twenty minutes.

2004 is here and this book marks the revolution. We seem on the verge of a new paradigm for lighting control. Digits and levers are about to be consigned to the dustbin of history. Lightboard helped break from levers and potentiometers to keypads and encoders; Whole Hog broke that pattern with touch sensitive screens. A number of individuals and manufacturers are exploring a future where the interface between the designer's imagination and the stage is very different. 'Intelligent' lighting today involves complications unimaginable a decade ago. The addition of integrated video light, undreamt of quantities of LED's, etc., will further add ever greater complexity. But the computer is not a dumb slave. Just as it aids the fighter pilot in landing on a carrier at sea, it should aid the designer by putting at his or her finger tips the resource capability when and where it is needed.

I fancy stroking my lighting onto the stage as an artist paints a canvas; yet our pictures are in four dimensions. We must move, colour, manipulate, edit, stretch, foreshorten as the player, our art and imagination demand.

Robert has made an amazing contribution toward the field of lighting. The combination of his design skills, operator dexterity and programming ability have changed our industry. His book brings together the moving stories of so many of his peers and gives us a glimpse of the extraordinary expertise that is needed. These are important stories that bring software and theatre lovingly together. As the book makes clear, other industries might be more lucrative, but none will offer richness, the passion and sheer thrill of a life in theatre.

This book shows ways toward a new future for stage lighting control. Robert is a young man. What surprises will he yet produce?

Richard Pilbrow

PROLOGUE

Thin Ice

From day one of my career I've worn two hats: one as the software designer and one as the end user. Without a doubt, this is the key to successful product design. There are many working environments in which software evolves, but when the person who is actually in charge of the design process is a number-one user, the results are so much more commanding. The other methods, that ultimately provide lesser results, include the design team that constructively consults with end-users and the end-user hack who tries to put together a product without the necessary software or architectural expertise.

When you are sitting at the office working with the engineers on the code, field experience makes your position and arguments much easier to convey. Finding and using real life examples not only makes the thought process flow, but also makes the conclusion much more focused and easier to arrive at. I find that people are not only interested in how it works in 'real life', but they can also connect the dots much faster than me. I just have to sit back and tell my story. It's a combination of having intimate knowledge of the software architecture and expressing the issues in the appropriate context.

Working in the field, where there are no code gurus around and you have a job to do is a completely different story. Everyone

on site is focused on the product, which at the time is the show. No one cares about your silly software; they just want you to produce the results. If I were not involved in product development and just had to light shows, the pressure would be much less. Doing both means you not only have to think about the big picture (the product), but the task at hand - which is the look on stage. As far as the production is concerned, things may be going just fine, but you may be up to your eyeballs in a bug and cannot think past it. Directors and producers have often caught me making notes that have nothing to do with the show, but to me are life or death issues concerning the code.

Unlike sitting in the office, being in the field is a lonely position. And I mean really lonely; you feel abandoned. I've often wanted the code guys right there by my side, compiling code on a laptop. Before the advent of cell phones it was even lonelier. At least now I can call them when I have a spare moment and describe my pain. In the ideal situation, by day's end I have new code and can continue the next day with a clean slate.

I've often described this feeling as "standing on thin ice". You know things are tenuous, but you don't know when, or if, you're going to crash through. One winter day I took my dog Miscou for a walk at the back of our property and found myself feeling this exact sensation. Luckily, I had the forethought to bring a plank of wood as a safety measure for crossing the river, but she didn't, and at the widest part of the water she fell through. Immediately the whole focus of my attention changed. No longer was I thinking of the objective - to get to the other side - but was completely focused on getting her out. I had to shimmy across on my plank, not knowing if a bad situation was about to get worse and was feeling very uncomfortable.

Working with WYSIWYG on site often proved to be helpful, but was never 'do-or-die' as far as the look on stage was concerned. From the software design perspective though, it proved to be much more valuable. I could log more bugs in one day on site than I could with ten days of testing in the office. If I had the dreaded crash through the ice, it was only my concern and never affected the production. If it preoccupied my thoughts to the point of distraction, that was my problem and resulted in me being a bad lighting programmer.

Working on and with control products such as Horizon is a very different story. If I have problems with the desk, it affects everybody, and the last thing I can do, as the product manager, is blame the product. You have to walk this very thin line between what was good for the production and what was good for the product.

Working with Horizon on Lloyd webber's *Starlight Express* with David Hersey offered me one of these invigorating experiences. The re-light of the show came up shortly after I joined Rosco ET and it was going to be Horizon's first West End show usind new beta moving light software. One day during pre-production, David took particular interest in a very specific gobo wash. We spent a good 20 minutes with him and an assistant on stage and myself at the desk, playing and tweaking all the wiggly lights. Just when he gave the focus his final stamp of approval (and feeling very pleased with the result) I went to record the cue and the ice broke beneath me. It wasn't a complete crash, but then again it didn't record the cue properly. The result was all the lights went to open white – 50:50. In hindsight, it was about half operator-error and half software issues, but in any case, it was my problem.

Feeling very ashamed, I had to ask David to re-do the focus from scratch. then, in one of my most abashed moments in theatre, I have to report that I lost the focus for the second time! David just dropped his newspaper and left the theatre for the pub. I sank back in my chair and wondered if my career as a board operator or as a product manager was over. It's amazing what a pint of Guiness can do to calm the nerves.

INTRODUCTION

In an article entitled *Control Issues*[1] Sonny Sonnefeld demonstrates how our industry, while it may be getting fatter, it is actually getting smaller. He lists companies that have forged the growth in lighting control systems since the 1950's (*Ariel Davis, Capital, Cutler Davis, Dilor, Eastern Stage Lighting, Electro Controls, Electronic Designers Inc., Federal Pacific, Frank Adams, Gallagher Dimming & Stage Lighting, General Electric, Hub, Kliegl Brothers, Lighting & Electronics, Lighting Methods Inc., Major Equipment Company, Mega, Metropolitan Electric, Newth, Rainbow, SCR Digitrol, Siltron, Skirpan, Stagebrite, Superior Electric, Theatre Techniques Inc., Trumbull, Van Buren, Vickers, Ward Leonard, West-star, and Westinghouse*). Even though the industry has grown five-fold, all of these companies no longer provide lighting control systems. The North American market is a little tighter than the European market, or even that of Asia, but organizations like PLASA and ESTA and technology like the Internet make it seem like a smaller place. There are still a lot of companies and tonnes of products, but from a historical perspective, if you count the real innovators, you may be surprised to find how small the number really is.

The specialized field of software development for entertainment lighting begins, coincidently enough, at about the same time as the popularization of affordable computer products. An examination of software development for our industry would be futile if you looked much before the mid 1970's. It's exciting to examine this chapter of our industry in light of the fact that it's beginnings were initiated by people that are still working in our day.

It's debatable where it all exactly began. Parallel developments in software solutions were happening in the UK, California and North Carolina and I'm sure other places around the world. Many of us consider the work Richard Pilbrow and Theatre Projects did with Rank Strand Electric on the Lightboard to be the most revolutionary and the first. The Lightboard, designed for the National Theatre and later sold to Covent Garden, Vienna, Berlin, and Hamburg operas, took concepts initiated by hard logic memory desks quite a few steps further by the use of proper data processing. For the first time the concept of 'groups' of lights were introduced allowing the operator to 'paint with light' by putting sections of the lighting rig on proportional controls. Pilbrow also

---

[1] Entertainment Design – December 2003

introduced the concept of simultaneously running cues because "light is, by its nature, the most fluid and ephemeral of substances, shifting and changing subtly or blatantly, slowly or quickly." Wally Russell, running the American division of Strand, was a big fan of these concepts and pushed hard for development of a much less expensive version for the American market. Light Palette, named after one of Lightboard's modules, became the defacto standard in North America as you will read in David Cunningham's interview.

A respected early innovator who is still working today, **Gordon Pearlman** was responsible for the very first digital lighting control desk used on Broadway for *A Chorus Line*. Before founding the firm Entertainment Technology he was responsible for control systems such as the Kliegl Command Performer, Command Performance, the Morpheus Light Commander and the Strand Impact console. At ET, he launched the GAM Access, Horizon and IPS dimming. Gordon, through a now famous USITT meeting, was also pinnacle in formalizing DMX as we know it today.

If you read Gordon's interview, you will see numerous mentions of **David Cunningham**. Gordon admits, that unbeknown to their bosses at the time, David and Gordon would often go out to dinner at trade shows and discuss ideas. David is without a doubt the most prolific, flamboyant and one of the richest men in our industry. It's impossible to work in theatre today and not be influenced by David's products. He's built 25 consoles, including the original Light Palette under Wally Russel's direction. The syntax used there changed the way we think about cueing and is still used on many consoles today. Dave also developed the CD80 dimmers, Colortran dimmers, Sensor dimmers, specified AMX, DMX and designed the Source 4 luminaire line.

Speaking of influence, **John McKernon**, a Broadway icon, has quite likely affected every assistant lighting designer and head electrician in America and to a lesser extent, throughout the world. There are more copies of Lightwright floating around than any other software in our industry. His paper-only method of rig organisation has set the standard for how people communicate to build a lighting system. After 20 odd years of writing software, Lightwright Version 4 is being released and includes some graphical elements for the first time.

Known around the industry as the 'Console Girl', **Anne Valentino** started in the earlier days with Gordon at Kliegl. Hopping from company to company, working mostly as a controls specialist, Anne has left a trail of successes. She has had a hand in a number of Strand's consoles and is responsible for ETC's Obsession and Vari-Lite's Virtuoso. She has astute insight into the language of lighting control and her interview has some very interesting quotables.

Tom Thorne is one of the founding members of Flying Pig Systems and has been the code architect for the entire series of Whole Hog Consoles – the only console to break it big on both Broadway and the touring rock scene. His interview finally puts pen to paper on the famed 'Cross-America' road trip upon which the Flying Pig business plan was formalized and much hilarity was had by all. Sadly, Tom is no longer working in this industry, but he leaves a great legacy.

Mark Hunt is of particular interest as he is one of a rare breed of developers for the Mac platform. He is solely responsible for Light and Sound Design's Icon desk and more recently wrote all the digital signal processing code for the Texas Instrument micro-mirror device that is used on the Icon M light – one of the most highly anticipated piece of kit this decade that unfortunately fell flat. All of that clever code now finds itself in the LDS MBox and joins an ever-increasing number of products that is breaking down the barriers between video and lighting.

While I was at CAST Lighting, **Tom Grimes** thought of himself as my nemesis. He was the one writing the clever micro code that allowed High End System fixtures to do all kinds of wacky things (without a control desk) and I would have to model them in WYSIWYG. Most recently he has kept himself amused writing Palm Pilot software for HES and working on ESTA's RDM protocol, for which he can take a great deal of credit.

Motivated by many of the problems that face us all, **Eric Cornwell** is the one-man shop creating highly useful little tools that are relatively inexpensive. In today's day and age of e-commerce, Eric has finally found a market place for his software where the marketing budget doesn't send prices skyward. His company, West Side Systems, has quite a reputation for translating old show files onto disks that can be used on today's consoles.

Before I was toying with PC's to draw lighting plans, **Chris Toulmin**'s peers were using mainframes from Cambridge University to do the same thing. He is really a lighting designer, but his hatred for drafting plans (similar to mine) landed him a job at Modelbox – the premier European CAD house. He took what was essentially an in-house tool for building hire pick-lists and turned it into a successful product. That then evolved into a services company that still exists today. Around the time I was at CBC, our paths crossed but never met.

Wayne Howell is a bit of a rogue developer – and doesn't have a fondness for American patents. I was intrigued by his Lamp-Tramp control system used by Pink Floyd and The Rolling Stones. He makes gadgets and solves problems. He makes PC controls systems, similar to the one I product manage and has evolved Lamp-Tramp into Colour-Tramp to control the ever increasing number of LEDs in our industry. A big proponent of ESTA's RDM, Wayne also pushes his open architecture protocol for Ethernet transmission of DMX in the theatre.

Trying to predict where we're headed in entertainment lighting software development is always tricky when done in isolation, so I asked two long-time friends, Richard Lawrence of Strand Lighting and Philip Nye of Engineering Arts to join in a conversation looking forward. These two gentlemen are the two longest standing members on ESTA's ACN task group. The vision these people have is enormous – in fact, it has often been criticized as too forward thinking. Only recently the task group proved the nay-sayers wrong and started to deliver what should be the next standard in computer communication in the theatre. The three of us try not to focus too much on ACN, but try to envision where the lines of control and data organization will cross and how to solve what we call 'the numbers problem'.

While discussing the progress of this book during its development, some people questioned my selection of individuals. I make no apologies for including or excluding certain people. The book, although substantial, never claims to be a full history of all people that have written or managed a software development team in our industry. We just can't include everybody – there are too many smart people. I considered interviewing more, but stopping at an even ten seemed to makes sense. The fact of the matter is, I felt comfortable approaching these colleagues and feel that the cross section of products they were involved in accurately represents a slice in time and epitomizes the ethos of software product development I wanted to touch upon. For their participation, I thank them all.

Entertainment Technology Press is the exact sort of medium in which this story should be told since software is an ever-changing thing. I've only touched on the very surface of this topic and having the ability to re-print on demand makes things like a Volume 2 very thinkable. For the opportunity, I thank John Offord. I am grateful for the patience and creative input of Jackie Staines who paged-up the book from my manuscripts and created the artwork for each chapter title page. Well done.

Also, a big thank you to Richard Pilbrow for early and continued encouragement. Having him write the foreword of my book means the world to me. Over the years, Richard has given me more time than I could have wished for and acted more as a godfather than a mentor. Finally, a huge thank you and hug to my wife Christine for pushing hard at the right times and laying off when I needed it. I won't make you read it again, I promise!

1 WHERE WE CAME FROM
The Four Yorkshiremen

In my short career as a code developer I have witnessed unprecedented advances in hardware technology. Sitting around talking about the old days back in the early 90's is almost preposterous, seeing they were only ten years ago. It reminds me of the Monty Python skit 'The Four Yorkshire Men' where:

> Who'd o' thought thirty years ago we'd all be sittin' here drinking Chateau de Chassilier wine?

The IBM PC (processor 8088 at 4.77 MHz) was release in New York in 1981, but it cost about $3,000. I got my first computer in 1982. It was the Timex Sinclair 1000 (processor Zilog Z80 at 3.25 MHz). Some of my wealthier friends had Commodore Vic 20s (1981 – processor 6502 at 1 HHz), a repackaged version of the CBM Pet (1977 – processor 6502 at 1 MHz) that we had at school.

The T-1000 was an unbelievable little toy that used Timex's own version of BASIC and actually did floating-point math. The base model had 2Kb of RAM, but Dad forked out the extra dough for the 16Kb expansion. Memory was so tight you couldn't type your code in plain text. Each keyword was a combination of shifts and key presses. Keywords were stored, internally, as extended ASCI tokens and

the video driver just used a lookup table to displayed words such as FOR and GOTO. It hooked up to your TV and stored programs on a cassette tape. I did create a number of silly video games with this computer, but seeing as I couldn't add any input device such as a joystick or output to anything useful such as a serial port or sound card, I quickly lost interest in it. I still have the machine in my basement and recently fired it up to have a play.

Aye. In them days, we'd a' been glad to have the price of a cup o' tea.

Well, at least I didn't start with punched cards. Dad did. I used to go to work with him and they had a Xerox 530 (1973) with a card reader. They graduated to a PDP-11 (1975) and it had a tape drive (no more dropped card stacks). Around that time, Gordon Pearlman was using a PDP-8 when he put the first digital lighting control desk (LS/8) on Broadway in 1975 when Tharon Musser designed *A Chorus Line*. Back then I didn't know where Broadway was. I do remember quite vividly when Dad was going to buy a VAX 11/750 (1980). He and his two partners had to re-mortgage their houses as it was going to cost about as much as a home did.

As a student working at Dad's mechanical engineering consulting firm, I spent a lot of time on the VAX. It was quite something as we could have up to sixteen people working on it at one time. (Well, OK, the printer was considered one of the people, so maybe fifteen.) Around that time, Dad bought me an 8088 clone. I had to buy a math co-processor so I could run AutoCAD Release 9 (1987). Up to that point, drawing in 3D on AutoCAD was really tough. It was Release 9 (the successor to Version 2.6) that added the proper 3D Object Snapping that made actually drawing in 3D viable. The math co-processor made it possible to do hidden line removal on a model without having to wait over-night to see the results.

The best WE could manage was to suck on a piece of damp cloth.

I remember the engineers at work really didn't understand what I was doing with my PC. They really were not interested in my 'toy' and it wasn't until I got LaTeX, a macro language that sits on top of the powerful text processing language TeX that they became interested. TeX allowed me to format professional looking stress analysis reports using a proper equation editor. WYSIWYG editors like Word did not exist yet.

House? You were lucky to have a HOUSE! We used to live in one room, all hundred and twenty-six of us, no furniture. Half the floor was missing; we were all huddled together in one corner for fear of FALLING!

One of my Dad's younger partners also toyed around with a PC. He found some weird modelling program that he could use to build finite element models that they would ultimately feed into the VAX for doing stress analysis. I was playing around with MS Windows V3.0 and knew the benefits of breaking the 640K memory boundary. I told him that purchasing more RAM might speed up his modeller. After great debate, the company decided to purchase 4 MB or RAM at a cost of $600. To his amazement, his models loaded in about a minute, as opposed to the 15 minutes it used to take. He summed it up by saying, "It must be easier to puke into a 45 gallon drum than a Campbell's soup can."

> Ohhhh we used to DREAM of livin' in a corridor! Woulda' been a palace to us. We used to live in an old water tank on a rubbish tip. We got woken up every morning by having a load of rotting fish dumped all over us! House!? Hmph.

As PCs got cheaper, and eventually faster than the VAX, my big job was to re-compile all the FORTRAN code from the VAX to run on PCs using FORTRAN 77. The VAX didn't have a floppy drive, so we had to use a terminal emulation package to capture RS232 serial dumps. It was a real pain. I eventually got the two devices to talk over Thick Ethernet – the one and only place I've ever seen ThickNet.

> Well we had it tough. We used to have to get up out of the shoebox at twelve o'clock at night, and LICK the road clean with our tongues. We had half a handful of freezing cold gravel, worked twenty-four hours a day at the mill for fourpence every six years, and when we got home, our Dad would slice us in two with a bread knife.

When we started CAST Lighting, we used Window for Workgroups 3.11 and Thin Net to tie our 'two' PCs together. We were using the Watcom compiler and in addition to the Thin Net, we had to have a Parallel Lap Link cable connected between the two machines to debug the software. Windows was a real bear back then. We would re-boot our PCs at least twenty times a day. If you think about all the time wasted, we could have released WYSIWYG a month earlier.

Memory was not cheap then either. The Watcom compiler had a DOS Extender so more memory was better. Again, sit down corporate decisions were made as to whether or not we should purchase more RAM. We paid over $80 a MEG. It's less than $80 for 256 MEG today.

But you try and tell the young people today that . . . and they won't believe ya'.

It's hard to predict where all of this is going and what we'll say about our

3Gig processors of today. There has never been a time in history where 20 years has changed so much. The larger debate centres around whether or not, as a society, we're better off for it. All I know is that I get to work at home and I can forget about the horrible commute into the city every day. That alone speaks volumes.

2 WYSIWYG SEEDS

My first lighting plot (1989) was done on velum with a mechanical pencil. As any of my friends can tell you, my penmanship is horrible and I cannot draw a straight line to save my life. The show only had 100 lights, but it took me forever to draft. All said and done, I was quite proud of it, and imagined myself making a career out of lighting. When I arrived at the theatre to do the hang, my entire crew was waiting on the stage with the electrics flown in and all the lights waiting in the wings. The director then popped his head in the theatre and said – "Oh, by the way – I've moved the set downstage about six feet. Hope that won't be a problem." The way it was built, almost every light on the rig had to move. I crumpled the plot up and threw it in the garbage. It was at that moment that I vowed never to do another plot with a pencil again.

I started building my own lighting template blocks in AutoCAD version 2.6, the version just before what they ended up calling Release 9. AutoCAD had it's own programming language called AutoLISP, based on LISP (acronym for LISt Processing) that allowed you to write code to extend it's functionality. I really got into LISP and wrote a lot of routines to edit the attributes of my blocks. I made things to rotate and scale the attributes, things to change their colour, things to copy attributes from one block to others. It was the only way I could make drawing with a computer as fast as drawing with a pencil. And – it was legible.

I was then asked back to my university to light a show on their main stage. They had acquired a whole bunch of new gear that I had never used and I didn't know what the capabilities were. The only information I had was the spec. sheets for the fixtures, the trim heights and an accurate 2D drawing of the venue which I completed in my graduating year. Wondering what could be done with this, I wrote some more code that drew beam angles and elliptical footprints in a plan view. It would also take empty space in my 2D drawing and draw a section view. The routine would draw two ellipses, one on the deck and one at six feet high. I then knew that the intersection of the ellipses was where the actors would be completely lit. This code, which by today's standards is quite juvenile, was really the seed of WYSIWYG.

On the strength of some of my lighting plots, I caught the eye of Gil Densham,

$$l = \sqrt{(xh - xl)^2 + (yh - yl)^2}$$

$$he = hf - he\_1 \quad (\text{if } he\_1 = 0 \text{ then on stage}$$

$$\beta = \tan^{-1}\left(\frac{l}{he}\right)$$

$$t1 = \beta - \frac{\alpha}{2}$$

$$t2 = \beta + \frac{\alpha}{2}$$

IF $t1 < -1.5$ THEN $T1 = -1.5$

IF $t2 > 1.5$ THEN $T2 = 1.5$

$$a = \frac{\left(he \times \dfrac{\sin t2}{\cos t2}\right) - \left(he \times \dfrac{\sin t1}{\cos t1}\right)}{2}$$

$$lce = \left(he \times \frac{\sin t1}{\cos t1}\right) + a$$

$$rd = \sqrt{lce^2 + he^2}$$

$$b = \frac{\sin \frac{\alpha}{2}}{\cos \frac{\alpha}{2}} \times rd$$

coordinates relative to focus point???

$$x1 = b$$

$$y1 = \left(he \frac{\sin t1}{\cos t1}\right) + a$$

$$x3 = -b$$

$$y3 = y1$$

to global coordinates

$$dx = xh - xl$$

$$dy = yh - yl$$

IF $\left|\dfrac{dx}{xl}\right| < 0.01$ THEN $\gamma = \frac{\pi}{2}$

ELSE $\gamma = \tan^{-1}\left|\dfrac{dy}{dx}\right|$

making it quadrant sensitive

IF $dx < 0$ AND $dy > 0$ THEN $\gamma = \pi - \gamma$

IF $dx < 0$ AND $dy < 0$ THEN $\gamma = \pi + \gamma$

IF $dx > 0$ AND $dy < 0$ THEN $\gamma = -\gamma$

IF $dx > 0$ AND $dy > 0$ THEN $\gamma = \gamma$

$$x11 = y1 \cos \gamma - x1 \sin \gamma + x1$$

$$y11 = y1 \sin \gamma + x1 \cos \gamma + y1$$

$$x31 = y3 \cos \gamma - x3 \sin \gamma + x1$$

$$y31 = y3 \sin \gamma + x3 \cos \gamma + y1$$

Original trigonometric solution for beam projections used in LXCAD

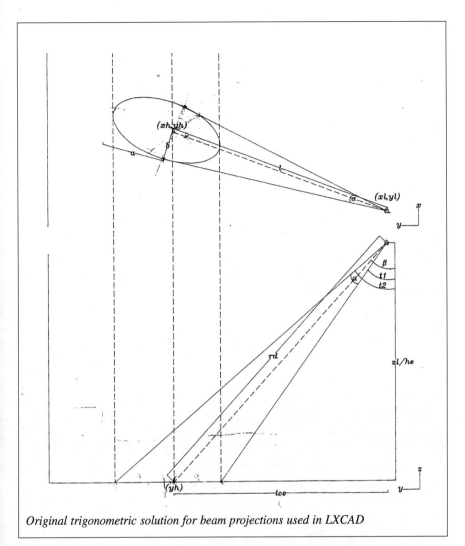

Original trigonometric solution for beam projections used in LXCAD

an LD for CBC who was doing similar drawings with Stephen Plotkin in AutoCAD and AutoLight from Modelbox at the Corporation. He got me a job there and I worked at CBC for two years in the lighting department. For the last six months of my term, I was transferred to the IT department to concentrate on polishing up some of my software. This time I wrote in C rather than LISP as the AutoCAD Development System (ADS) was unveiled in Release 11 (October 1990).

One day I discovered a wonderful command in AutoCAD called RULESURF (first appearing in 1988). Using the system variable SURFTAB1 to determine the number of faces, RULESURF connected a series of polylines between two objects to create a surface. I found that if I put a tiny circle in the nose of a fixture and drew the ellipse calculated by my trigonometric code, I could use RULESURF to connect the two to create a cone of light. That was so exciting I started to skip the whole idea of drawing a plan and section view separately and drew everything in 3D.

We then wanted to see these cones move. I wrote an editor where you could enter raw cue data to produce an AutoCAD script that would draw a secession of these cones. I then let the machine (a 386) chug away as fast as it could and each time a frame was drawn, I captured the image on a Leich Still Store. I then played back these frames as fast as I could to record it on a Digital Beta Cam. Playing back that video at 2X speed, I made a video showing virtual moving lights in a 3D environment. It was enough to convince CBC to fund my development a little further.

It was then that I called on an old high school friend, Rick Szijarto, to help me beef up some of my math routines so this thing could become a little more "real-time". He came up with an algebraic algorithm that was much faster than my trigonometric solution, plus it gave us the ability to project gobos. Using a DMX-PC card from Pthalo Systems, you could receive DMX from a Compulite Animator and capture it real-time into dual ported memory. This memory was visible by the code and we no longer needed to create an AutoCAD script to generate the cones. Instead of creating real entities with RULESUFF, we used AutoCAD's GRDRAW routine (sadly not available in AutoCAD's current VBA) to draw vectors directly on the graphics screen. This, too, was much faster as the main database did not need to be altered. I convinced CBC to buy me a Pentium (quite likely the first Pentium in the city) and before too long, we had beams screaming across the screen in tune to the cues written on the console.

This demonstration attracted the attention of *Lighting and Sound International*'s then-editor John Offord, columnist Tony Gottelier and visiting lighting designer Richard Pilbrow who was in town designing *Show Boat*. Collectively, they convinced me that this concept was marketable. For love nor money, I could not convince CBC management of that and I shortly left CBC to explore other marketing possibilities.

I wrote letters to every lighting manufacture I could find in the industry resource guide. A few people flew to Toronto to meet me, including Flying Pig Systems' Nils Thorjussen. It was at that meeting he showed me preliminary designs of the Whole Hog II in an effort to convince me that they too were on to something. He flew home and somehow convinced his partners that we could pull it off. With seed money from them, I went down to the registry office and incorporated CAST Lighting. Shortly later, Rick and I started to write original code using concepts proven at CBC. We set up an office in my living room and worked fourteen hours a day during the summer of 1994. Minutes before the PLASA show opened at Earl's Court in London that September, we had completed the compilation of a very shaky WYSIWYG Version 1.

Many people who first saw it there could not get their head around the concept. They thought they were watching a computer animation. It wasn't until I pulled the DMX line out of the back of the console and the beamsstopped moving did they understand it - or at least paused to think about it.

WYSIWYG has grown leaps and bounds from that point. We made what was essentially a rental house product more into a consumer-based product by introducing WYSIPAPER and WYSICAD and the product line now comfortably holds the standard for lighting visualization in our industry. CAST Lighting is still based in Toronto and is headed by Gil Densham and Rick Szijarto. ETC now markets the boxed products as WYSIWYG Report, Design and Perform and has integrated into a lighting control product line under the Emphasis label. And to boot, I can draw a straight line with it.

Excerpt from document entitled
LXMOV – A Lighting Designer's Virtual Reality

Document prepared for Canadian Broadcasting Corporation Programme Production Services, Toronto Production Centre by Robert Bell, CAD Consultant

December 3rd 1993

By the end of November 1993, LXMOV (moving light simulator) was in its third stage. The original concept sprung from LXCAD's Beamproj routine, which produced elliptical 2D representations of a light source at Z = 0'0" in the plan view of a lighting plot. Triumphant tests using the different photometrics of several light sources encouraged me to expand the projections into three dimensions.

The first version of LXMOV used a combination of AutoLISP routines and C++ code to produce the images of four moving lights. The operator entered "end cue" states in an "off line" editor that produce more accurate "moves" in the form of formatted files for the LISP code to read. The four lights projected coloured elliptical images generated by trigonometric mathematics onto a crude 3D set. The images took about 1 or 2 seconds to produce on a standard 386 based computer running AutoCAD 12. These images were captured by an industrial still store slide file and later played back in rapid succession to produce a moving image. The objective was to capture the concept on video for documentation of the idea and to persuade further developmental funding. It worked.

Version 2 of LXMOV continued with the same algorithms, but it now worked for any number of moving lights, and in real time. This was accomplished by allowing the lighting console to do the math for the cross fades (not the off line editor) and the virtual lights reacted as quickly as possible. This allows the operator to work on a console he is familiar with and there is no need for special training on a new piece of software. It was only at this stage I realized the average PC was going to be plenty powerful enough to simulate a handful of moving lights that encouraged me to take it to the next step.

There were two very special cases of lights —lights on the ceiling projected on the floor and lights on the floor projected on the ceiling. Beams of light shone through walls and disappeared when they reached horizons. This method, although accurate for beam placement, was deceiving, as lights that were fired (on) may not be displayed if they were above their horizon. Also, some lights approaching the horizon were shining miles away on the floor (or on the same plane as the floor). Colour, size, pan, tilt and speed were all accurately represented in version 2.

A fundamentally different mathematical approach was utilized in version 3.0. An algebraic solution was developed which solves simultaneous parametric equations instead of using pure trigonometry. This allowed for two new features greatly improving the virtual reality of the system. Every light used by LXMOV now recognizes both the floor and the ceiling as well as any number of walls and set obstacles (i.e., stairs, risers, flats). The second improvement this new algorithm features is the ability to project gobos or patterns. Lights are no longer bound to projecting elliptical images. The user can draw any number of gobos in as much detail as he wishes to see how the effect will work in real life. This is also used in gobo design, to predict how a pattern may look if it is stretched down a wall or passing through simulated studio smoke. LXMOV version 3 also has a facility to program lights with a hard edge focus...blind.

Specifics of Version 3

The latest version of LXMOV is extremely versatile and realistic. There are many features of this program that we did not anticipate to have incorporated in the scope of this project. The accuracy and reality of the simulation are so good that the original intent has been surpassed and LXMOV is being used in situations we did not originally plan for. LXMOV does not live in an office and is not used strictly for pre-production purposed as intended, but has found a home right in the studio and is used in both rehearsal setups and live show situations.

One of the most valuable assets of the program is the manager module that allows multiple drivers for moving light fixtures to exist simultaneously. This means that many different types of lights can work at the same time on the same 3D image. In the fall of '93, LXMOV was tested with four types of moving light drivers —Summa 8; Summa 12; VL5 and Dummy. The dummy driver is used when no moving light console is available. Other drivers would not be difficult to add to the manager module.

Lights that are capable of using gobos are easily configured in LXMOV. The patterns must first be drawn (only once) as a separate AutoCAD drawing and registered in the\source directory. Each light can accept any valid number of gobos and as they are placed in the lights, a rotation angle can be used for correction.

Surfaces must be inserted in a drawing so a light has something to strike. If the light goes to infinity (10e50 units) and strikes nothing, no beam is drawn. At least six surfaces should be drawn and all moving lights encompassed within these surfaces. That way every light will have something to hit in any direction. These primary surfaces should be unbound —that is, they stretch to infinity in all direction within the plane they define. Any number of unbounded surfaces can be added. Other bounded surfaces are more useful for describing set pieces, such as flats, risers and stairs. Any number of bounded surfaces can be added.

LXMOV also offers Preset versus Live modes of operation. Live mode operates, as you would expect; such that when you bring up a light on the console, the light appears on stage as well as on LXMOV's screen. This is the normal mode of operation. It is also valuable to be able to set a light in position, size it, assign it a colour and pattern without bringing up the dimmer in real life. This can be used during live show situations to preset lights without seeing them move on camera, a very handy innovation to have when key lights burn out during a show. It is also used in programming, to find the position of lights not being used in certain cues. This allows you to check for possible preset positioning in other cues.

3 GORDON PEARLMAN

Introduction

I don't know when I first met Gordon. It seems as though I've known him for years and years, but I don't think it's been that long! On serious recollection it must have been during the WYSIWYG days because since then I've been working for him, and before then I was nobody. We did accept an award together at LDI 1999 for incorporating Horizon and WYSIWYG onto one computer.

Gordon is well known in the industry for having an 'opinion', much more often than not, quite valid. He just likes to let you know it. He is a damn bright fellow, and is famous for putting the first computer-based lighting control system on Broadway with EDI. That was in 1975 and it was for Tharon Musser's lighting design for *A Chorus Line*. Since then, the LS-8, as it was known, enjoyed a spot at the Boston Computer Museum until it closed in 1999.

From EDI, Gordon went to Kliegl. In fact, he refused to go to Kliegl in New York, so they happily let him stay in Portland where he hired Steve Carlson and founded Entertainment Technology (ET). Apart from making good money on consoles for Kliegl (including the Performance and Performer lines), they built the Morpheus Commander and the Strand Impact. They also worked on a

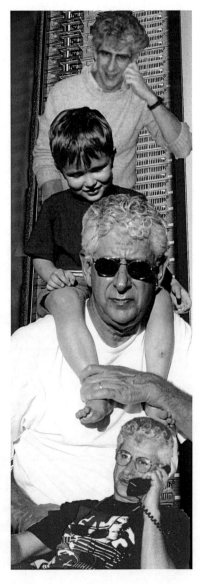

number of dimmer projects, including the unsuccessful K-96 dimmers. (I worked in a studio full of them at CBC.)

After Kliegl, ET built one of the most successful consoles ever, the GAM (Great American Market) Access. Gordon will happily tell you that it only cost $140 to build and they sold it for many times that amount. They couldn't manufacture enough of them and they sold over 1000 in the first year alone. He still thinks that it was one of their best products. Gordon, unlike me, looks at the whole picture. He looks at a product for what it is, what it cost to make it, and how many you can ship. I prefer the sex – what it does and how it looks.

When Steve and Gordon weren't messing around in the theatrical business they built architectural controls for Steve Carson at Lightolier, now a division of the huge architectural lighting corporation Genlyte/Thomas. Carson was setting out to forge his own division, Lightolier Controls, and ET's Lytemode wall box dimming/control system, helped make it all happen.

In 1995, colour giant Rosco purchased Entertainment Technology and branded it Rosco/ET, and it was through Rosco that ISP (Intelligent Power System) dimming was popularized. This was an all-new, all-electronic dimming system that greatly reduced electrical harmonics and audible noise by the way it chopped the sine wave. The problem was that it was expensive to manufacture and had only limited applications.

To sell dimmers, everybody knows you need a console, and that's where Alan Martello of Horizon Control comes in. He went to LDI '94 in Reno looking for a manufacturer for his control software and Mike Connell, a regional sales manager for ET, put him in touch with Gordon Pearlman. The funny bit was that Alan (for whom I now work), and I crossed paths at this exact moment in time. He was at the TMB booth showing his wares, and I was there setting up our first ever sale of a WYSIWYG system. We shared the same table but neither of us can remember the occasion.

Gordon grew tired of making, what he and I commonly refer to as, furniture. He understood better than any of us that the consumer market was driving technology much faster than we could keep up with it, and there was no reason you couldn't run a show using a PC. Alan was clever enough to demonstrate real-time fades on a non-pre-emptive operating system – Windows 3.1. This was not thought possible at the time, but leveraging on the friendly graphical user interface of Windows, Gordon thought he could outwit all of his competitors and do it at a fraction of the cost.

It was after I left CAST in 2000 that Gordon hired me. I was at Rosco/ET for a year before I found out it was time for Rosco to get out of the dimming business, and in walked Steve Carson (Steve Carlson had left ET a number of years earlier to pursue other interests). Genlyte purchased ET for its IPS intellectual property and got Horizon as a bonus. I moved over to working for Horizon Control Inc. and Genlyte shut the Portland factory and moved it to Dallas.

In 2002, Steve Carson made all our heads spin when he purchased Vari-Lite. This interview took place in a hotel bar the day we all met in Dallas to do the great big family group hug (Genlyte Controls, ET and Vari-Lite). Here the regional sales managers found out that Vari-Lite's Virtuoso was to be withdrawn and that Marquee (based on the Horizon engine) would be the console we manufacture for all three divisions. So, it was back to furniture after all.

Interview

GP: I was teaching at the University of North Carolina in Chapel Hill. It had a pretty good theatre department, certainly the best in the South. I was the technical director and lighting designer and started playing around with computers. It was about 1970 and we were doing this fun show where we took a big library-like hall and built a vinyl balloon inside it. We sealed all the doors and windows and put a window fan in the ballroom and evacuated the room, sucked this thing up and made a bubble inside it. The fire department would have had a fit because it was made out of polyethylene – the cheapest polyethylene sheeting we could get.

It was a graduate student project; I designed the dome but a student organized the project. He had 35 slide projectors and was doing a sort of multi-media thing. Computers were really only big mainframes in those days and we had two at the university. One was at Chapel Hill and the other was off in the Research Triangle[1] at IBM. It was a great big brand new IBM 370 but was only as powerful as calculators are these days. To begin with, the only way to communicate with them was with punch cards and four hours later you went up to the desk and got the printout from the one and only line printer.

The student wanted to control his slide projectors. He had 200 slides in each of the 35 slide projectors for an hour's show. I went to the state surplus warehouse in Raleigh and they had an old paper tape reader. I didn't even

[1] An area with intensive research between Raleigh, Chapel Hill and Durham.

Gordon Pearlman (L), technical director for the upcoming Carolina Playmakers production of "Amanita: The Death Angel," and Howard Cherniak (R), computer coordinator, work over one of the many instruments which the multi-media production necessitates. "Amanita," which premieres next Tuesday in the Graham Memorial Lounge Theatre, will use music, lights, and over 20 various projectors in its performance. Tickets are now on sale at the Playmakers Business Office and at Ledbetter Pickards.

Original Slide Projector at University of North Carolina.

know what the paper tape reader had been for, but it simply drove a bunch of relays and every time it saw a hole it would drive one of these relays on. It certainly did a lot more after that, but I could get to that point where I could see it drive the relays. We matrixed those relays so that we could control all 35 projectors. We matrixed the 8-bits – it was digital. I don't think we thought of it as being digital at the time, but it was. If one was down, you got one, if two was down, it would fire the second projector, and so on. That was pretty simple. Then we started to wonder how we were going to punch the paper tape. The show was an hour long and if you wanted to make one change in the middle of the show, you would have to punch the whole paper tape. But there was no other way to do it!

I had a graduate student who had a friend in the city-planning department and he advised me to contact a guy who could write a little BASIC program. At that point we had input/output devices that were Teletypes. These were the first real-time inputs and outputs we had from this computer. This machine could time-share and do that kind of stuff, which was relatively new at that point too, but there were no CRT terminals. They were unheard of. So your input/output device was a Teletype. And, guess what, a Teletype has a paper tape punch on it!

So first of all I had to teach myself BASIC because I didn't even know what a computer was.

RB: This is like Line 10 blah, Line 20 blah blah?

GP: Yes – BASIC, with all its GOTO's and all of that.

RB: BASIC on the IBM 370? Not Fortran?

GP: I did do a Fortran project later, but this was BASIC. Fortran was very bizarre, but then I did one in Pascal that was even more bizarre. Pascal got close to C.

This IBM did have BASIC and it was sort of interactive. You could run your little program. You didn't have to input and come back to get the results. It would time share into the machine. But you have to remember this was 55 baud, which was extremely slow.[2]

RB: You could type faster than that!

GP: The Teletype typed very slowly too because every time it typed a character it punched the punch and all of that. It was a very crude kind of printer – like a daisy wheel.

So I wrote this program that is not that much different from our programs today. It allowed you to insert cues and say what the cue was. In this case there were just 32 on and off bits – that's all there was. You could say what they were driving and you could insert them and get it to re-punch the paper tape.

RB: It was like a console with one 8-bit channel.

GP: Or a 32-channel console with only levels of on and off. A 32 channel non-dim console is basically what it was. It was extremely crude. I don't even remember if you had to type an octal number in to say what the setting was or whether we actually did a little thing that said this projector, that projector. But since you wanted to minimize the Teletype from typing as much as possible,

---

[2] Baud rate is a measure of the rate of signalling level changes. Using direct serial communication (such as RS232) the baud rate is the same as the bit rate. With modems that need extra things like start and stop bits to pad the byte and other control codes, 300 baud is just a little faster than I can type. Most dial-ups are 165 times faster than that now and standard networks are over 300,000 times faster.

you tended to do as much as you could with as few characters as you could.

So I did that project. Then I got fascinated with it. This will be more interesting to you than anybody else, but I found this guy who had written this 3D modeling program that was a batch 3D modeling program[3]. It was called Blocks. Basically what you did was to draw blocks – and the primitive by which you drew everything was rectangles. It didn't do any shadowing, but it did remove the hidden lines.

RB: This was probably the early stages of using a computer to model systems with finite elements. I think they graduated to using tetrahedrals eventually.[4]

GP: He had written the program to do the hidden line facility and I wrote a more practical interface to it where you could enter and edit things in real time. We could then plot this thing off – they had a Calcomp single pen plotter. I followed that by doing a bunch of set designs on it to show directors what their sets were going to look like.

RB: This is very impressive for 1971.

GP: By 1973 we got some CRTs. You could type in the description of the block and then you could see it on the screen. That was an interesting project and it was fun. I went to an ATA[5] convention and got a dial up connection to the mainframe in Chapel Hill and I demonstrated it in San Francisco. It blew everybody away.

RB: You should have been in Detroit demonstrating it to the auto manufacturers and you would have been a hell of a lot richer.

GP: Right. Nobody could believe this. Joel Rubin, to this day, says that it was an absolutely stunning event. He came into this room and I was doing

---

[3] By Batch Modeling Gordon means that you would use a text file to describe shapes, normally a series of 3D vertices connected together in long strings, separated by commas and fed into the computer to generate a graphical 3D model.

[4] Working for my father who owned a mechanical engineering firm that did stress analysis on nuclear reactors' plumbing, I had quite a lot of experience building "batch models". We used an in-house system written by dad and another engineer that used rectangular blocks as its primitives, but when I left dad's company in the late 80's they were starting to use third party CAD applications that built models using more complex primitives. The basis of finite element analysis is that you can break a solid into a finite number of simple parts and then study the stresses on each part to see which area of the model has the greatest stress and will likely fail first. This is much more a science of materials (which I don't understand) then of computer CAD applications. The CAD is just the front end.

[5] American Theatre Association – the predecessor to the American Eductaional Theatre Association (the only trade show at the time)

renderings on a CRT. Everybody does this today – MS Paint almost does it now - but it was unheard of in those days.

RB: AutoCAD wasn't even around.

GP: It was ten years before AutoCAD.[6] Soon after that, several big-CAD programs came onto the market, but this was the very beginning of interactive computing. Until this time, computers were always batch machines.

Doing this, I got to be a pretty good programmer but it was just recreational.

RB: Had you studied theatre?

GP: I have a Master of Fine Arts from Tulane, which in those days had a very good theatre department. It published the Tulane Drama Review. I studied scene design and lighting design. I worked at the University of North Carolina for nine years – lit four or five shows a year and set designed at least two shows a year. Then I got involved in outdoor drama (another part of my life).

At the time I was doing this 'recreational' coding, my next-door neighbour was the Digital Equipment Company salesman. You may not even remember DEC.

RB: Oh yes, my dad had a PDP-11 and later a VAX 11/750, which I worked on quite a bit.

GP: Well DEC was building personal computers for years before IBM had even thought about it. They had a good operating system and just had the most inept marketing strategy in the entire world. PDP-8 had a perfectly useable multi-threaded operating system. It worked perfectly fine and the PDP-11 had a better operating system than that. They were multi-threaded; they were multi-tasking, they supported terminals, it was . . . well, what we're finally getting to today in Windows.

RB: DOS never had any of that.

GP: DOS never figured out the basics. DOS started out with nothing and never went back and did the basics. DEC built a machine that was a desktop machine, that had a decent operating system on it which was certainly better than DOS. Gordon Bell, the president, just could not imagine that every engineer would have their own computer and, in doing so, missed a chance of a lifetime.

RB: This was the PDP-8. The PDP-11 was way more successful.

---

[6] First release of AutoCAD was 1982.

GP: Yes, but not for near as long a time. The PDP-8 was the only computer that people could afford to have in their lab for probably a ten-year period.

RB: What would they cost?

GP: By the time I bought one, they probably cost $10,000. My brother, a doctor, had a PDP-1 in his lab, which was really the same machine, and used it to process data. It was a whole rack tall, and I'm sure they paid over $100,000 for it.

RB: $10,000 in 1970 would be, what, three times more expensive than a new car?

GP: Maybe two times.

So having a DEC salesman as a next-door neighbour, I thought it would be nice to do a lighting console. The history was that England had done several lighting consoles, but they were not processor based. They were pure hard logic. There was no code written at all. When you pushed the '1', transistors latched up a '1' in a latch somewhere and you pressed '2' and you press RECORD and it put the data on a specific place on the memory that was accessed just through flip-flops and latches.

RB: Can you name these?

GP: I don't know about the Strand ones because I had nothing to do with them, but going to work for Kliegl I knew all of the Kliegl products.[7] The ones I knew were built by Thorn. The Q-File and Q-Level were the two that came to the United States in abundance and Kliegl sold a lot more of them than Thorn did.

RB: This is why a lot of people will say that the British were doing computer-based consoles early because they did Q-File.

GP: Q-File was not a computer-based product. These things were just latches – relay logic is the best analogy you can come to. It was all done solid state, but it was basically relay logic. They did some very slick things with them, no doubt about it, but they were not code based.

RB: Sort of like an FPGA[8] but hard wired with many chips.

---

[7] Kliegl Brothers Props was founded in 1896 by John and Anton Kliegl. It's sales department was managed by Joel Rubin when Gordon got there and was famous for fixtures, dimmers and eventually Gordon's Performer, Performance and Command Performance consoles.

[8] Field Programmable Gate Array – see Mark Hunt page 238

GP: No chips – this was before chips. Just transistors. The first Q-File that came to the United States was three racks of electronics. Three racks of electronics! There were no chips, so if you wanted to make a gate, it took three transistors. The first Q-Files were discrete logic. They were just card after card after card of these enormous card files and back-plane wires all over the place and they would cost $100,000 - the first ones were more than that.

RB: What sort of dimmers were they driving? Broadway at this point was still running on piano boards[9], which were resistance dimmers.

GP: By 1959 Strand and Kliegl were building *exactly* the same type of dimmer that is being built today.

RB: SCRs[10]

GP: An SCR, a choke and a timing circuit. Today the timing circuit is mostly digital; in those days it was all analog, but it's still a timing circuit.

RB: How did you talk to it? Did you feed it an analog signal?

GP: Yes, so there was a D-A[11] converter at the output of this Q-File.

RB: And it would produce 0-10v.

GP: Or whatever – more like 0-32v.

RB: That is what would feed directly into the timing circuit?

GP: It's the same circuit as wall-box dimmers use today; most dimmers have a digital counter that does it, but you know how a dimmer works. You sense zero crossing, you take a voltage, you pop it into a resistor and a capacitor network, it takes a certain amount of time to charge up, and after it's charged up it releases and it fires the SCR. The lower the voltage, the longer it waits and . . . you've got a dimmer. It's a circuit that takes about four parts and frankly the wall-box dimmers we build today have the same four

---

[9] They were called Piano Boards because the cases that they were packed in for touring or transport looked like an upright piano. These were large resistance or autotransformer consoles that typically had 14 circuits, each controlled by a large handle moved manually by an operator back stage. Rows of these would be lined up and there would typically be more than one operator running a show.

[10] Silicon Control Rectifier or basically a transistors that turns on a circuit, albeit at a very high frequency (120 hz) to chop a sine wave.

[11] Digital to Analog converter

parts in them[12].

RB: But, for historical perspective, Broadway was still running on resistance dimming. Now (politics aside) technologically, were those running on DC?

GP: They would run on DC, so that is why they were there, because half the theatres in New York were still DC. The real reason they were there was pure economics. Four Star Lighting owned literally a basement full of piano boards. The place was packed with these great big green boxes. A lot of them were resistance dimmers, and some of them were autotransformers.

RB: Explain the difference.

GP: In the manifestation that you've seen them, they look exactly alike. A resistance dimmer is putting a toaster in series with the light. Put in more toasters and the light gets dimmer and dimmer. An autotransformer is an actual tapped transformer so you really are varying the voltage you supply to the lamp. In physical build, they are almost exactly the same, but in one of them there is little resistance in the wire.

RB: Autotransformers didn't get warm like resistance dimmers.

GP: They got warm, but they didn't get hot. A resistance dimmer has to give off all the heat the lamp is not consuming.

RB: So working those things was wicked.

GP: Just brutal. Resistance dimmers will work on DC (or AC), but autotransformers, well, they're transformers – they only work on AC.

So Four Star didn't see any reason why they should invest any money in electronic equipment because they owned all this other equipment. There was also a union that said they didn't want electronic equipment on Broadway.

RB: Is it fair to say that Broadway was using piano boards longer than any regional theatre?

GP: Absolutely. Q-Files were being put in all over the place. The Guthrie had

---

[12] When Gordon says "we" he means Genlyte/Thomas. For years, Gordon has done work for Genlyte, a massive architectural lighting company that makes hundreds of thousands of wall box dimmers a year. Entertainment Technology is now a division of Genltye. ET holds the North American patent to produce IGBT dimmers. This is an Insulated Gate Bipolar Transistor that is capable of chopping either the front or back of the sine wave (forward or reverse phase control dimming). The advantage of RPC dimming is lower audible noise (no choke), lower neutral line harmonics and absolute voltage regulation (you sense the voltage and turn it off when it's at the right level, vs. approximating it and turning it on when you think it's there.)

a Q-File long before Broadway. The University of Iowa had electronic dimmers probably in 1950. We're now talking 1975. Twenty-five years earlier there were electronic dimmers (not SCRs) in theatres in the United States. Broadway was very resistant to change. It was clear that it would have made much more sense for them to put in electronic dimmers. It was a strong union and Four Star owned the market. You couldn't get any more equipment from anybody else. That's the history of SCR dimmers.

RB: How about the history of code based desk?

GP: There were a couple of other early code-based machines built in the United States. I'm not sure whether Strand's MMS's were all hard logic or processor based[13]. Lightboard (from the UK) was certainly a processor-based product, but it was introduced as the same time as Kliegl Performace and Strand Light Palette. There had been a processor-based one built by a guy named Etlinger for TV. It was very TV oriented. First off, it used a light pen[14] to run it. It was basically one step above what my code did to run the slide projectors. It could record cues, play them back in order, and you could insert cues. It had very low resolution. I think it was 5-bit storage or 32 steps, but so was Q-Level and those others.

RB: But historically, piano boards were only five steps.

GP: Piano boards were infinite.

RB: But on paper, it would be Out, ¼, ½, ¾ and Full.

GP: No, I think most cue sheets were written 0 to 10 plus ½ steps. When Skirpan build Autocue for CBS (CBS commissioned this from Etlinger), it had those values on it. The first one to use percentages was mine, but this thing they had was cute. It used a PDP-8 as well and it worked really nicely, but it wasn't very theatrical. It was designed to bring the next light cue up in a TV studio.

---

[13] Two years before producing the digital MMS (Modular Memory System) in 1973, Strand sold the DDM (Digital Dimmer Memory) to the Royal Shakespeare Theatre. This system also used core memory as Gordon is about to explain, but were logic-based systems – not using processors.

[14] A light pen is a wired device that had a light collector in the tip that you touch to the screen (like a touch screen today) and using calculations based on the scan rate of the CRT, it could give XY coordinates into a primitive Graphical User Interface – popular before the mouse, which was invented in 1964 by Douglas Englebart. (Englebart, by the way, is also responsible for hypertext and windowing systems). The Vista console by Jands was unveiled at PLASA 2003 and also uses a light pen. The word is that it is much faster than a mouse to manipulate things on the screen, but you do have to take your eyes off the stage to use it.

RB: You knew of this product by this point in time?

GP: I had seen it. Skirpan took it over and sold it. I think he sold two or three of them. It was all light pen driven which was OK as there was no immediacy needed in a TV studio.

Then David Cunningham was working for Van Buren out on the west coast and had done some real simple consoles. One of them had 16 channels and had a lever that would take you through the 120 cues. They called it the Sweet Sixteen. They were console looking – they looked like a two scene preset desk. They didn't have CRTs or any of that kind of thing.[15]

So I went to my next-door neighbour and told him I wanted to do this project and asked him what sort of equipment I would need. I still knew little about computers. I'd taught myself to program, sort of, but I certainly didn't know how to put together a computer or build a D-A converter or anything like that. But the psychology department at the university had used enough computers for experiments that they actually had an electronics technician who worked for them full time, also a neighbour. This guy helped me design the hardware.

So I got a PDP-8. It's fascinating in today's numbers. It was a 12-bit machine, unlike the early IBM PC's that used a 16-bit word. It had 8k of core memory[16]. I find it interesting that my son has two friends that have just graduated with masters degrees in computer science and neither one of them knew what core memory was. This machine had core memory that was four boards deep, each about 12" x 12". The glory of core is that when you turn it off, it does not forget. That made building lighting control consoles a bit easier because you didn't have to worry about losing it. That memory had to store the program and the cues, so now you see why compression of cue storage became such a big issue. Autocue would only store five bits for each level, where I actually went right up to eight bits or 256 steps.

So I got the hardware and really didn't have to do anything with it initially. I just started by writing the program. But I did build a front panel with a matrix of 125 push buttons on it, one for each channel[17]. It also had a '10-key' to

---

[15] See Cunningham page 77

[16] Core memory uses matrixes of ferrite donuts hand-wound with a number of wires producing a magnetic field, representing either a 1 or 0.

[17] Gordon is talking about the early development of LS-8 which was made famous by become the first computer desk used on Broadway for a Chorus Line in 1975. Many years later, the Artisan and Icon Console also have used this idea of a matrix to access channels. See Anne Valentino page 167. We've also put one on Marquee.

access the cues, but not the channels. That didn't come until Performance for Kliegl[18].

RB: How did you arrive at 125 channels?

GP: It had to do with the mechanicals of how the buttons would be laid down. I believe there were five rows of 25 across.

RB: Oh – so you're to blame for the 'twenty-five across' stigmatism.

GP: The first was 100 channels, but then it became 125. It may have had to do with *A Chorus Line* and what they required.

   Apart from the matrix and the 10-key, I took a pot[19] and put it in the center of its travel, and built this really crude mechanical thing with two springs so when you pushed the pot up and let go it would return to center. That was the way you set levels. It actually worked very nicely.

RB: So you could take a level of 30% and push it up…

GP: Or pull it down.

RB: Could you see the channel level on the screen?

GP: Yes – absolutely. And it tracked[20]. One of the unique things that I added to the business was the translation table between 100 and 256. The table to this day is the one I wrote in the LS-8. Everybody uses the same translation table. There is no formula for that because if you divide it doesn't come out even; so where do you put the remainders? It is kind of top loaded and bottom loaded. You loaded the bottom so you didn't have to worry about jittering pots and silly things like that. I don't know if it's written down or not, but everybody uses the same one.

The LS-8, similar to the one used on **A Chorus Line***.*

---

[18] The Kliegl Performance was released in 1979.

[19] Potentiometer or slider.

[20] By saying 'it tracked' he means as you ran cues, you could read all the 'live' channel levels on the screen. LS-8 and all of Gordon's earlier desks were preset desks, not using the tracking style concept. See Anne Valentino's description of the difference between the two on page 152.

RB: I believe the Lil' DMXter[21] uses a different one - they just round. If you look at Horizon with a percentage value of 10, on the DMXter you will see 9. I saw this the other day when we were testing the +10% and –10% buttons on Maquee.

GP: So this was the first console that stored things to that level of preciseness and it was the first console to display levels on the screen. Well, Autocue had, but it had done it pretty slowly and it had done it as $1:\frac{1}{3}$ or $2\frac{1}{2}$.

So I just started writing this program. You have to understand that the development system amounted to two cassette tapes. That was very revolutionary because DEC had just done it. Everything earlier had been paper tape. They had, if you can imagine, high-speed paper tape readers and paper tape punches and everything was done that way. So if you wanted to library off the work you've done, you would library it off to paper tape – that was the only way.

To turn on your machine in the morning, you would switch it on, and then toggle in a sixteen instruction boot strap - literally toggle it in on the front panel, then it would be smart enough to read the paper tape through the Teletype. It would read in a little bit of tape from there, and then it would be smart enough to read the cassettes. That's what I had to do every time I wanted to turn the machine on (assuming that the core had forgotten). Since it was core, you really could just shut it off then turn it back on again and it would just start running exactly where it had left off.

RB: Where we're getting to now with PDA's?

GP: Maybe. Certainly all of us who had PDP-8's could do that 16-instruction bootstrap in our sleep. It was 12 switches and you had to put all 12 into an order, then you hit a button, then put another 12 in order and hit a button, and there would be 16 instructions like that and that gave it enough knowledge to read the paper tape.

All the code was written in assembly language because you couldn't waste instructions on high-level language. You had to be in control of everything it was doing, because like I say, there was only 8k to store the program and the cues.

RB: What about the operating system?

---

[21] The Lil' DMXter was one of the first very popular hand held DMX test tools used by technicians. It was (and is) made by Goddard Design. The firmware was written by David Dexter McNeil in 1991.

Here you can see the 'boot toggles' on the front of the LS-8 (right).

GP: There were no operating systems in these early machines at all. These things were just simple round-robin programs. You booted right up into the program running this little round-robin loop of some kind.

So I wrote that in my spare time in my office. It took me five or six months to write it.

RB: The University was still paying you?

GP: I was still working there and still the lighting designer. This was a kind of a hobby. I had to get the money to buy this equipment so I applied to the faculty grants committee. The university gets a certain amount of money that is for anything. Well, nobody from the theatre department had ever applied to the faculty grants committee for anything before. So my chairman signed the thing, laughing. He didn't think there was any chance in the world I would get the money. But he didn't know that another neighbour of mine was the chairman of the faculty grants committee!

So I got the money. It wasn't very much - it must have been $15,000 or

$20,000, but I bought the PDP-8. You asked if we displayed the channel levels live. We could do that because of this very slick hardware. Most monitors (or terminals really) were serial devices. In those days, to change a character half way down the screen, you had to re-write the entire screen.

RB: It was just a 25x80 array that you stuffed.

GP: It was just a great big FIFO[22]. I bought this terminal that looked like RAM. To the machine it looked like an array of addressable memory. So if you wanted to write a '1', you put hex '31' in that particular byte.

RB: These were the ASCI codes of the day.

GP: We didn't call them ASCI back then. Everything was in octal because hex didn't work out with 12 bits. Everything was in three bit chunks, so the way you mnemoniced everything was in three octal characters to make up a 12 bit word. But yes, it was the same sort of things: you wrote things that looked like ASCI into that RAM and it would appear on the screen. You would

LS-8 screen

---

[22] First In First Out – a common serial communications method where the oldest command is handled first, often implemented on COM ports with UARTS (Universal Asynchronous Receive/Transmit microchips)

have one spare bit that would make it flash or bright or something. It was very crude, but it did allow you to refresh the screen as fast as moving the pot up and down. Remember, these machines were really slow, and I mean *really* slow.

RB: So you had a monitor and a front panel. How did you think you were going to talk to dimmers? There were no standard protocols then - just analog stuff.

GP: Yes, they just took a voltage. I bought an off-the-shelf D-A converter and put it on a card to sit right on the bus of the computer. It was real expensive – I think it cost me $300.

RB: So then you had 125 bits of copper coming out of the back?

GP: Yes. We did that all the way through Performer[23] – 125 signals coming out the back. Obviously it was multiplexed internally. The D-A converter talks to a bunch of samples-and-holds and they sample-and-hold the data to put out the voltage. I think Autocue had done it with a D-A converter for each channel instead of sample-and-holds.

David Cunningham gets the real credit for figuring out that the de-multiplexing should go out in the dimmer rather than at the back of the console. That made a tremendous difference. That's all AMX[24] was. He just took that same bus that had a timing bit and analog data just sitting on there, then he shot it down to the dimmers and did the sample-and-hold at the dimmers. A very bright thing to do.

RB: And analog consoles before that were just a large power supply with a group of control pots outputting to the same 125 bits of copper.

GP: They would tie the wiper of the pot to the other end and turn the resistance pot into a mini autotransformer. It makes the circuit easier to build. Basically that's what they were – they were a little dimmer system of their own that then put out this zero to ten volts.

RB: So you built this thing and installed it on your stage?

GP: Not easily – we didn't have any electronic dimmers. Universities had

---

[23] Performer was produced from USITT Seattle 1979 until Kliegl died in the early 1990s

[24] Analog Multiplexed – Strand protocol developed by Dave Cunningham (see page 87) that controlled 192 dimmers on four conductors (clock plus; clock minus; data and ground). Used as a standard for years and made popular by the Strand CD80 dimmers.

autotransformers in those days because nobody could afford electronic dimmers.

Ward Leonard[25] slid the wiper across the top of a coil, instead of putting it around the outside, like all those you've seen. I can't imagine they did this for any reason except to get around GE's patent. Arial Davis (another genius in the business – not around anymore[26]) took their wiper off and put six little wipers on. So you took one 60-amp Ward Leonard dimmer, and put these six wipers on and made six 20-amp dimmers, which gave you much finer control and they had nice little sliders on them. They were about 6" wide and 2' long and had these six coloured Bakelite sliders that slid up and down. Obviously you could only put 50 amps total on it, but you could put 20 amps on each of the sliders. It really made a tremendous difference because all of a sudden, you had finer control. Instead of being 50 amps and very expensive, you had six dimmers. We had a bunch of those as everybody did. Apart from those, we had one EDI 12-Pack. EDI built electronic dimmers in Portland, and that's what I ran with this thing. It used a 2 to 7.5 volt control voltage to fire the dimmers. I had to build a D-A converter with a 2 volt offset and only had 5 volts gain in it. (Later when I worked at EDI[27] we figured out how they got at that voltage. That's the break over voltage of the transistor and they looked at it and that was full – so that was it.)

Then Joel Rubin sent Jolene Polanski (a name only us old timers remember) down to Chapel Hill to see this system because he'd got wind of it. So I demonstrated it for Jolene right in my office.

RB: So you had 125 buttons on the face panel and you were in your office driving 12 dimmers.

GP: Hey, this is the old fantasy of trade shows! At this point I'm not driving any dimmers, I'm just changing numbers on the screen. Two weeks later Joel comes down to Chapel Hill because he wants to see it too. Meanwhile I'm going through some negotiating because I decided to quit teaching and work for Kliegl in New York. They were going to buy this system and manufacture it. Remember, Kliegl's got Q-File and Q-Level at this point.

RB: Are you married to Sondra at this point?

GP: Yes.

---

[25] Ward Leonard was one of the leading Canadian manufacturers of dimming systems in the 60s and 70s. Bruce Whitehead of Lumitrol was on the engineer design team.

[26] Ariel Davis was president and founder of Electo Controls.

[27] Electronics Diversified Inc., the manufacturers of the LS-8

RB: Was she nervous?

GP: No - we were kids. What did we know? I was making $14,000 a year teaching – starvation wages. She was teaching high school for $5000 a year. So I quit to go to work for Kliegl.

RB: So then you met John Kliegl?

GP: Yes, but Joel ran all the sales and engineering. That made it complicated because there was something going on at Kliegl and all of a sudden I didn't have a job. So then I decided that I had to hawk the product and the only people I knew were Electronics Diversified. Probably the worst decision I made in my life was to not pick up the phone and call Strand (Century at that point). I was told that by Strand years later.

In those days, when you worked for a university, the software belonged to the author – copyrightable material belonged to the author, and patentable material belonged to the university. So, since software was copyrightable, I could sell it. This isn't true nowadays. The universities have fixed that little loophole. Anyway, I licensed it to Electronics Diversified and I went to work for them.

RB: So they went out and bought the hardware needed to put one together.

GP: They bought their own PDP-8.

RB: Did you manage to get the face panel out of the university?

GP: That's where Steve Carlson[28] came in. They had just hired Steve, a young engineer out of school and he redesigned all the electronics because mine were horrible. I didn't really know what I was doing. I didn't even know there was anything like a de-coupling capacitor[29] or anything like that that you had to worry about. They actually re-built my design for the very first system, but after that they used Steve's new redesign.

I went out to work for them as Vice President – I wasn't even doing R&D for them at that point. I picked up my wife and two little kids, sold our house in Chapel Hill, and we all moved to Portland, Oregon. By some quirk, we changed moving companies at the last minute, and that resulted in us having to drive non-stop across the country. We were going to spend two weeks

---

[28] Gordon and Steve later become partners in Entertainment Technology and develop various consoles including the Performer, Impact, Light Commander, Access, IPS (Intelligent Power System) dimming and Horizon.

[29] Capacitors placed around circuits to limit noise.

going across the country but arrived early and moved all our stuff into the house. It was the Fourth of July weekend, and we didn't have a telephone. I was tearing one of the toilets out in one of the bathrooms because the carpet was all rotten and somebody comes and knocks on the door. It's Paul Bennett – the President of Electronics Diversified. I'm not supposed to go to work for another week or so, but he tells me that they were designing a system based around one of those little 4-bit processors that came out way early. It was an Intel 4040. This system was supposed to be like Dave's Sweet Sixteen – pots and levers – no monitor.

RB: Like the Mantrix?[30]

GP: Yes – similar to what we're trying to build today[31]; something that had a pot for every channel and no CRT. They had sold this to a show in New York. They didn't know what the name of the show was, they just knew they had sold it to some Broadway show in New York and they weren't going to be able to get it done so they would have to ship one of my systems.

Now, they had built one of my systems to show at USITT about three months before that, but it didn't drive dimmers. We were on the floor – we didn't need to drive dimmers, right? They hadn't done the D-A section or anything like that. So I go out to the plant and Steve Carlson is there and we build his design (which has never been built before) for the D-A converter. I believe we used my design for the front panel. We did this in 24 straight hours. This was before FedEx – so people were putting stuff on airplanes to us from LA and New York. We finally get it done – but only just!

RB: You took the code from the old cassettes.

GP: The only way you could load the code onto this machine was from paper tape. From toggling in the bootstrap to loading in the program, it would take you 45 minutes. We loaded this thing on an airplane and I got on the same plane and flew to New York, red-eye over night.

RB: Just left Sondra…

GP: Right – with two kids and the bathroom torn up. I was just supposed to be there for two days and come back. I get to New York; they pick me up in an

---

[30] The Mantrix was a Strand memory desk that had pots and a record button, but could be operated without a CRT. The MX succeeded it.

[31] Gordon, Alan Martello and I at the time of the interview, were building the Marquee console for Genlyte. The design spec for this thing was to be a high-end memory desk when hooked to a PC with a monitor, but should be simple enough to operate as a two-scene memory desk with no monitor present.

old beat-up van from Four Star and we seemed to drive around Manhattan for hours. This guy keeps getting out of the van and calling the theatre, then getting back in and driving some more - not telling me what this was all about. It turns out that David Merrick was in a big fight with Four Star over some fixtures that he had owned and stored at Four Star. It seems the sheriffs were at the theatre repossessing all the lighting equipment for *A Chorus Line* and they didn't want to put our console in there in the meantime. Eventually they got this sorted out and we finally arrived.

RB: Can we back up a bit here? When the thing was spec'd, did Tharon Musser say she needed such and such a thing that could do so many channels, etc?

GP: No. Tharon had been convinced by Gary Bennett and Bob Krugel, the Four Star Guy in LA, that the 4-bit thing (that they couldn't build) was going to do the job. She would have gone absolutely berserk. She didn't just want to do crossfades…

RB: She wanted a lot of bumps – fast cues in succession.

GP: And things running on the other fader at the same time.

RB: Piano boards just couldn't do this show. You can't bump a resistance dimmer.

Gordon visiting the Computer Museum Boston in 1991 where the LS-8 was on display.

GP: That's right. And you certainly couldn't have five cues in three seconds or more – which we did a lot of in *A Chorus Line*. So that's what Paul Bennett came to tell me that day we moved in. They can't build it and all they have is mine even though they've never built one with outputs. So we built one in a day-and-a-half and shipped it to New York.

Apart from the fact that we needed to tweak the power supply a little bit and the guy from Four Star didn't unplug it before he did that and blew the thing to smithereens. I mean absolute smithereens. Apart from that – it all worked fine. That was about two weeks after opening, and that's when I met Steve Terry for the first time. Gary Shevett was the master electrician and brought in Steve to help me, you know, go-for-things and that sort of stuff. Steve was the master electrician at the Harlem Ballet.[32]

Before that, I was there for all the rehearsals leading up to the opening. I dropped in there every night with Tharon and Gary and every night I'd tell Tharon "Tharon, I have this young wife at home, two little kids… I've got to go home!" But she wouldn't let me go home. Finally, Gary says to me, have your wife come out for opening night and Frank promises to pay for her expenses. To this day he hasn't! It cost $300 – a lot of money then when I wasn't making any. They put me up at the Piccadilly Hotel, which was the about the worst dive you've ever seen. It was just horrible. But! We did go to opening night. We walked into Sardi's after the show with Tharon and went to the after-show party and waited for the reviews - and all the things that happen on opening nights of Broadway shows. It was great fun.

That thing was a PDP-8 M with the toggle switches are on the front, and by the time the first one blew up (and we fixed it), we went home and madly started to build another using a PDP-8 A. It had this marvellous thing in it called ROM (Read Only Memory). This was a PC board of 32 rows of 12 diodes each. What you did was clip the diodes out. That was ROM. Wherever there was no diode, that was a one, and where there was, that was a zero. You clipped it out to make the bootstrap. So now you could just turn the thing on and it would boot up by itself and it had… 'Floppy Disks'! These were brand new things. They were invented by IBM to boot up their machines. We had two floppy drives and the belts kept falling off the bottom of them.

Our machine would actually boot up out of ROM then it would continue to boot on the floppies (when the floppies worked, which was rarely). The

---

[32] Steve Terry was one of the owners of Production Arts for years and sometime after its acquisition by Fourth Phase moved to ETC.

At Terminal with the prototype of the Performer in 1978, with the Command Performance in the background.

miraculous thing was that we left that machine there at *A Chorus Line* for four months and they never had to reload the program. And they never had to go to the paper tape. That was an absolute miracle!

RB: The show was stored in core?

GP: Stored in core and backed up on paper tape.

RB: That desk has gone from one museum to another.

GP: Not that actual one, but the second one we built. The first one got destroyed. I don't know where it went. The second one – the one that then ran for 13 years – when they finally replaced it with a Light Palette, Steve Terry asked them what they were going to do with it. They were going to throw it away so he took it and put it in his warehouse. One day he told me he had it so I asked him to ship it to me, collect, and I would put it in my warehouse. He shipped it to me, just about the time we were starting to work on IPS dimming. Then two guys from Bayview,[33] who were both old DEC people, knew Mrs. Bell (Gordon Bell's wife) who was starting a museum. They called her up and asked if she

---

[33] Entertainment Technology bought patents from a company called Bayview that covered the use of Insulated Gate Bipolar Transistors (IGBT) for use in dimming. ET built these into their line of Intelligent Power System (IPS) dimmers.

would have any use for this kind of interesting piece of memorabilia. Three or four weeks later she called me back and said: "We understand you have…" and I said 'yes' - and it still works! She said: "Don't tell us that!" They would then have to preserve it working and they didn't want to do that. It sat in this computer museum until it closed and they moved all the contents of the computer museum out to Livermore somewhere where there will be a new museum. So now it's just in storage. You can take a look at it on their website.[34]

RB: So how many LS-8's were built?

GP: There were three sold. The reason for this was that Steve Skirpan sued for violation of his patent to use a CRT to display lighting, which as a law suit goes, was, in my opinion, very bogus. This is where Dave Cunningham came in.[35] Frank DeVerna didn't have the guts to buy more, so he went to Strand and said build me a copy. So Dave built Multi Cue, which was a copy that I don't think was anywhere near as good. It didn't originally have split cross-faders. Maybe Dave had been working on it before – I don't know, but he also used a PDP-8. He used a PDP-11 when he did Light Palette, which was a very good move on his part because the 11 got reduced to a chipset and the PDP-8 never did.

RB: So how complex was cue structuring on the LS-8? Did you have things like Up and Down times?

GP: The original one didn't have times. It had an A/B fader, which was a manual cross-fader and a C/D fader where you set the times by setting these pots to different levels. You didn't record times in the original software that was on *A Chorus Line*. Very shortly after that we added the ability for the C/D fader to record times.

RB: So where did Steve Carlson and you go after LS-8?

GP: I worked for EDI for another nine months and sold one to ACT[36] in San Francisco. They loved it. They not only ran their lights on it but they inventoried all their scenery on it. And they ran the box office on it - doing all kinds of things with the lighting computer. The other one was sold to Arvada Community College outside of Denver. All three ran for a long time.

---

[34] http://www.computerhistory.org/collections/index.page

[35] See Cunningham – page 79. Also see Cunningham page 86

[36] American Conservatory Theater, the big resident company in San Francisco, not to be confused with Bob Gordon's company A.C.T. Lighting.

Then I went to New York and met up with my friend Michael Connell who was at Kliegl and told him I was unhappy at EDI. When I got back to my hotel room, Joel Rubin called me. So then I went to work for Kliegl and Mr. Kliegl said to me that he wanted me in New York. I said, OK, if you double my salary I would be happy to move to New York. He said, OK then, stay in Portland. So I did - and I hired Carlson.

Kliegl had been burned badly by trying to build a memory lighting console. System 70 was the one they tried to build themselves, and it was an absolute disaster. It cost them a million dollars and they got nothing out of it and a million dollars in those days was a lot of money. Kliegl's gross annual sales were probably three million dollars – maybe not even that. John Kliegl was running the company and was really convinced that System 70 killed his father. Joel really wanted to hire an R&D director, which he couldn't do. So he hired me to be the Western Sales Manager, but he doesn't give me California or Nevada. So I had the wonderful territory of Oregon, Washington, Alaska and Hawaii, where sales are nothing – ever. He gave me a salary and I was supposed to make commission, but there was no possible way I could ever make any quota, but he let me hire Carlson. In my bedroom, four days a week, we would do R&D and one day a week I would go out and sell. I was still the Western Sales Manager for a year-and-a-half after we introduced Performance.

Steve and I did Performance in about three or four months. It was a really slick system. It had interchangeable front panels, all ribbon cabled together. It was microprocessor based – the first time anybody had really built their own microprocessor board. Cunningham was building Multi Cue using off-the-shelf stuff from DEC. We built all our own processor boards. We had this wonderful thing called EPROM,[37] which was the most marvellous thing we've ever seen. I think the first one we got was maybe 4k and I think it cost $75. We were using a TI 9900 microprocessor; it was a really nice microprocessor; much nicer than Intel had at the time, but they didn't have the marketing that Intel had. This is about the time the Altair computer[38] was out and early Apple

---

[37] Erasable Programmable Read Only Memory, similar to today's Flash RAM, but you needed to remove the chips and expose them to ultra-violet light to erase them.

[38] The Altair 8800 was manufactured by Micro Instrumentation Telemetry Systems in 1975 and used the Intel 8080 microprocessor. When it was first released, the only way to interface with it was with the binary toggles and lights on the front, but for the home enthusiast this was a huge leap forward in technology and it was huge success.

The creative lighting control system designed for those who demand the highest standard.

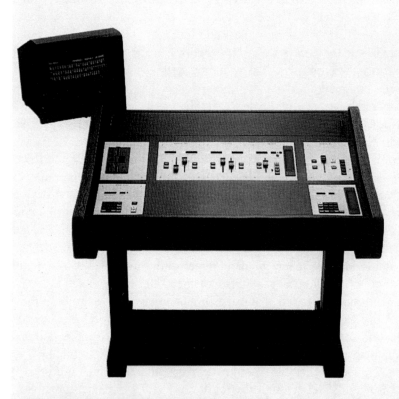

In just two years, PERFORMANCE® has gained phenomenal acceptance world-wide from those who recognize the need for reliable and sophisticated lighting control. Not only has it captured the imagination, but it's an affordable system employing the most advanced electronic technology. It is backed by the dependability of Kliegl expert engineering and service.

PERFORMANCE® has been installed in every type of facility from intimate community theatres to grand opera houses, television studios, Las Vegas showrooms and Broadway productions. PERFORMANCE® is now performing on four continents.

The growing list of satisfied users includes leading lighting designers who have "fallen in love with PERFORMANCE®," who term it "the lighting designers' fantastic tool" and who state emphatically "PERFORMANCE® really performs!"

PERFORMANCE.® The smart choice for tomorrow is here today.

Performance

- way before the IBM PC was released. This was a 16-bit processor that could do task switching very quickly so you really could build a real-time system out of it.

RB: But there really were no high-level development tools - you did this all in assembly language?

GP: Once you understand the concept of assembly language, you can program anything. Assembly language is assembly language, at least at the 16-bit level. You know, there aren't that many instructions. There aren't that many variations on the 16 bits as you have to use 8 bits as pointers. The instructions are simple. There's Jump and Adds.

So we built Performance, which was a very nice system. We introduced it at USITT in Washington DC 1977 and that was the same time that Strand brought Lightboard to the United States for the first time.[39] Fred Foster of ETC showed up at the same conference, and in his hotel room with his brother he had an absolute copy of Q-File written on an 8-bit Altair computer, thinking they were going to sell it to Kliegl because their mentor was Gil Helmsley, who was one of Joel's best buddies. They were convinced they were going to show it to Kliegl, but we're there with Performance all done and on the floor being shown and sold, and so on. (Fred himself has told this story a number of times.)

So Performance sold very nicely, and then I convinced Kliegl that what we needed was something portable. What was needed was something that sat on a tabletop. So then we did Performer.

RB: Much more suitable for touring. When did you do the Command Performance, because we had that at CBC?

GP: Somewhere in there!

RB: Didn't it have something crazy like bubble memory?

GP: Yes it did. I don't know how that actually worked, but I can tell you what they told me. It was a bunch of magnetic things they called bubbles, but I don't know what they were. It was an enormous shift register. If it was an 8k device, it had 8k times eight bubbles (plus, like any serial data, some header and trailer bits). So, you just shifted these bubbles around in a circle and you read them as they moved through the shifter. But it was very unreliable.

Performer really changed the whole business. Strand was still building Multi

---

[39] See Cunningham page 85 showing Light Palette at the same time.

Cue. At around the time we introduced Performer they introduced Light Palette, but the entire rental business went to Performers instantly. We just couldn't make them fast enough.

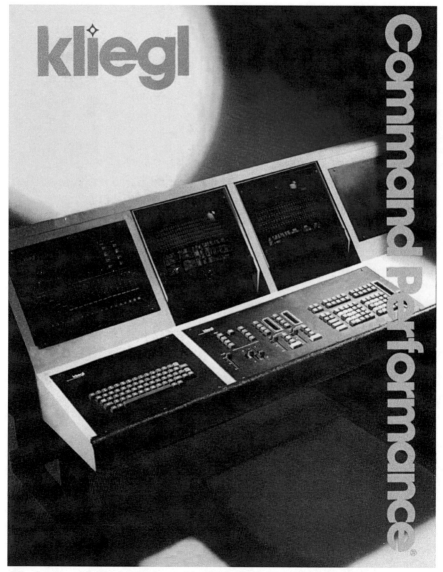

The Command Performance as used in CBC's Studio 7 with the K96 dimmers.

Then came Performer II and a whole family of Performer. They were all based on this TI microprocessor.

RB: So Steve and you are both at Kliegl?

GP: We were both working for Kliegl and we now had an office out in Portland with three or four employees and a regular R&D staff;

Performer 1

a PC board layout guy and a secretary and finally someone who was the Western Sales Manager, Lee Magadini. She was really working for me, because I was still the 'real' Western Sales Manager. It was all such a charade.

Also a spin-off of Performer was the Morpheus Commander.

RB: Where was Strand's Impact?

GP: Impact was just Performer III repackaged for Strand, with a few changes

in it. It was Performer II that spun into the Pan Commander. The Pan Commander was really the first generic moving light control console - the first one to look at the problem of, not this fixture or not that fixture, but as a generic thing.

John Richardson of Morpheus Lights had been using Kliegl Performers for controlling his new fixtures. You know: Channel 5 is Pan, Channel 6 is Tilt. He came to us and asked if we could modify the software to be more automated light friendly. So working with John and his senior operator Brad Malkus we developed the Commander line of consoles. Those were the days when automated fixtures were so new you had to keep making new

Unique new features provide the mastery performers demand.

PERFORMER® became an instant success when introduced to the entertainment market.
PERFORMER II™ incorporates the outstanding characteristics of PERFORMER® with unique new features.
PERFORMER II™ is the most versatile and effective lighting control system for those who demand the ultimate in control.
PERFORMER II™ provides the mastery many performers demand.

Performer II

The Commander is the automated lighting industry's only fully integrated system controller.

Commander

Impact 2

features on the console for the features on the light.

RB: You did a lot of the processing up in the 'Truss Boxes'?

GP: Originally we didn't do any. Everything was done in the desk. It was a DMX out console; the DMX did everything. Later, John Richardson[40] added some processing up in the truss boxes that did some swirls and turns and spun the gobos and that sort of thing.

RB: That philosophy of applying mathematical functions, as he did, was the basis for the Hog II Effects Engine.

GP: On the 'M' cues.

RB: Yes, because it is basically just taking the base value of a parameter and adding a dynamic profile of a waveform and altering the size and rate and offset into the function.

GP: And that is what he did up in the Truss Boxes.

RB: That's what we're all doing nowadays.

DMX was pretty new at this point.

GP: DMX came in at Performer II. I think the only difference between Performer and Performer II

---

[40] John, a lighting designer, founded Morpheus Lights in 1971 with his brother Brian. The console, the lights and the truss, which sort of acted as one and made them a choice for touring acts for quite some time.

is that Performer II had DMX and Performer had analog outputs.

RB: How was the DMX standard ratified?

GP: This was at a very quick meeting at USITT which Steve Terry had initiated to try and come up with a standard. Strand was of course pushing for their standard, which was analog.

RB: AMX.[41]

GP: Right. An analog bus with a digital clock. And Colortran wanted their standard, which was basically DMX at 152k baud (instead of 250k baud). The Colortran scheme made much more sense. First of all, it was digital. But the thing that made sense about it was that you didn't need any processor to receive it, because it used the break as the reset and any UART has a break detect in it.[42]

RB: You didn't need a processor for AMX.

GP: You didn't need anything for AMX. You just needed a demultiplexer. The problem with AMX was that it wasn't digital so it suffered from all the problems of any analog signal. It was very noise sensitive and it obviously attenuated over a length of wire and had all kinds of problems of that sort.

So Steve Carlson and I were still using analog on our desks and we decided that what we really wanted to use the Colortran standard.

RB: So you felt that you needed to make a quantum leap - not just go to multiplexed analog.

GP: And we were designing a pure digital dimmer called the K96[43] at the time and we thought it would be very nice to get the data digitally. We didn't want to put an A-D converter on the other end to get it back to digital.

---

[41] Analog Multiplexed (4-wire) – originally developed for Strand by David Cunningham. Dave also did the Colortran standard digital protocol.

[42] A UART is a Universal Asynchronous Receive/Transmit microchip – used on all serial ports. These chips can sense that a line has gone low for a set period of time (much longer than the average bit) and cause an interrupt, or another pin to go to a certain state. Monitoring this pin allows processors to 'service' the UART – or empty it of it's data. Most UARTs can hold about 16 bytes before needing to be serviced.

[43] One of the studios I did an awful lot of work in at the CBC had racks and racks of K96 dimmers. Gordon admits that the dimmer may have been ahead of its time causing it to be a disaster product. Its tragic flaw was that it didn't do enough samples to regulate out little bumps in the line. So if you had a little dip in the line, which of course the dimmers could cause, you could get lights going up when they should have been going down.

So, I wrote up this proposal and took it to the meeting and basically it was the Colortran standard, spelled out in really tight parameters, but also moving it up to 250k baud.

RB: And how did you learn about the Colortran standard?

GP: It was published; everybody knew it. We may have already built it into some product by that time.

So I just stood up at this meeting and said: "Here's what I propose". The only thing that I had over everybody else at the meeting was that I had it all written down already. So I passed it out to everybody and they passed it. That was it. That was the whole 'shabang'. It all happened in 20 minutes – and we've been fighting about it ever since!

RB: At that point, you and Steve were Kliegl employees. Where did Entertainment Technology come from?

GP: Well the way the deal with Kliegl was structured, I got a very small royalty on each system sold. Kliegl had one very basic rule: no one could make more money then John Kliegl and Performer was so successful that I was bumping up against that limit. So we split off the R & D department in Portland and Steve and I formed Entertainment Technology Inc.

RB: So Kliegl was the first and main contract – but there were others?

GP: Yes. At first we did do a little bit of other work for the phone company but mainly we were working for Kliegl. Then one day I get a phone call from a guy named Steve Carson (not to be confused with Steve Carlson). He says he is in San Francisco and would like to fly up to Portland the next day to meet us. No mention of what he wants. This is, of course, the same Steve Carson who is now the General Manager of the Vari-lite and ET divisions of Genlyte/Thomas.

RB: So what did he want?

GP: He shows up, blue serge suit, white shirt, tie, clearly not in our business. He is starting a new division of Lightolier (another Genlyte company) to build and market architectural lighting controls. They have a source for the normal "wall-box" products, but Steve had another Genlyte division design them a board-room/conference-room preset system.

RB: And what was it like?

GP: We have taken to calling it "The Big Ugly Black Box" ever since. The plan was to build a four channel - five scene preset system that could mount in the wall. The way they had approached this problem was to cram twenty trim pots, six preset buttons and the crossfade electronics into a box. This thing also contained four 600-watt dimmers and their electronics!

RB: I see why you called it the Big Ugly Black Box.

GP: So Carson says, "We can't get this to work. Can you fix it?" My immediate answer was, "No, we can't fix it but we could give you all the functionality and fit in a standard four gang box if you let us start over." We talked for a while and he said he'd be back in two weeks with his boss.

RB: So I assume you prepare to stand by.

GP: Not quite. They returned two weeks later and we had a complete working prototype. What we knew, which no one else had figured out, is that you can fire the Triac directly from the microprocessor. Except for a little electronic "glue" this unit contained a microprocessor, fourteen buttons, four triacs and four chokes. Everything including firing the triacs was done in the code. That product became the Lightolier Scenist. They are still manufacturing the same product today almost 20 years later.

RB: That's some resilience when you consider the average product (especially a code based product) is obsolete in three or four years.

GP: Well we were quickly doing much more work for Lightolier then we were doing for Kliegl. It was a good thing because John Kliegl had fired Joel Rubin and the quick slide to oblivion had begun.

RB: What other products did you do for Lightolier?

GP: That day when we showed them the first prototype of Scenist we negotiated a contract to design all of their multi-scene controls and dimmers. But while we were doing these projects we got the idea that you might be able to put a microprocessor in a single wall-box dimmer. On our own, we developed the "touch it fades up-touch it fades down" wall box dimmer and it had a single preset. All this was just building on our theatre experience.

RB: Sounds like your spring pot on the LS-8. What kind of microprocessor do you put in a wall box dimmer?

GP: A four bit processor that sells for less then fifty cents each, even way back then. This was a real challenge since you had 16 bytes of memory (RAM) and 512 bytes of code-store (ROM). Just so you're not confused here that's

16 Bytes not 16k or 16 meg.

We licensed that project to Lightolier and now there are hundreds of copies.

RB: This stuff took off. Why? What were you doing different?

GP: Everybody was looking at processor-controlled systems at that time. We had done one for Kliegl called Ambiance. But these systems all had a central processor and were designed for big spaces. The problem with central processor systems is that one half cent component can black out the whole building. What we did was to decentralize the whole project. If you had five meeting rooms then you had five separate controllers talking to any number of dimmer units. It let the sophistication of processor-based systems be used in the smallest of projects.

RB: So what did you do when the whole system had to combine into one big ballroom? Those are the systems I remember.

GP: We didn't want to give up the reliability that came with decentralization so we devised a scheme that was basically a Local Area Network. Originally we had a "traffic cop" server board to handle the communication, but we soon gave that up for a peer-to-peer network. Now you had the reliability of the decentralized system and you could still do all the room-combine stuff that only the central processor based systems could do. This style has certainly won out in the big picture; most installs are done this way today.

RB: So ET graduated to the real world and started making real money, but you didn't give up "Show Business".

GP: No, we probably should have, but we didn't.

RB: What was your next product for the entertainment market? (The name of the company didn't change!)

GP: My wife and I went on a trip to China with Illuminating Engineers Society; they had recently made me a Fellow in recognition of all the innovative controls.

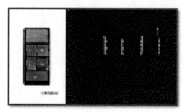
Scenist.

Joe Tawil of Great American Market was also on that trip. He kept pushing me to make something he could sell. So when I got home, Steve and I went to work on a low-end processor based lighting control system. We took the same processor we were using in the Lightolier multiscene products and basically did the same thing.

RB: What do mean by the same thing? There were other processor based controllers – you built some of them.

GP: Yes, but the GAM Access did everything in the code just like the Scenist. Its hardware was simple. It had seven sliders, a handful of buttons, a video chip from a cash register and a serial port to output DMX. Total manufacturing cost was well under $200. Considering its closest competitor sold for well over $7000, it was a great time.

RB: ET evolved from a consulting firm to a private label manufacturer. What made you decide to market your own line of products?

GP: In retrospect I guess you would have to attribute that decision to poor judgement, but it was time for a non-SCR based dimmer. So when we met the guys from Bayview Technology and saw they had an IGBT[44] dimmer they wanted to licence, we changed into a marketing and manufacturing company. As it turned out their product worked great on the bench but was not ready for real world electrical systems. A year later, after much work by Steve Carlson and I with the boys from Bayview, we had a product.

RB: IPS[45] dimming. How did that whole adventure work out?

GP: We have sold and continue to sell a lot of IGBT based dimmers. The whole idea seems to finally be taking off. I guess my desire to always live on the ragged edge of technology has its good and bad sides.

RB: Was it about this time that Rosco came into the picture?

GP: Not quite yet. First I came across this very bright PhD who had caught the "Show business" bug. Alan Martello had written a very interesting program called Fire Fly that used a standard PC as a lighting controller. He had solved the major

Great American Market Access (cost $140 to make).

---

[44] Insulated Gate Bipolar Transistor – see footnote 12 above

[45] Intelligent Power Supply ®

problem of making Windows, a non-realtime operating system, perform at what could be called realtime.

I could see that with my experience in console design and his software knowledge we could put together a real revolutionary product. We went to work on Horizon just about the same time as Rosco came into the picture. We were doing reasonably well for a very small company, but I was not having any fun and all my previous projects had basically been fun so I was looking for a way to get back to the fun.

RB: And Rosco provided that means.

GP: Or at least I thought they would. Stan Miller approached me at an NBC convention and asked if we might be interested in some type of merger/takeover. As I said I was ready to get back to the fun so we started to talk. It didn't take too long and Entertainment Technology became part of Rosco.

RB: The Rosco arrangement didn't last too long. What happened?

GP: You may think it wasn't too long, but from my end it was a long five years. What happened is that I still ended up running the business. So I didn't get back to fun. I just lost control. I must say the company grew over five fold during the Rosco years, so things were going along nicely, but it just wasn't a good fit. They sold expendables and we sold capital goods. Completely different things.

RB: But Horizon did get a start during those years.

GP: Yes, Alan and I continued to develop Horizon and Rosco gave it a grand send-off. They are still the major outlet for Horizon and they do a very good job. The problem was that while I was still doing *some* development, mostly I was running a bigger and bigger division.

RB: Enter Genlyte.

GP: I guess you could say that. I was down in Dallas for IAAPA[46] and I give my old friend Steve Carson a call, just to go out for a drink. He mentioned that he might be interested in licensing our IGBT technology for the architectural market. Well, to make a long story short, we negotiated a deal for him to buy ET from Rosco and get him in the entertainment business and me back to having fun developing new products.

RB: That pretty much brings us to today.

---

[46] International Association of Amusement Parks and Attractions

Windows Based Programming and Control

Hand-held Controller

Horizon control console

GP: Pretty close. The funny thing is how much this changed his business. We joined Genlyte Control as a little entertainment division of a big architectural company. Then he and the Genlyte/Thomas management see the entertainment business as a very open field and go out and acquire Vari-Lite. Now Genlyte Controls is a big entertainment lighting company with a smaller architectural division.

I am back doing development, which is my first love and they are growing ET by leaps and bounds. You never know how the cards will play out!

Capio Dimmers using the IGBT technology – now made in Dallas after the aquisition.

4 DAVID CUNNINGHAM

Introduction

If you've ever seen David Cunningham at a trade show, he was probably wearing black: black shoes, black socks, black trousers, black shirt – no tie, no hair, two girls. It is somewhat odd for a guy who likes to play dress-up. You see, since 1996, Dave has not had to work much and spends most of his time throwing lavish costume parties at his house in the Hollywood Hills.

He is categorically the most eccentric person in our industry. And quite likely the wealthiest. He is a genius of product design and business sense unlike any other, and has a better knack at combining the two than most. Very early in his career, he got into the habit of arranging business deals in which he would make a royalty on product sales. In the early days, this was tough, and as you will read, during ENR dimming days with Colortran, it can be even tougher. But through and through, this scheme has paid off in abundance, particularly with the success of ETC's Sensor dimmers and the Source Four line of lighting fixtures.

He has a way of making companies wealthy. His products first launched Strand to success, killing Kliegl in its path. Then he moved from Strand to Colortran, leaving Strand in the dust while rocketing Colortran to top position. When the

Colortran days ran their course, he helped ETC move from a console manufacturing company to the most successful theatrical manufacturer ever, making fixtures, dimmers and consoles. It's rather frightening to think what he might do next! During my interview, I asked him what his predictions of the future hold. He's pretty sure that the next revolution will be an alternate source of light, and he goes on to add: "But I'm not sure if I want to do that." The thing is, if he put his mind to it, he could.

Dave invited me to his place to do the interview. I was a tad nervous because I had heard of the infamy of 'The House' and I wasn't sure if we would be alone or with company. It's hard to separate the house, the place, and the events that go on there. It truly is a mix of Warhol and Hefner (but up a notch or two). Dave has hired 20 artists for the past six years to decorate the house. Each room has a theme. As you enter, the dining room is classic romantic with much inlaid woodcarving and detail. It looks out to the balcony, which has an Hawaiian theme. The main living room is art deco and comes complete with disco lighting and a control console that can reposition moving lights for photo opportunities. The kitchen is 'Western' with a wagon wheel chandelier and a miniature Cowboys and Indians scene playing out across the kitchen sink. The fridge has only water, beer and wine in it. The garage is decked out to look like the bat cave, complete with stalactites and a bat computer. You get the idea. And those are the rooms that don't have beds in them.

A few years ago, Dave would have up to one hundred of his friends around for movie nights or costume events that would last for days. Participation was mandatory. On one wall upstairs, 200 photo albums chronicle the events, in full-on fashion. Dave asked me not to take photos as one day he wants to publish his own book.

Interview

We did the interview in the main living room drinking bottled water and eating candied hearts that lay in a dish before us. I sat on the couch and Dave sat on the head of a huge Polar Bear rug.

RB: You have a physics degree?

DC: Sort of. I started in physics as UCSD[1] in 1965. You've got to remember, this is the beginning of the 60's. About half way through, I switched over to philosophy and chemistry and that's what I finished in. But I started teaching when I was 19 at UCSD.

---

[1] University of California, San Diego

RB: Teaching what?

DC: It's a little hard to explain, but I was doing acting and I said I wanted to do my own theater. So we got a building, we got funding for it, and set up a theatre on campus. This was mostly a science school (similar to Caltech[2]). There were a dozen Nobel Prize winners on the faculty. So I had all these science people - and artists too. It was an interesting mix of the two. So I was doing this as a teacher but I hadn't even graduated at that point. It was a unique time. There were only a few hundred undergraduates when I started and now there are something like 20,000. It's a big school now.

RB: Did you put together the funding and organisation?

DC: Yes, that's how I learned the whole business of running a creative group. I would go and hustle. I told people that this technology was going to change the world. I was just bullshitting, but it actually ended up happening.

There were two parts to the group. There was the performing group that was doing street performances like the San Francisco Mime Troupe and Open Theatre – and was involved in political activity. Then we created an indoor theatre and tried to do environmental work, which was tough. You couldn't do it then because there was no equipment. The objective was similar to what Cirque du Soleil is today. Everybody wanted to see visuals. Things were moving out of traditional theatre into psychedelic theatre.

RB: But without black lights, without Parcans . . .

DC: There was no equipment.

RB: No decent gel even.

DC: And, no computers. It was all manual. So what we did was get computers from the Physics Department and hooked them up to the lighting. This was in '68 or '69. Gordon Pearlman was doing the same sort of thing at the University of North Carolina.[3]

RB: He was doing it with slide projectors.

DC: And he was using a LS...

RB: LS-8 is what it ended up being. He was using a PDP-8.

DC: We were using some 'scientific' computer; some sort of microcomputer.

---

[2] California Institute of Technology

[3] Gordon started messing around with computers in 1970. See Pearlman – page 38

RB: And what were you finally driving with that?

DC: We built SCR dimmers and we built the lights and, well, we just built all the equipment, because we needed it. The dimmers were triacs.[4]

RB: Were there commercially available dimmers? What was Strand producing at the time?

DC: Edkotron six pack portable dimmers. They were SCR dimmers, but they were big and expensive. Edkotron was named after Ed Kook, who was running Strand at the time.

So we built all our own equipment. Every cent that I had went into the theatre. I was earning $300 a month.

RB: As a teacher?

DC: As a teacher. But then I got transferred because it was too radical for the school. Ronald Reagan[5] was cracking down on everybody doing weird stuff. There were all the radicals and the hippies and the Philosophy Department at UCSD was pretty extreme. It was at the centre of the new left. Herbert Marcuse taught at UCSD. I went to school with Angela Davis[6] and Eldridge Cleaver lectured on campus.

So we built all this equipment and the sixties ran out. I wondered what I could do with the designs. Then I met George Van Buren who won the Wally Russell Award[7]. The fact that he got it meant a lot to me because he was one

---

[4] Phase control dimmers use either triacs, SCRs, FETs or IGBTs. These are all devices that work as switches, turning the line on or off 120 times a second to "chop" the sine wave (100 times a second in Europe). SCR's FETs and triacs commonly use forward phase control, chopping the sine wave as it rises, and smooth out the waveform with a choke, while IGBT dimmers can use reverse phase control, chopping the back end and don't need a choke due to their ability to provide longer transition times between states.

[5] Reagan was Governor of California between 1967 and 1975.

[6] Davis closely studied the Communist party at USCD. In 1968, she became a member of the Communist party and joined the Black Panthers. The Black Panther Party were the FBI's public enemy of the then sixties "...racist pig power structure." It was her involvement in these radical groups that caused Davis to be watched very closely by the United States government. She was fired from her position as assistant professor of philosophy after teaching for only one year. In 1970, Davis became only the third woman in history to appear on the FBI's most wanted list.

[7] Wally Russell, a Canadian, ran Strand Lighting for years and was a mentor to many. First presented in 1992, posthumously to Wally, the prestigious Wally Russell Lifetime Achievement Award is presented annually to a leading figure in the entertainment design and technology field. Past "Wally" winners include: Jimmy Fuller in 2002; Jim Bornhorst in 2001; Stan Miller in 2000; Don Stern in 1999; Bran Ferren in 1998; Fred Bentham in 1997; Francis DeVerna in 1996; Tharon Musser in 1995; George van Buren in 1994; Robert Bell (New-Comer) in 1994; and Charles Altman in 1993.

of those people that nobody knew anything about. Very few people knew that he actually started the whole memory board thing with the Sweet Sixteen. The Sweet Sixteen was a 'hardware' system.

Wally Russell - 1934-1992.

RB: Latches and gates and that sort of thing.

DC: Yes, but I did a computer system for Van Buren. They sold a total of six systems. I learned a lot about how *not* to do business from George. He was brilliant, but he would take game show specials and that sort of thing. He loved the challenge. He was great in that respect. But he would take these jobs, under-bid them, and take on way too much work - but he would always make it happen.

RB: The company was called Van Buren Industries.

DC: Yes, that was his own company, but when he ran out of money, he made an exclusive deal with Strand and they just killed his business: they killed the competition.

RB: So George got the second Wally, after Charles Altman. But what happened to the New-Comer Award?

DC: It was hard to find new-comers. We could find lots of old people that had done things, but it was hard to spot someone that was coming up with something new. So you got the first and last one.

RB: I'm sad (especially because I'm Canadian) that I've never got to meet Wally. He died just before I got into the industry in earnest.

DC: A lot of people don't know how much he did. He helped create Vari-Lite, behind the scenes. He was Rusty's[8] advisor. He also influenced Strand, Colortran, and Theatre Projects.

---

[8] Rusty Brustché and Jack Maxon founded Showco, a sound and lighting equipment rental house, in 1970 that turned into Vari-Lite in 1981 after the prototype of the VL Zero was shown to long-time clients Genisis and they put in an order for 50 units. The original intent was to create a whole new fixture that changed colour, using dichroic glass rather than adding gel to a conventional fixture. Adding two more motors to the fixture for movement set the path for Vari-Lite to change the face of the industry. Vari-Lite went public in 1997 and in 2002, Genlyte Thomas Group acquired all assets of Vari-Lite's manufacturing and sales division.

Working for George was interesting. I learned a lot about the business and of course it was an opportunity to do a software system.

RB: He originally designed *Sweet Sixteen*, with its bunch of hardware logic gates. Then you came in and used a microprocessor to re-build the same spec. How did the product evolve once you jumped in?

DC: I think I just drew some sketches of what the system was going to be and George said: "OK, go do it. You've got six months; we've got to deliver one to UCLA." It was done on a PDP-11. So a programmer from UCSD came up and the two of us did the whole system. Unfortunately, George didn't have the marketing set-up, and we only sold six.

RB: What were the specs on the thing?

DC: It had 120 scenes and it had a full manual wing because nobody was ready to go away from that yet. It was all analogue in and out. It was designed to simulate an analogue board. It was a single scene preset and 120 memories and two cross-faders. But they were not dip-less cross-faders because I didn't understand what the point of a dip-less cross-fader was at the time.[9]

RB: Had you heard of Gordon Pearlman by this point?

DC: No, not at Van Buren. Gordon was working with Kliegl, which was the dominant company at the time. Their sales were about $10 million, in 1970 dollars. Strand was starting to pick up and it eventually developed into a big duel between Strand and Kliegl.

RB: So you went from Van Buren Industries to Strand?

DC: No. After Van Buren, I got a backpack and went to Europe for six months. Then I lived in Berkeley and did the whole Bohemian thing. When I got back, I wanted to do another project. By that point, the salesman for Van

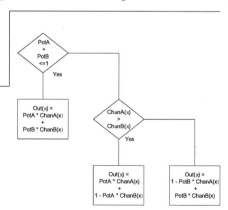

[9] Dip-less cross-faders are important if you want to go from one look to another where the lights should just move in one direction. There are combinations where if you just do an electronic cross-fade, the lights can start moving up, then dip down for a second in the middle of the fade and ultimately settle at their higher, desired level.

Buren, Don Hamilton, had started to work for Wally Russell. He said I had to meet this guy Wally, as he was really cool. I sat down with Wally and I said we could sell 50 systems - because that's where the price break was.

RB: Where was Wally then, Strand?

DC: Wally had just left Strand Canada. They moved him down to run the US operation, but the US operation was at $1 million in sales and falling. They were told only to sell the British product – the MMS.[10] That was a real complicated system, with all these circuit cards.

RB: And again, logic gates.

DC: All logic gates.

RB: Was Richard Pilbrow doing Lightboard yet?[11]

DC: That came years later. Wally was told to only sell the British products and Kliegl was the dominant company with the Q-File, which was pretty economical compared to the MMS, but it was very limited. Wally was under strict orders not to develop anything. He decided that Strand was going to go out of business if he didn't get any new products, and that he was basically there to shut the company down. He said he needed a memory system for a secret project (he had two MMS's sitting in the wings in case we didn't get it done, but he never told me that until afterwards). He said that I had five months to deliver the system. I said: "Sure we can do it in five months." We really did get it done, but I had no idea how ridiculous it was to do a complete system in that amount of time. I only had two other people, a draftsman, and a programmer.

RB: This is Multi-Q?

DC: Yes. So we just started working on it and a week before the deadline, I found out that it was for *A Chorus Line* – the touring production. It was because Electronics Diversified was in a lawsuit with Skirpan over the use of CRT's so Four Star didn't want to buy Gordon's console because they were afraid they would get sued.[12] So Wally promised a whole new system, and they

---

[10] Modular Memory System. A console that could control between 60 and 480 channels by adding more modules.

[11] Lightboard was built in 1976 and used a processor. The MMS using hard logic was released in 1973.

[12] Stephen Skirpan manufactured high end dimming and control – mostly for TV. Gordon's LS-8 was used on the Broadway Production of *A Chorus Line*, but it used a CTR to display the channel levels, apparently in violation of a Skirpan patent. See Pearlman page 58

ordered two of them - one for the Toronto show and one for the San Francisco show. I had no idea what it was for.

So Tharon Musser showed up a week before delivery and I showed her the board. It didn't have any split cross-faders. She looked at it and said you need split faders. So we added a split cross-fader off to the side.

Chuck Levy was involved. He was the Strand guru. He knew all the New York designers and had excellent connections. And Wally kept Ed Kook in the background as a business advisor. Ed Kook started Century (later to become Strand) and had been at the company forever. (That is where Leko comes from – Levy/Kook.)

So Wally did the new system – even though he was told not to. When it went out on *A Chorus Line* everybody wanted one. So Broadway went from road-boards to memory systems overnight. We went to a trade show and there were 50 sales already. They weren't expecting it to be so successful.

RB: They also had to get solid-state dimmers in the theatre too.

DC: That was the second project. I hated patch panels. I said there should be a dimmer for every light, but you had to make the dimmer cheaper. So we did the CD80, which was the first economical SCR dimmer with the elimination of the wiring, and it evolved through the years.

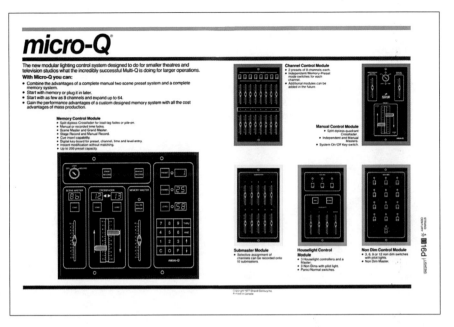

RB: I guess this would have been about 1980.

DC: Yes. 1979, or '80.

RB: I had the misfortune of being at CBC where we had CD90's.

DC: CD90 was after my time . . . Strand went backwards. CD80 was a two- or three-fold cost reduction over the old dimmers. It cut the price of the dimmer in half, which let you eliminate patch panels.

RB: You built the tower first.

DC: Yes, then the CD80 Pack, then Environ, the architectural system. The development group at Strand was a very productive group and we would come out with five or six products a year while Kliegl was coming out with one. Performance was their response to Multi-Q. By the time they came out with Performance, there was Light Palette. As soon as they would come out with something, our new product would be ready, because I was always developing the next generation. After Kliegl did Performance, they did the Performer.

RB: That's where things get a little strange and it all overlaps. Strand took the Kliegl Performer and branded it as the Impact.

DIMMER MODULES

CD80 series
STRAND CENTURY

Compact, economical plug-in modules
• Ideal for dimmer per circuit applications
• Heavy gauge aluminum chassis
• Heavy duty, self-aligning power and control plug
• Two silicon controlled rectifiers
• Toroidal chokes
• Plug-in non dim modules available

STRAND CENTURY

STRAND CENTURY INC.
20 Bushes Lane
Elmwood Park, New Jersey 07407
U.S.A.
Tel: (201) 791-7000 (212) 564-6910
Telex: 130322

STRAND CENTURY INC.
3432 West 102nd Street
Los Angeles, California 90045
U.S.A.
Tel: (213) 776-4600
Telex: 653508

STRAND CENTURY CO. LTD.
6520 Northam Drive
Mississauga, Ontario, Canada
L4V 1H9
Tel: (416) 677-7130
Telex: 06908646

DC: Performer was actually a very popular product. Impact came after I left Strand.

I developed Multi-Q and Micro-Q. Micro-Q was the mini version of Multi-Q. The next generation was Light Palette, Mini Light Palette and Mini Palette.

RB: Then they went into Light Palette 90 and Mini Light Palette 90…

DC: Anne Valentino had been influenced by her time at Kliegl in the Light Palette 90 design. But at ETC she was trying to put move/fades and presets together on the same desks. I guess it sort of worked, but they really are very different lighting philosophies.

The cool thing about Light Palette was that it was done as a move/fade board.

RB: Because all the earlier computer desks were mimics of preset desks it was easy. It was just like a PLD[13] storing a bunch of values. You start here, go to here and make a nice easy transition.

DC: Move fades came about after talking to Chuck when I went with him to New York. He said the new boards were great, but there were things that you couldn't do that you used to be able to do with autotransformers. Light Palette was an autotransformer emulation board. The electricians would take the handle and say go-to a level… It would just be move-to instructions. So Broadway loved Light Palette because they got back to what they were used to, but they could do hundreds of changes instead of being limited to the number of arms and legs of the electricians.

RB: Anne described to me in detail about Chuck building the syntax because he went into the theatre and listened to how the designers were talking to the electricians.[14]

---

[13] Programmable Logic Device

[14] See Valentino page 152

Light Palette

DC: That's what *I* did. But Chuck is the one who got me into the theatres. We would have endless discussions about the board design. Chuck helped keep me on track, and Wally was also very design oriented. So at five o'clock when Wally was sick of doing all the accounting and boring bits of running the company we would hold these design meetings between the three of us where we would discuss how the console would work. Wally was extremely insightful because he had done lighting design and Chuck knew all the Broadway people. He totally kept things on track. So it was really this creative team that actually made it happen.

Chuck and I went out with Jules Fisher with the first version of Light Palette on *Beatlemania* in Chicago and it was awful. I sat there and watched the electrician go through ten operations to get one thing done. That's what Anne was talking about. I would watch them and see how they used the board, then go back and change it. That was a good design strategy.[15] Because a lot of people who were engineering the boards were just engineers, they would think in terms of engineering solutions, and they couldn't relate to board operators, who were all union. So these guys were pretty . . .

RB: . . . hard to convince.

---

15. See Thin Ice on page 13 for a discussion of "From Spec" vs. "On Site" design approaches.

DC: Yes. Also, they were not very communicative. You would just have to watch how they were running the board.

RB: The Light Palette syntax has been persistent through the years. It has been the root of the design of so many desks since then.

DC: I think they have finally gone away from it – the whole command structure.[16] The idea was you would type in what the lighting designer would say to the board operator.

RB: Group 5 @ 80.

DC: Or Channel 15 @ Full. Then Enter.

RB: That was the big thing - the termination of the command. Can you remember the syntax of the older stuff?

DC: The preset desks didn't really have a syntax. They were: 'Record'. You set the handles, typed in the preset number, and hit 'Record'. So it didn't operate like a syntax; it was more like a… I don't even know what that is. You would set things up then push a button to make it do what you wanted. I did every single IC on those early boards. I did the trace layout (not always personally, but I would check it all) – some of it on the back of napkins.

RB: There was no routing software back then.

DC: No, there was nothing. It was all IC logic. I only had a draftsman to help, so I would figure out all the logic circuits and the hardware and we would just put it in a box. But using the PDP-11 as a buy-out, that got a lot of the computing stuff out of the way.[17] So basically, you would use a buy-out computer then you would interface it to the real world through A-D converters and D-A converters.

Light Palette was the first one that did the A-Mux. I remember saying: "There's a lot of wires in here. It would be cooler if there were just a few wires." So it was just a clock with an analogue line on it and sample-and-holds at the dimmers. So the CD 80 had sample-and-holds. Then it would persist; I think it had a half-second hold time. We were doing a 20 Hz refresh, which was fast enough to keep the levels stable. So there was a lot of analogue hardware in there: D-A's, sample-and-holds and multiplexers.

---

[16] Again, Anne thanks Flying Pig for finally breaking the back of the rudimentary structure that Broadway was stuck in for so many years. See Valentino – page 159

[17] See Pearlman re: embedded systems page 59

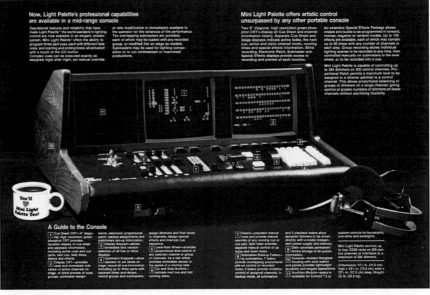

Light Palette

RB: I remember when the Advanced Electronics came out on the CD80's we were all very happy. At CBC we had tons and tons of CD80 Packs with just AMX boards. So we always had all these converter boxes. We called them Higgins' Boxes.[18]

DC: Did that switch them over to digital?

RB: You could use DMX or AMX or SMX (the Strand protocol that never really came about) and you also had the individual dimmer test buttons right on the front, which was a huge deal. I guess you were gone by that point.

DC: Wally lasted until about 1982 at Strand. But because he was doing stuff they told him not to, he got fired – even though the company went from $1 million to $25 million in sales under his guidance.

Wally was always rebelling. His first rebellion was when they told him not to do any development, because the British wanted the US company to sell their products. I remember when Richard Pilbrow demonstrated Lightboard at the same convention where we introduced the Light Palette[19]. In one room was the Lightboard at $250,000 and in the other room was the Light Palette

---

[18] Dave Higgins founded Gray Interfaces, now Pathway Connectivity.

[19] USITT 1977 – Washington DC L'Efant Hotel Gordon was also showing Performance – see page 61

and they walked in and looked at it and said: "Oh shit!" – because it did the same thing for $20,000. Lightboard was a move fade board like Light Palette because Richard believed in move fades.

RB: That was it for the British and tracking desks. Even today the Strand 500 series (running GeniusPro software) comes up, by default, as a preset desk. Much of London's West End still thinks that way.

DC: But Richard, as a lighting designer, was the one that gave them the idea of the wheels and groups and 'painting with light'.

RB: That was pretty revolutionary stuff.

DC: But the changes happened simultaneously in the US and the UK, because Richard was working with the British and we were doing the Light Palette. But Light Palette was more successful because it was a $20,000 board and Lightboard wasn't.

RB: Imagine if Richard had emigrated from the UK to the US during those days what you and he could have come up with.

Now Light Palette had a CRT. How did you get around the Skirpan patents?

DC: Multi-Q had a monitor, rather than a built-in CRT, which may have been the difference. Skirpan exhausted himself going after the LS-8 in the lawsuit and both companies just got worn out and they never went after us.[20]

RB: What was his story?

DC: Skirpan had a lot to do with the television networks and he got the reputation of having super high quality, high performance equipment. He ended up being the TV guy. He made it hard to break into selling to television with things like high rise time chokes on his dimmers[21]. But he didn't keep up with the volume.

The big change with Strand was high volume/mass production. The manual systems and even the MMS's were custom built. Every console was custom built. So basically you would specify how you wanted it to look: I want this here, I want that there. So the big change was basically making the Model-T: a modular dimmer and a standard console.

---

[20] See Howell on thoughts of patents page 353

[21] Chokes are the large coils of copper and iron that smooth out the choppiness of what the SCR do when they cut up the sine wave to make a dimmer. TV studios are particularly sensitive to the noisy filament hum when you use low quality dimmers. Rise time refers to the amount of rounding a choke can do to a chopped waveform. Bigger chokes give higher rise times.

There were even arguments about standardization. In Multi-Q the panels had sixteen faders. They said: "What if somebody wants thirteen?" I said we would give them sixteen then, give them the extra ones. They said people would never go for that. In the old manual systems, they would wire in each potentiometer in a custom punched panel that was designed and approved by the lighting consultant. So every single board was a custom board.

RB: Just imagine the documents that would have to follow that.

DC: You could never do it. So ours was the beginning of 'mass production'. The CD80 and the Multi-Q helped do that for the industry, which I think was a really good move. It brought the cost down and let you do dimmer per light. It then let memory systems get into high schools and colleges, where they could never have been afforded before because you went from a $200,000 console to a $5000 or $10,000 console. I think Micro-Q was down around $5000.

So the market went from sales of 20 consoles a year to hundreds of consoles a year, which was a big move.

RB: So you did AMX when you developed CD80 and Light Palette?

DC: The first Multi-Q was analogue, then Light Palette was AMX. There was an option to go fully analogue, although nobody ever bought it. The original Multi-Q had a full preset wing. The first few consoles went out with them and then people said: "We don't need this". They realized they could control everything by the wheel.

RB: I'm still fighting that with Horizon. People still want individual faders to control each channel. I say that is very good for building the first cue, and maybe the second cue because you may add something, but in the third cue when you want to pull something down, but it's on-board, you have no choice but to grab it by the wheel. You can't use a pot to override what's on-board.

DC: The whole preset wing is a hold-over from preset lighting, which made sense in the early systems. It was a hold-over from two scene/three scene presets and they didn't want to give that up.

RB: It's still a spec thing. I guess we'll have to wait for all the old specifiers to die. Having lots of pots for channels is very silly, except maybe when they move by themselves. I've recently been using the grandMA with flying faders. You can now go to a cue and the fader will follow it. If you don't like the look, you can just grab them and move the level.

DC: Siemens had a system like that in the '70's, but it was one of those $200,000 - $300,000 consoles. You could call up a preset and all the handles would move, then you could adjust them. They did that a long time ago, but it was impractical because the hardware was impractical.

RB: MA Lighting has managed to find hardware, in this day and age, where it actually works. Mostly due to the audio industry, I think.

DC: Sound guys still want all those knobs.

RB: You know what – they are actually getting away from it. For years I worked on the Canadian music awards shows and we, obviously, had memory desks and took up a small footprint, but the audio guys still had these huge desks. That show would be about 192 inputs so they were just surrounded by hardware. But then Céline Dion would come on the show and insist on her own mix. She had a Soundcraft Broadway desk that you basically plug into a 120v outlet and a Cat5 cable that goes to the stage. All inputs terminated at the stage in this telephone booth and all the processing is done locally there. The desk is very small and looks like a lighting board. It has flying fades and you bang through groups. You mix the drum group, and then hit a button and it throws up the horn group and you mix that. Then during the show, if you want live fades you just hit a Go button. So, audio desks are finally getting to the position you brought us to in the 70's.

DC: Especially since everything is digitised. There are those who still say analogue is better. But if you like that, then you just simulate the noise.

RB: Exactly. If you're sampling it at twice or more the rate of your highest frequency, you can hardly beat that.

DC: But there are still audio people who want tubes. I don't know if they still exist, but tubes had a quality that people liked.

RB: Yes, they distort the even harmonics rather than the odd harmonics.[22]

DC: But if you really understand what it's doing, then you can simulate it digitally.[23] It's finally happening, but audio is even a worse industry because there is so much subjectivism.

RB: Everything can be done on a PC nowadays. But Horizon is still losing

---

[22] Transistors produce hard clipped harmonics when overdriven, which can sound hollow or dry, were as the softer clippings of a tube produce even harmonics that sound warmer.

[23] See discussion on Nicholas Negroponte page 290

that battle. Today – in 2003 – people still want the furniture.

DC: That was an opportunity I missed because I stopped doing consoles in 1990. I had just done too many. I think it was 25 consoles if you count all the little variations. The last one would have been a motherboard (a PC) with an ergonomic interface on a little cord. That is what Gordon is still fighting. But you don't need a big piece of furniture; you just need this little custom piece with some wheels and some handles.[24] You still have to deal with the human operator.

RB: David Hersey was doing a re-design of a West End show and I was asked to program it. I told Gordon that I wasn't going to go until he gave me some wheels. I was not going to pan and tilt lights with a mouse, or mix colours on stage using three dialog boxes on the screen.

DC: Did he ever make a little add-on that plugged in the back?

RB: No, what we did was go on-line to xkeys.com and we bought these little USB keypads that are built for video editing. They have a row of buttons on the side, a row of buttons on the top and a jog/shuttle wheel in the middle. So I got three of those and plugged them into a USB hub.

DC: So it was basically a soft console and you programmed in what all the handles do and you interfaced it to Horizon.

RB: The funny thing is that other industries are split on the issue. All movies are edited on Avid systems and Avid's just take the average 101 keyboard and put funny coloured keys on it with labels, and people are quite happy editing Star Wars with a 101 keyboard. But our industry still insists on having a certain amount of tactile feedback.

DC: Lucky for the manufacturers.

---

[24] At the time of this interview, I couldn't tell David, but we were in the middle of development of the Marquee console. Marquee is Horizon software running a Windows XP Embedded PC hooked, via USB, to a sexy pace panel that has 48 pots, two split cross-faders, some wheels and programming buttons. Since I joined the Horizon camp (fall of 2000) I've wanted to build a desk, but mergers and acquisitions and lots of other business had continually delayed the efforts. I have always had faith in the core Horizon software, but it never sold as well as many desks because of the lack of a good user interface. Nowadays, many new consoles are using the Windows OS – mainly because Microsoft has finally made Windows stable and processing power has become so cheap and so fast that you no longer have to worry about getting the system to be truly real-time.

The idea of using a 'face-panel' and a PC is not at all new. The Flying Pig Whole Hog I did it quite successfully, whereas the High End Status Cue didn't have such a good go at it – even if they sold more than the Hog I.

RB: Well, today, everybody has an off-line version of their console that runs on a PC and with Pathports and Art-Net nodes and all these other Ethernet based things. You don't need all the superfluous furniture.

DC: So you can do all the work ahead of time then just load it into the console when you get there.

RB: Or not bother.

DC: Or not bother. You just run the program and say 'this is it'.

RB: Flying Pig had the ability to release Hog PC years before they did, but...

DC: . . . they didn't want to eat up their hardware sales.

RB: You only make money when you ship boxes out the door. That was the stigmatism we had with WYSIWYG. We were trying to sell . . .

DC: . . . software. And people don't get it. The software industry works that way, but it's a tough business. You have to sell a chunk of something.[25] And if you don't have good copy protection then you have multiple copies.[26] I don't know how well you were able to protect WYSIWYG.

RB: On the first WYG we had the DMX interface card that would do all the DMX reception.

DC: So that was your key.

RB: Then in the newer versions it was done with a dongle. Some people say just hide keys in the registry, but then he calls back saying his hard drive crashed or worse still he figures it out and tells his friends. I still want to ship something out the door.

DC: Who knows where it's going. What is going to happen when we get the next generation of interaction with PC's such as voice recognition, when you eliminate the mechanical interface altogether? That is going to be a hard one to beat. If you can just talk to the system, then you just tell it what to do. Although, that doesn't seem to have happened yet.

RB: Didn't Avab try it years and years ago? I know there was a desk at the National Arts Centre in Ottawa that talked to the operator.

DC: But voice recognition wasn't very good then.

---

[25] See Cornwell page 269 regarding how he had to build boxes to sell his software.

[26] See McKernon page 139 regarding his efforts to curb piracy.

RB: You need massive processing power.

DC: Voice recognition was one of Wally's dreams.

RB: Well, you have figured out the language for us.

DC: It would be a command structure anyway. It was like writing down a sentence then saying 'go do it'. It actually was a good idea; it's just that the equipment wasn't available for it to happen.

RB: You could probably do it now with two buttons - a clear button and an enter button. You clear, then you start talking, then you look at it and say that looks good and you execute it.

DC: You would need a wheel.

RB: Yes, I guess you would want to look at the stage and feel it.

DC: There is that one tactile thing.

RB: So what happened to Wally?

DC: Wally rebelled against the British and eventually got fired, which was awful. They gave him two weeks notice and told him he was 'out' after he had done so much for the company.

RB: Who did it?

DC: It was the Rank people. Although frequent management changes saved him for a while. Somebody would get shifted right before they were ready to fire him. So he kept getting reprieves.

He was very customer oriented. He used to say: "I want to do this because it makes cool lighting. Not because I'm trying to get the last dollar out of people." But the products were incredibly profitable.

RB: High tech marketing experts say you should market towards the end user – not the people with the buying power.[27]

DC: That's where he was going and that's why he succeeded. Because he loved theatre and had done lighting and he had been technical director for the Canadian Opera. So he wanted to make cool products for theatre and that was a winning business strategy.

RB: That is a common trait among the vast majority of us in this industry. We do it because we like it. There are so many people in our industry that are

---

[27] See Valentino and Geoffrey Moore page 173

passionate about what they do, and they do it because they want to make good theatre at the end of the day. Most of us are not driven by pure business sense.

DC: Another strategy is to do things to bring the costs down, like we did with CD80. On the CD80 we went through every single part. There was nothing in there that wasn't necessary. Strand's original product, the CCR 300, was a 2k dimmer that was huge and had a lot of wiring in it. The CD80 was about getting rid of all the wiring and you got exactly the same product but the manufacturing cost was a one-third. So then you cut the price to the customer in half and you still get high margin product. So the customer wins and the company wins. Also, the customers buy more product, because it's less expensive.

RB: But you wonder why the philosophy that Wally pursued on this side of the pond didn't fly on the other side. Was it just British arrogance?

DC: You worked at the CBC. You know the mentality that you get there.[28] "It has to have the rise-time of 500.1…" Do you need it? No. Three hundred was OK. It was just that the lamps didn't make noise anymore. There was a rigid mentality about what products had to do and how they had to perform and how it had to be packaged and how it had to look. A lot of it is really protectionism. It was the British market protecting itself from the Germans, from the French and from the US. Some progress is being made and things are beginning to change.

You were talking about the commercial side of things. If you bring the manufacturing cost down – if you really do a number on it – then you end up with not only a profitable product, but also a really good product for the end customer. You can see this in consumer electronics. You see how much you get in a CD player. But that is because you spend an enormous amount of money tooling it and engineering it and making it low cost. If you went out and wanted to build a CD player yourself, you couldn't do it. But if you're going to make hundreds of thousands of them or even millions of them, you can deliver a lot to the end user and still make money.

---

[28] When I took the concept of WYSIWYG to my bosses at CBC and told them we could market it worldwide, they stated (rightfully so), "We don't make software; we make television." With that, I was out the door.

[29] Christie Lites Manufacturing is now called Spectrum Manufacturing Inc. and was purchased by AC Lighting Limited in 2003.

RB: It's like Christie Lites Manufacturing[29] did a lot of tooling for the injection moulding for the Chroma-Q scroller. The whole thing is fully plastic (or composite).

DC: Are they the people who bombed the price of scrollers?

RB: Oh yes. They halved the price or more, because they spent thousands and thousands of dollars on tooling. But, instead of bending metal and punching it and riveting it together, and mounting PC boards inside it on stand-offs, and fly-wiring off to the connectors, they spent tons of money building this tool. Now they just go boop, boop, boop. Everything about it, the hinges, the springs on the door - everything is all part of the same injection.

DC: If you go back to Strand in 1975, where everything was a custom console, that mentality persisted for a long time in the industry, and I still think there are vestiges of it.

RB: When you talk of these custom-built bits of furniture, that must have flowed over to the software (or logic) side of development too.

DC: That was another reason why the Strand thing worked. There was a bit of a fight. Sales wanted to sell whatever it took to get the job and they were used to saying: "OK, you want another cross-fader? OK, I'll give that to you." "You want 200 memories?" "You want it to do this?" I said 'no'. It either had to be standard or we would have to develop a new generation product that covered the requirements. That is what kept the specials under control at Strand and Wally backed that philosophy. Because if you just have sales selling whatever they want, then you will get into a lot of problems. I still see that with giant projects like LDS. [30]

RB: It killed it.

DC: Large projects like the MGM and the other Vegas hotels normally required something very unique. But rather than make special software or special hardware, you basically look at the demands of the market and build it into the next generation of product. So when you do the next product, you then have something that will meet everybody's needs.

RB: But even presidents of companies are so easily driven by these specials.

---

[30] The huge Church of the Latter Day Saints job in Salt Lake City that ETC took. The spec demanded so many modifications to the Obsession code that it just overwhelmed the R&D team and fragmented the code base.

They look at the spec of a job and think they just need to put two guys on it for six months to do the modification and they've got the order – 2500 dimmers out the door.

DC: It's a three million dollar order and they say, "Yes great!" But what you miss is the twenty million dollars in business that the same investment in development could have achieved. So you get a one-shot special bid – and, worse yet, you never bid it right. I'm sure you've worked on special projects where they go out of control and things don't work out.

RB: Some of them pay off. Sometimes because it's R&D you wanted to do in the first place, or other times because of the publicity it gives you. We did the Super WYG for the Millennium Dome. We got a lot of distributed processing and multi-threading R&D out of that job. It also got a lot of press.

If the project works, it can be a feather in your cap and you can use it as a marketing tool. But then you have other projects where it just sucks you dry.

DC: There were a few projects that almost killed both Strand and Kliegl. I think they were the two MGM's. They were big prestigious projects at the time, but they almost bankrupted both companies.

So, back to Wally, He left Strand in 1982 and then they brought in the 'business' people: the corporate people, the bean counters. They were actually OK people, but they didn't have the same passion for the theatre. I remember after Wally left, I gave them two years' notice.

RB: So you were on staff?

DC: I was working there. I had a very small salary but I had other arrangements that were related to the products.

RB: So you had your royalty arrangements set up that early?

DC: From when I was with George. Of course, he never sold anything so it didn't matter much then.

RB: But you are rare. So many of us will just prostitute ourselves for anything - the chance to work on something.

DC: Yes, I don't know where the idea came from. It just kind of happened and it wasn't worth very much in the beginning, but it certainly ended up being a good business model. Controlling the patents and doing patent licences is just better from an inventor's point of view.

So I stayed at Strand one year and nine months after Wally left. There were

25 people in R&D then and I was Vice President R&D. In the meantime, I learned a lot from all these business people. In the board meetings, everybody wanted to educate me. It definitely was an education!

RB: There are people who don't have a passion for the theatre but they look at certain companies and realize that they could have been run better and think there is money to be made.

DC: Yes, and there probably is, but it's a combination of how you get the passion and the understanding of the business and the products and run it like a business. Then you have to manufacture the products with proper quality control. You don't want to make equipment that doesn't work.

When I left Strand I really didn't have any plans at all. There were only three companies - Kliegl was out by that point - so Stand was the dominant company, and then there was Electro Controls and Colortran. So I went out to Electro Controls and they were interested, but the vibe didn't connect.

Then I went and talked to Ken Boyda at Colortran and he said: "Perfect". They really didn't have a development group. They were buying consoles from ETC. So I started Entertec, which never really got to be more than 12 people. Eventually, all the good people at Strand left and came to Entertec.

So it was much the same group, and these guys are still together. They moved from Strand to Entertec and now they're at ETC. Everybody thinks the same way. It reminds me of doing theatre. It was like I'm the director, and this was the lighting guy and the sound guy . . . but instead they were programmers and engineers. It was a very creative environment and everybody knew exactly what to do since they had been working together for years. It made it very efficient.

RB: Where was Entertec?

DC: It was in Century City in LA, then down to the bottom of the hill on Sunset Boulevard. Then it moved into the house, because I didn't want to drive down the hill. So Source Four was built in the Moroccan theatre room downstairs, which was the light lab.

RB: Is it now defunct?

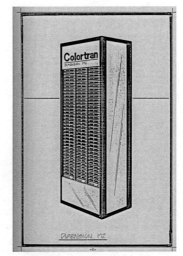

Dimension 192

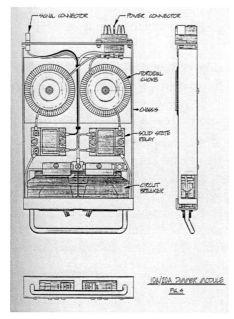

Colortran ENR dimmer module concept.

DC: In 1996, everybody moved to ETC so they would have jobs.[31]

When we first started, even some of the sales people came to Colortran because they didn't like the bureaucracy at Strand.

RB: I asked the people in Portland - as they were meeting the people from Dallas for the first time after Genlyte bought ET - what were they like? I had not met any of them yet as I was in Toronto and the people in Portland were all about to lose their jobs. Their answer was: "Shiny shoes".

DC: The corporate guys.

So I ran the R&D group from outside Colortran and licensed things to them. The products that I worked on for them were the Dimension 192, the Prestige series of consoles: Prestige 1000, 2000, and 3000, and finally ENR (Electronic Noise Reduction).

RB: What year would that be?

DC: It started in 1984 and went through to 1990.

RB: And that is where you did the Colortran digital multiplexed protocol?

DC: The first console we did had a RS232 protocol that became DMX.[32]

---

[31] Dave 'retired' in 1996 after the success of Sensor and Source Four. I remember a very amusing event at the 2000 Broadway Lighting Master Class. On the big night they had, what I called, the Four Yorkshire Men. It was a panel of Wally nominees moderated by Steve Terry, including Dave, Sonny Sonnefeld, Stan Miller and Don Stern. The other nominees are all senior to Dave and Steve asked: "What do you see yourself doing from here?" These guys, who have lived very busy lives and contributed masses to the industry, each in turn, gave a detailed description of what they aimed to achieve. From the audience, you could clearly see that they all should have been sitting by a pool in Florida sipping Martinis rather than slogging on in this sometimes thankless industry. Knowing the plethora of gear Dave is responsible for inventing, everyone was on the edge of their seat, thinking we were going to get a sneak preview of amazing things to come from the genius himself. His answer was, bluntly – "I'm pretty much retired."

[32] RS232 and RS484 are very similar. 232 is strictly point to point, where you can have multiple drops on 485. These are just electrical interfaces – the same protocol can be used on either. 485 is also (cont...)

Steve Terry wanted to change the baud rate so we just had to switch the clock rate. I wasn't at the standards meeting.[33] I guess that was one I should have probably been at. I was happy that everyone finally agreed on a standard. It allowed people to buy consoles from one company and dimmers from another and lights from another.[34] They could just go to the lowest bidder. Everybody would buy Altman's lights, and often you would try to get the dimmers and the console together if you could. DMX allowed the consoles to be broken out. So now you could get the best consoles, the best dimmers and the best lights. In the past, you used to have to have them integrated because they didn't have a common protocol.

RB: So ENR got a little messy, didn't it?

DC: It got messy, because the plastic . . . was pushing the engineering limits. The D192 was a metal dimmer, but it was still a cost reduction from the CD80. Then the ENR was the ultimate cost reduction. It was all injection moulded. There was a sequence of weird events that brought about the problems with ENR.[35]

It was actually caused by the contacts on the choke. The chokes were being made in Mexico and during manufacturing they were all thrown on top of each other and the weight would crush the contacts and spread some of them open. It was one of those things that shouldn't have been done, but instead of copper bus bars, we used aluminium bus bars with nickel plating. Then the company making the bus bars, instead of plating them, anodized them, which makes them more resistive. So, we had these open contacts, mating with aluminium bus bars, and they started pitting and corroding and elevating the temperature. Then there was a Lexan block holding the contact which caught fire and ignited the plastic side rails. The big problem was that it didn't happen for a year. By the time it happened, there were over a thousand installations. So we had to go into the field and rebuild the units.

RB: Was it this problem that bankrupted the company?

DC: No. The problem was handled, and I ended up paying for half of it.

RB: The other side of getting the royalties?

(...cont) balanced and differential, which makes it much more noise immune and can travel hundred of feet, whereas 232 is only good for about 30 feet.

[33] See Pearlman page 64

[34] See Tom Grimes page 247 regarding his same thoughts.

[35] They caught fire.

DC: That was a rough one. The good part is that Colortran handled it well. Unfortunately, a lot of the problems were in manufacturing, but Entertec couldn't control the manufacturing process. But on the other hand, it would have been better not to have used certain kinds of plastic in there. It was high temperature plastic, but it couldn't handle a thousand degree arc on an aluminium bus bar.

RB: Did the situation ever go to court?

DC: No – there was never one lawsuit. There were two fires, one at Universal Studios, and one at the Mirage Hotel in Las Vegas. But we figured out, pretty quickly, what the cause was. It took a year to retrofit and cost three or four million dollars. We had to do the work at night because they were operating venues. A quick inspection could tell if there was a problem about to happen because you could see the pitting. It got handled and the people were impressed by the recall. It actually turned into a positive thing because it proved that the company stood behind their products. Once the changes were made, it was a good product, but a stigma stayed with it. It really didn't hurt the company financially. At that point, Colortran had knocked Strand down and was the dominant lighting company. Colortran went from about $8 million in sales when we joined them to about $30 million at the end. It basically replicated the original Strand dominance in the industry.

RB: So how did the Colortran link end?

DC: The ENR problem soured the relationship and they brought in a new president. Lee Lighting owned the company. Lee started growing and ended up owning 30 companies. The Lee brothers were from the theatre, so that was good. They were gaffers so these guys understood the lighting business. But then during the stock market crash at the end of the eighties they ran into trouble and over extended themselves. They bought Panavision. They paid too much for it, then the stock market crashed. They had no reserves, and basically lost their companies. Then all the groups got divided up. An investment-banking firm from New York bought Colortran and they didn't like the way it was being operated so they changed the management. This was right around the time of the ENR problems. So it became a very cold relationship instead of the warm fuzzy one with Ken Boyda. It was at that point I said: "Enough consoles". So the Prestige line and the Scene Master 60 were the last consoles.

Up until 1990, I hadn't designed any lights. Wally had been pushing me to do fixtures, and it ended up with Source Four. He figured someone should do a new light since nobody had done anything with lighting in 30 years. The Altman 360Q was the best light. When we measured it, it was better than the Colortran and Strand lights, even though they looked nicer. So basically we set out to do a high tech 360Q.

RB: So, had you already found Fred Foster of ETC?

DC: In the beginning, I financed it myself and decided I would figure out who to give it to later. Once we had a prototype, I met with Fred at ETC and we just clicked. He is a lighting person. He loves the theatre and said: "This looks good!"

RB: Had you known him before that?

DC: No. I think Anne Valentino made the original introduction.

RB: And you had to develop the HPL.[36]

DC: Nobody even thought about making a new lamp. Lighting manufacturers would just take whatever was out there and use it.

I started looking at the light as a system, which was the lamp, the optics, the reflector and the lens. What could be done with the whole thing? Source Four ended up being a three million dollar project. Nobody had ever decided to put that kind of money into a $160 light.

RB: Did you know about moulding and casting by then?

DC: Yes. A lot of the designers (Gregg Esakoff, Mike Kiktavi, David Lui) were good in this area because we were using it in other products. We just engineered the hell out of the product.

Dichroic reflectors were only used for dental mirrors at the time and they cost $60 to $100 a piece.

Dave Cunningham's Source Four 'to-do' list.

---

[36] The lamp used in all Source Four fixtures.

We had to make the light for $100 if we were going to sell it for $160. That's still not a big margin, but the reflector can't take your whole budget. We pursued how to make the glass, how to make the coatings, and we finally got a very economical reflector. Each little part of the product became an engineering project on its own to get cost out of it.

RB: Who made the lamp for you?

DC: I went to GE in the beginning, but they wanted to charge too much for the lamp. So that didn't work. Then Ushio didn't want to sign a non-disclosure. Finally Sylvania made the lamp. Now GE and Ushio also make it. I brought Ushio along because we needed a second source, and GE for European distribution. Philips just came on last year. The HPL is the largest selling specialty lamp in the world. There are now about 25 different variations on the HPL, but Sylvania did the first one. HPL was a whole project on its own, because I had never designed a lamp before.

We wrote software to analyse the light output from the fixture. Manufacturers would only publish centre foot-candles and it didn't have anything to do with the uniformity of the image or the distribution of the field. So we developed, with Radiant Imaging, a software system based on a CCD camera that would allow us to fine tune the optics of the reflector. We built a modeling program that took the filament geometry into account. All other modeling programs were ray-traced, but they didn't take into account the unique aspects of the filament geometry. So the idea here was that you took images of the filament and projected them through the optics and onto the target and overlaid that millions of times. So basically we could model the performance of the reflector, the optics and the lenses all in the computer but based on taking photographs of the filament. You would scan the lamp with a

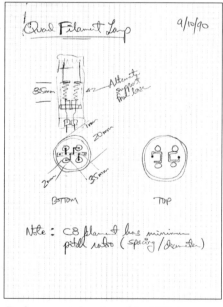

Early concept drawing of the HPL lamp – the core of the Source Four.

goniometer and build all these images of what the filament actually looked like, then you did the modeling. Then we would build the optical prototype and check it against the model. The software we co-developed with Radiant later became ProLight and ProMetric. [37]

RB: Have you ever met Robert Shakespeare? [38]

DC: No.

RB: I met him in Vancouver at a lighting symposium that I was invited to talk at during the very early days of WYSIWYG. It's where I met Larry Kellerman, who put my name in for the Wally Award nomination. Shakespeare has been doing very complex lighting modeling for years. He used his software to design fixtures for lighting things like bridges.

DC: Well that software we used was key to the development of the Source Four. We never could have done it otherwise. It's very complicated. Just little things like the end of the lamp as an optical element. The glass in the lamp is an optical element; it changes the beam distribution of the filament. So all of that is taken into account when using these techniques. Before that, they would do ray-tracing to try to aid the reflector design, but they would assume a point source. And then they would bend reflectors in a sheet metal shop. It was very crude optical modeling on those early fixtures.

I think Source Four was the first fixture to use heavy computer involvement in its development. It turns out that some of the results in the software were not as accurate as we thought. So we made a guess and it turned out to be right and we just hit the sweet spot. Years later we went back with much more sophisticated software and it showed just how lucky we were. Sometimes all the modelling doesn't make any difference if you don't start in the right direction.

RB: Garbage in, garbage out.

DC: Thomas Edison didn't have any modeling software.

RB: At least you weren't rolling filaments with your bare hands!
So the base objective of the Source Four lamp . . .

DC: . . . is the efficient collection of light.

---

[37] www.radimg.com/products_overview.htm

[38] Robert Shakespeare is a Professor of Theatre and Drama and Director of the Theatre Computer Visualization Center (TCVC) at the Indiana University Bloomington.

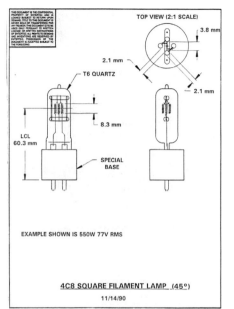

TOP VIEW (2:1 SCALE)

3.8 mm

2.1 mm

T6 QUARTZ

2.1 mm

8.3 mm

LCL
60.3 mm

SPECIAL
BASE

EXAMPLE SHOWN IS 550W 77V RMS

4C8 SQUARE FILAMENT LAMP (45°)

11/14/90

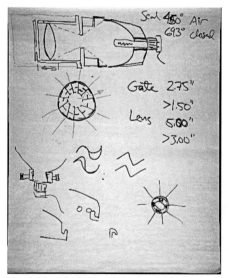

From the flipcharts nicknamed 'Codex Cunningham'.

RB: Point source.

DC: Actually, it's not a point source. It's a source that puts the light out in a perpendicular pattern from the bulb. In the FEL, the coiled coils spray the light all over the place and HPL actually focuses the light into the reflector. You just get more light out of the system and the filament's more compact.

RB: And the heat sink on it was unique.

DC: Each part was its own engineering project. Wally was an advisor to Entertec. He would come out about once a month and hang out and check how things were going and we would talk about what we were working on. To his credit, he was the one that pushed me on the rotating barrel. I wasn't convinced about it. I thought it would be too expensive - but we ended up finding a really good mechanical way of doing it. At the same time, he was also working with Theatre Projects and Vari-Lite. With us, it was rather more of a hobby project.

So about a year-and-a-half into the project I met Fred and he said ETC was interested. So the first products with ETC were the Multiplexer and the Source Four.

RB: And the Sensor.

DC: The Sensor wasn't conceived

at that point. I had some general ideas and said: "Well, I can do a dimmer too." Fred said they needed one that was less expensive than the LMI dimmer. So we agreed to do that product too. I had patents filed on the ENR. I looked at the patents and it was clear there were ways to steer around them. But at LDI in 1992 when Source Four and Sensor came out, ETC's booth was across the aisle from Colortran's booth. There were a million people in the ETC booth and nobody much on the Colortran booth - and they were a bit upset. Basically Sensor is a metal version of ENR.

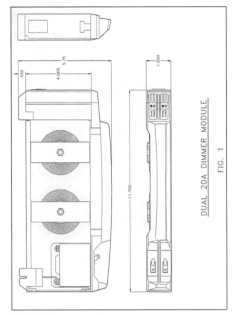

Sensor dimmer module.

RB: So ENR has a CEM[39] in it? There was no microprocessor in each dimmer?

DC: Yes, it had a control module and a custom SSR[40] with all the leads on it. It was highly integrated, with no wiring. But Sensor was die-cast metal, so there was no way you would buy ENR, with the plastic stigma following the fires.

RB: But you said you had patents on ENR?

DC: Yes, they were assigned to Colortran. But none of the patents were infringed by the Sensor design. Colortran was annoyed because of the earlier ENR problems - and they didn't want to work together anymore. So they stopped paying the royalties on ENR. I said: "That's OK, we can work it out." But then the combination of Source Four and Sensor caused them to lose a lot of business. The investment banker running it just said: "We're not going to pay anymore." So then they filed a patent lawsuit, saying Sensor was infringing. But it wasn't. I had been very careful to ensure that it didn't infringe. Unfortunately, I got an impromptu degree in patent law through this whole

---

[39] Central Electronics Module
[40] Solid State Relay

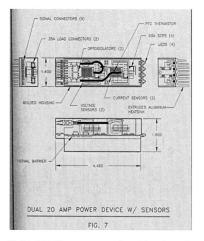

SIGNAL CONNECTORS (9)
PTC THERMISTOR
35A LOAD CONNECTORS (2)
50A SCRS (4)
OPTOISOLATORS (2)
LEDS (4)
1.400
MOLDED HOUSING
VOLTAGE SENSORS (2)
CURRENT SENSORS (2)
EXTRUDED ALUMINUM HEATSINK
THERMAL BARRIER
4.450
1.600

DUAL 20 AMP POWER DEVICE W/ SENSORS

FIG. 7

process. They had stopped paying the royalties, and they were suing for patent infringement. Then they made their own product to compete with the Sensor (which later was the i-Series, which went to NSI and Leviton). However, there were patents filed on the Sensor. They copied the way the modules were made and stepped all over the Sensor patents. So there was a counter-suit for the patent infringement against Colortran.

RB: Was that an Entertec counter-suit, or from ETC?

DC: Well, we were in this together. So they were suing for Sensor infringing on the ENR patents (I was getting sued for my own patents) then ETC was counter-suing for the patents Colortran had stepped on and they were also not paying royalties.

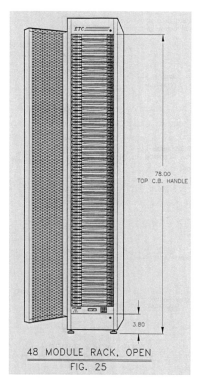

ETC

78.00
TOP C.B. HANDLE

3.80

48 MODULE RACK, OPEN

FIG. 25

However, I had an arbitration clause in the royalty agreement, so I forced it into arbitration and they fought that like crazy because arbitration gets settled quickly. They had figured they would just beat us down by dragging out the litigation. So I pushed it into arbitration and I won. Then they bankrupted the company so they didn't have to pay. The investment banker put 120 people out of business so they didn't have to pay, and that was the end of Colortran. I tried to settle. I have never been able to not settle a dispute. Fred Foster and I have gotten into disagreements sometimes, but then we would just sit down and work things out!

RB: It helps when people are talking to people rather than lawyers talking to lawyers.

DC: It was the president of Colortran who had a problem about the ENR thing and the success of the new products. He just didn't understand the history. We finally released the bankrupt company from its obligations, and that's why those products are still out there.

RB: Did you do the 77-volt version of the HPL right out of the gate?[41]

DC: There was going to be an integrated dimmer in Source 4 and at some point I just pulled back and said this is too much for the industry to swallow at one time.[42]

RB: You were going to send DMX to the light.

DC: The original concept actually went further, but then we just ended up doing line voltage. The 77-volt was just for the multiplexed fixture, which is finally starting to get used on Broadway.

RB: ETC still has a hard time explaining to people how the hell to even patch it.

DC: Yes, I know. If it had been handled better from a marketing point of view, it probably would have taken off. The multiplexer was a good concept, but it didn't make it.

All the ETC products were conceived in 1990 (the Source Four, the Source Four Junior, the Zoom, the Source Four Par, the Parnel, the Multiplexer, the Sensor) and we started working on them all simultaneously, but just handling the success and the volume of the Source Four was overwhelming for

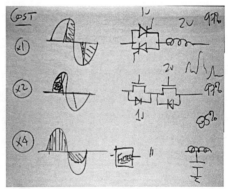

When developing the HPL lamp, there was a desire to reduce the voltage to further compact the filament. The top sketch was the innovation that led to the Dimmer Doubler.

---

[41] The idea of the Multiplexer was that you could use one dimmer and just two conductors to drive two separate lamps, each with their own control. The Multiplexer itself is a special two-fer you put near the lights, saving half the wire to power a rig. The dimmer would chop the bottom and the top of the sine wave based on different control channels. One light would use the top half, and the other the bottom. The RMS voltage of half a sine wave is 77 volts. A single 2.4 kW dimmer could handle two of these 77-volt lamps.

[42] The Source Four Revolution moving light was introduced at PLASA 2003.

the company. They had never made a fixture before. We had talked about a volume of 10,000 fixtures a year. It ended up being 12,000 fixtures a month. It's a ridiculous number. They started going into places like hotel lobbies...

RB: Well, as soon as you made them white...

DC: We had estimated the size of the market at 60,000 fixtures a year and we were getting a 200% market share. The market expanded with the capability of the fixture. The Par also took off. It took almost five years to get all the products to market, even though they were all invented at the same time.

RB: So, the Parnel was the last one out. Then you retired?

DC: I think the Colortran fight, which was in '93 - '94 wore me out. Even though there are projects that I think I may still want to do, I realize that I'm not going to live forever and I want to do some other things.

RB: So then you got into the renovations on the house and the performances, which were full time happenings.

DC: It was the theatre of the sixties re-done in the nineties. It supported about 20 artists for six years - it's the LA artist's welfare society! But that has sort of run its course now, so the question is what to do next.

RB: Between work and play, how do you handle all the dancing?

DC: Somehow I live in the art world and the business world at the same time. It's worked out so far.

5 JOHN McKERNON

Introduction

John is a lighting designer - not a software programmer – and he just happens to be the author of the most popular paperwork program that has ever existed. He's always been flattered that other designers think enough of Lightwright that they rely on it for their work, require their co-workers to use it, and even evangelise for it. It all happened because he hated doing things twice and he kept asking himself why he should be stuck killing trees when everyone else was having fun at the beach.

Unlike all of the other subjects of this book, John has a singular project: Lightwright. It was first released under the name ALD and sold by Rosco, but now, after twenty years and only four versions later, John sells his wares through City Theatrical. His program is, without question, the standard on Broadway. It is the method whereby almost all Broadway shows are documented, and countless other theatre companies around the country archive their lighting plots using his software.

The only reason its massive success is not world-wide is only due to the fact that Europeans have a much different way of documenting shows. West End designers generally walk into the theatre with one piece of paper and it has all the information

on it. Fixture templates have everything related to the fixture surrounding them, including channel number, dimmer number, colour, gobo and accessories. Hookup notes and followspot colours are in legends around the side. It's all there, and generally the designer doesn't need much else at the production table.[1]

Whether it is for organizational purposes (labour or otherwise), things on Broadway are much different. People love to surround themselves in paper: dimmer hookups, instrument schedules, magic sheets, gel swatches, cue synopses. The more paper the better. Then come the people to manage all the paper: the associate designer, the assistant lighting designer, the tracker, and the head electrician. There is an obsession with documentation. There are fears that the console is going to crash and lose all of the cues. The head flyman may get drunk and crash the set into the electrics. The show may get canned, but we damn well better make sure there is enough paper so we can get it back.

I come from television, and television doesn't tour. We normally don't even have a 'tomorrow'. On Broadway tomorrow is very important, and documentation is key. Shows come back. Shows move from bigger houses to smaller ones. Really successful shows go on tour and you don't want to be caught with your pants down.

WYSIPAPER aspired to be what Lightwright is. It never was. We had so much else on our plate that we could only get by with what we had. What we did have was what John still has not been able to achieve. That is the connectivity to a really good CAD program. Paper alone can never do the job.

At the time of this interview, John was working feverishly on Version 4. For me the race was on, whether or not I could get the book out before he got his code out.

Interview

RB: Eric Cornwell was telling me about his success and frustrations of trying to read and write Strand file formats and I asked him what sort of good is the proprietary approach compared to the open architecture approach.[2] I used the example of Vari-Lite and Series 200 gear and then Vari-Lite and the Series 300, saying that if they sold the VL5 when they first came out, they probably

---

[1] See Toulmin page 311 or an example of how this proves true.

[2] See Cornwell – page 282

wouldn't have had the financial problems they had later.

JM: I think you're probably right.

RB: We went through this same thing with WYSIWYG – we would read your Lightwright files, but certainly I wasn't going to write your files.

JM: Well, my files are pretty cryptic. There is something about having an amateur writing software code, which means it gets done, but it's probably not the cleanest or prettiest way of doing it. Lightwright gets out the door, it's useful, it's wonderful, I'm happy, everybody else is happy, but just don't look at the man behind the curtain. It might not be pretty. I never took any software classes or anything. It was just, "do it".

The whole proprietary thing, yes, I guess Lightwright is proprietary, but it's because I want to do stuff that a normal database can't necessarily do (like collapse worksheet rows), and if I did manage to shoehorn it into a regular database such as Access (which isn't even available on a Mac, and I don't want to lock anybody out), your data files are going to take up sixteen CD's just to put *Showboat* on it – and that's ridiculous.

RB: You can also make it come up faster. My original code was done in AutoLISP[3] and the data structures were so big and laborious and slow…

JM: …you can't do anything. Frankly, you can't have the data sitting on the disk because it takes you a year to get to it to play with it. And normal sorting things don't work because theatre people are weird; we do strange stuff.

RB: Well, who would think that you want the 1st Electric, then the 2nd, then the 11th. If you sort alphabetically you don't get them that way.

JM: Computers go "1, 10, 2". Thank you, yes. Makes perfect sense – to the computer, but not to us mortals! Then again there is the method everybody has to use in Excel, which is a second column that has the sort order in it. Excuse me, no. I'm stupid.

---

[3] AutoLISP was the first tool AutoDesk gave us to customize AutoCAD. It was based on the LISP (LISt Processing) language and was rather a funny beast. The only language that is older and still in use today is FORTRAN. There are no complex data structures available or dialog box editing tools and everything took quite a lot longer than you would hope. Then again, you could get at and manipulate the underlying AutoCAD database which was remarkably powerful. I did the prototype to LXMOV using AutoLISP. See WYSIWYG Seeds – page 27. Now AutoCAD supports VBA (Visual Basic for Applications) which is much more powerful and building applications take one tenth the time. Things also run much faster. In between AutoLISP and VBA was ADS (AutoCAD Development System), which was based on C. This is what I used to build LXMOV, but is no longer supported.

People are always surprised when they come to see me light a show and I don't have the computer on the desk in front of me. In fact, I may not even use the computer during the entire tech week. The assistant probably has it, but maybe not. Even when I assist, you make changes on the paperwork until you can't see it anymore, then you go and make the changes and print a new set of paperwork, but I don't bury my head in the computer at the production table.

RB: Does the head electrician get nervous when he does a show with you?

JM: Well, he has all the paper work - that's his job. He's got his computer there and he's usually the one keeping it all up-to-date, nice and tidy. Yes, I totally believe that everything has to be in all the paperwork. It all has to be 100% there and 100% correct, but I have this strange left brain/right brain thing, where when I'm writing software code, then I'm this person that thinks about nothing but numbers and the minutiae of it all. But when I'm designing a show, I don't want to know about numbers and things. I can't remember a channel number to save my soul and don't even ask me about what Lee 205 looks like. I haven't got a clue. Oh, that's the warm that's in the sidelight. Great. Fine. I saw it one day when I was holding the gel book up and it looked nice, so I picked it. But there is no computer brain going on. Well, there's some. You may have to talk "Light Palette" or...

RB: ...figure out how to mark your moving lights or what have you.

JM: There's that. But it's not what I'm thinking about at the production table. I'm not thinking about what unit number is up there except that it's number 1,

Type	Watts	#Stock	Label	Size	# Per ckt.	Per sheet
5° ETC	575	18	D	14.00" x 14.00"	1	1
10° ETC	575	48	C	12.00" x 12.00"	1	2
19° ETC w/Iris	575	0	H	6.00" x 6.00"	1	12
19° ETC	575	46	H	6.00" x 6.00"	1	12
26° ETC	575	208	H	6.00" x 6.00"	1	12
26° ETC w/iris	575	0	H	6.00" x 6.00"	1	12
36° ETC	575	38	H	6.00" x 6.00"	1	12
50° ETC	575	14	H	6.00" x 6.00"	1	12
PAR 64 NSP	1000	0	B	10.00" x 10.00"	1	4
PAR 64 MFL	1000	46	B	10.00" x 10.00"	1	4
2LT STRAND FAR CYC	1000	0		0.00" x 0.00"	1	0
6'Ministrip 75w WFL	750	12	I	4.75" x 3.38"	5	28

COLOR FRAME SIZES KEY | Color sheets are 20.00" x 24.00"
A	7.50" x 7.50"	F	3.75" x 3.75"	K	P
B	10.00" x 10.00"	G	8.75" x 13.00"	L	Q
C	12.00" x 12.00"	H	6.00" x 6.00"	M	R
D	14.00" x 14.00"	I	4.75" x 3.38"	N	S
E	15.25" x 18.50"	J		O	T

Point to any changes you want, then type then in. <Ctrl+PgDn> moves to bottom. <Alt+O> changes order; <Alt>+<S> changes sheet size; <Esc> to exit.

Lightwright v2 Equipment Details.

2, 3, 4, … ah, 5. Or, to the assistant, "find me a spare overhead that can get to that window over there."

RB: When you're sitting at a production desk, do you use magic sheets or an assistant?

JM: I use magic sheets. I could never have an assistant pick channels. It's a very personal thing. Ken Billington has always laid out his channels on the screen, according to purpose, so that you could look at the console's monitor and see what's up generally by its area on the screen. I've been taking that to an extreme. Doing a ballet, the bottom row of the screen is the first wing, the second row up is the second wing, the third row up is the third wing, and the top row is the last wing. And if it's stage right, it's on the left side of the screen, and if it's stage left, it's on the right side of the screen, because that's the way it looks when I look at the stage from out front. So, hopefully, I have less memorizing of channels to do. Also, the other reason I do a magic sheet, even if the screen isn't organized very well, is because half the time you're looking at the screen thinking, what's channel 42? Then you have to look at your magic sheet and find out what channel 42 is. If the magic sheet is in order by number, you can do that. On the other hand, it may not be the right way to write the show by starting with numbers.

RB: You know that in Horizon you can label your channels.

JM: Which I've never understood the virtue of. It's just one more layer of information I have to process. You still need the number there so you can say channel 42 at full. And under that, how many characters can you get? Four characters doesn't get you very far.

RB: You can get a couple more, but point taken. If you're not shouting at a board man and you're not afraid of picking up a mouse, it can be much faster, because it removes a layer of thinking.

JM: But everybody does everything differently, and I don't run the board unless things are really desperate. When I teach kids about doing light plots, all I want to see on the plot is the unit number because the plot's only purpose is as instructions on how to hang the light - nothing more. If you're Andy Bridge, you're cueing off the light plot, then you want the channel, and the colour and everything on it. Find that fourth boom right, and the third unit down and ah, channel 65 and call it that.

RB: Very British. They don't do paper. They do 'a' piece of paper.

=================
"ANNIE WARBUCKS"
=================
Variety Arts Theatre
New York City

=================
CHANNEL HOOKUP
=================

Page   1
8-8-93
Lighting by Ken Billington

Note: Asterisks indicate color scrollers

Chn	Dim	Position	Unit	Cir#	Type	Watts	Purpose	Color
(1)	64	FOH #3	1		36' Source 4	575w	Apron L	L-136+R-119
	"	"	6		"	"	"	L-161+R-119
(2)	62	FOH #3	2		36' Source 4	575w	Area DL	G-106+R-119
(3)	60	FOH #3	4		36' Source 4	575w	Area DL/ C	G-106+R-119
	"	"	14		"	"	"	L-203+R-119
(4)	59	FOH #3	7		36' Source 4	575w	Area DC	G-106+R-119
	"	"	15		"	"	"	L-203+R-119
(5)	58	FOH #3	8		36' Source 4	575w	Area DR/ C	G-106+R-119
	"	"	18		"	"	"	L-203+R-119
(6)	56	FOH #3	12		36' Source 4	575w	Area DR	G-106+R-119
(7)	55	FOH #3	16		36' Source 4	575w	Apron R	L-161+R-119
	"	"	21		"	"	"	L-136+R-119
(8)	12	FOH #2	1		36' Source 4	575w	Area L	G-106+R-119
	"	"	5		"	"	"	L-203+R-119
	"	"	9		"	"	"	G-106+R-119
(9)	9	FOH #2	6		36' Source 4	575w	Area C	G-106+R-119
	"	"	10		"	"	"	L-203+R-119
	"	"	14		"	"	"	G-106+R-119
(10)	5	FOH #2	11		36' Source 4	575w	Area R	G-106+R-119

Typical printout from Lightwright 2

JM: Well, it's a miracle that anybody is using Lightwright over there, but they do. I don't know how much they really use it. But they buy it, and they do keep up with the upgrades, so that says something, I guess.

RB: So tell me about the beginning of it and when it was ALD Pro.

JM: In 1979 I was running a scene paint shop along with Campbell Baird, my partner, and I was also lighting a very small dance company, touring around the countryside. And every half a week or week we would hit a new space, normally a university. We were not touring with our own equipment, but we used the same light plot everywhere we went. But this week, what were PAR cans last week, are Lekos this week, or Fresnels next week.

RB: Fresnels from the front of house?

JM: Yes, exactly! Because that's all the university had this week, but it was still the same plot. So there was all this stupid paperwork. OK, I guess this week it will be the eight inch Fresnels instead of PAR's. Fine – lay it out and tell them. I actually drafted a light plot where all of the symbols were Lekos, without crosses through them or anything. They were all the same symbol. And the key had fifteen lights on it and they were all the same symbol. Then you said, OK, a Leko symbol with a cross through it is now an eight inch Fresnel symbol. I made that as generic as I could. You still had to make up a dimmer hook-up and an instrument schedule, which is extremely boring.

Then there was the famous weekend where the company went off to play at the beach for the day while I was left behind at the hotel doing the damn paperwork. I got very frustrated. I think my exact words were: "this is stupid, any idiot can do this; an assistant could do this, a machine could do this." Because it really was just that repetitive. Then I said . . . a machine! I went to the local shopping mall that was in Raleigh, North Carolina, and there was a dealer there selling Apple computers and a Radio Shack store selling these computers.

RB: Tandy's. That would have been 1977.

JM: It was 1979, but yes, the TRS 80 Model 1's. The Apple people were mostly showing graphics and games, and the Radio Shack guy had a payroll program and a thing called BASIC which you could write your own software with. The other thing we were really hating those days was doing the bookkeeping for the painting business and the payroll in particular. So I called my partner in New York and said... Campbell, I think we should buy a

```
*** SYSTEM REQUIREMENTS ***

"ELECTRIC ASSISTANT" REQUIRES A TRS-80 MODEL I WITH 48K OF RAM, AT
LEAST  ONE DISK DRIVE, AND AN 80-COLUMN PRINTER, SUCH AS THE RADIO
SHACK LINE PRINTER II OR EQUIVALENT.  IF SOUND  OUTPUT  TO  SIGNAL
WHEN  PRINTING  OPERATIONS, ETC. ARE COMPLETED IS DESIRED, A SMALL
SOUND AMPLIFIER AND SPEAKER  CAN  BE  CONNECTED  TO  THE  CASSETTE
RECORDER PLUG.
```

computer to do the books because then you can do it while I'm out of town. Never mind that he doesn't want to hear about these things. Then I called my sister and said, Alice, there is this thing called BASIC and they say you can write your own programs with it. I know nothing about computers. I've never had a course in one, I've never put my hands on one, because in high school, there wasn't any such thing. She said, yes, anybody can do this - you can learn it! And with that, I spent $3000 out of the business to buy a computer to do the payroll.

Great! Ship it to New York. Learn about the horrors of saving code to cassette tape. Did the "Hello World" exercise in the book and learned BASIC. One thing led to the next and I learned assembly code because BASIC was too slow. Then the IBM PC came out and a friend of mine had one of those and I thought it was neat.

RB: DOS. Disk drive.

JM: Then I read an article in Theatre Crafts or Lighting Dimensions, whichever one it was at the time, that was talking about a piece of software somebody had written to do paperwork. I said, mine works better than that! I thought Rosco should be selling mine, not this other one. At the time, I think mine was called Electric Assistant or something stupid. So I go see Bob Saturn at Rosco and Bob looked at the software and said that if I got rid of all the bugs and made it work on the PC, then sure, they could sell it for me. They named it ALD,[4] which I thought was sort of academic I suppose. We made a deal and then it became ALD Pro. Then I realized I wasn't making enough money on it to make it worth doing (it never made enough money to pay the rent – ever!). Then it turned into Lightwright, because people thought ALD Pro sounded stupid ("what is it, dog food?"). Then I came out with the Mac version. Then I moved away from Rosco and signed a new contract with City Theatrical. Now I'm actually paying the rent with Lightwright. First time ever!

---

[4] Assistant Lighting Designer

Print options in Lightwright 2.

Now I probably make more money from the project than City Theatrical does. It blows me away that other people like my way of doing things. I think Lightwright's terrific, but then again that's because I write it to work for me, as a designer. I never really know if a new version I've written is any good until I actually do a show and try it out and that's when I react and deal with different features.

RB: I was saying to Eric that I attribute the success of his products, your products and my products, because we all work in the theatre.[5]

JM: Written by people that are using it.

RB: I can track ten times as many bugs in a day at the venue than I can in a week at the office.

JM: One day in the theatre I will run into fifty bugs that nobody else has run into in four years. I don't know how that works. Makes you wonder if anybody at Microsoft has ever actually written anything in Microsoft Word!

RB: As a side note, do you find that once you find a bug in your own mature software, you will get another three reports within a week, reporting the same bug? You think that it never should have run.

JM: I know. There are things in the program where people will say they can't get it to do such and such and I'll go look at the code and see that there is no way that it ever could have worked, ever – and it's been out the door for four

---

[5] See Cornwell – page 285

years. No one has ever tried this; none of my beta testers has ever pointed it out. How did I get through it when I was writing the code? Yes, it happens all the time. Baffling!

RB: What baffles me is the phone call from the guy in Japan who coincidently comes across the same bug and you wonder "did the moons line up?"

JM: I think they do.

The only thing I fear for now, as the operating systems become more and more complicated, is that it gets harder and harder for one person to write a piece of software, single handed, and understand all the platforms. The Mac is easy; you write it for one platform and it runs on everything. Yes, OS X will

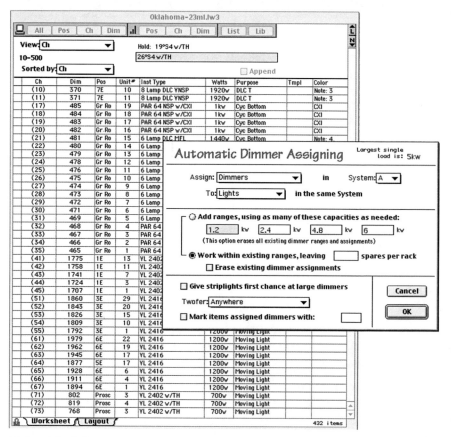

Lightwright 3 dimmer assignment wizard.

be a challenge. But Windows… 95, 98, 2000, ME, NT…

RB: XP…We have this problem with Horizon.

JM: XP stands for Extra Pain. I had someone call the other day, stuck in the registration window for Lightwright, and the whole window was white; no text in it.

RB: "Can't be my fault!"

JM: I didn't do this, but it turns out that if you go to one of those famous settings in Windows and choose one of these different themes (never mind that I'm just using the colours that Microsoft provides) it makes the foreground colour the same as the background colour. Hello Microsoft, I'm writing it with a Microsoft product. Why doesn't it work on a Microsoft product?

RB: What are you writing it with now?

JM: Visual Basic.

RB: And the Mac version?

JM: Future Basic.

RB: And how do you maintain the two? Are you always simultaneously jumping or do you have some engine structure that is the same?

JM: When I first wrote the Mac version, I took the DOS code and had to completely start all over again, basically because it was event driven and mouse driven and all that stuff. A few bits of code transferred over, but basically it was all from scratch. But going from the Mac to the Windows version was pretty straightforward because a mouse click is a mouse click wherever it happens. So I actually wrote a translator to convert Future Basic code into Visual Basic code, then, of course, had a whole lot of handwork to do to finish it. But it got ninety percent of it over. So the routines and functions are all the same names in both of them and many of the lines of code are the same. But yes, there are two separate computers and I swivel my head from the right to the left and copy back and forth.

RB: Do you try to work on them simultaneously or do you stick on the Mac then every month try to do the transfer.

JM: No, you have to try to work simultaneously. I suppose if I was a really organized person I would just change this line to this…but no, I just plough ahead and I don't know what I've done at the end of the day, but now it works

– on both platforms. If I had to take a day's work and go back and ask which of seventeen modules I worked on I couldn't do it. So I end up working on one tiny section at a time on both platforms.

RB: Without a doubt, that has been the profitable method. But it must have been a pain.

JM: It gets it out the door. I was looking at RealBasic, which is really only available on the Mac, but also creates programs for Windows. And there is something new called Revolution that has just came out of Scotland that I was looking at that is very similar to RealBasic in that it's one of the programming shelves in which you add buttons and things and put code behind the buttons - which is very much like Visual Basic and supposedly it generates code for both platforms at once.

Where they all fall down in is in printing. And inevitably there are things, like some mouse moves, you can't do without going to the Windows API or Mac Toolbox and I don't see any way out of that. So I look at these things like RealBasic and ask what happens when I use a Mac Toolbox call, how do I come up with the equivalent Windows API? That gets messy. And printing is a totally different world and completely different to both platforms.

RB: Much to Richard Pilbrow's chagrin, when we went from WYSIWYG 2 (which, even though it was DOS he was a big fan of it) to WYSIWYG 3, we got Microsoft Development Studio 4. As advertised, it allowed you to hit one button and get a Windows EXE then hit another button to build a Mac based thing. We bought a Mac, and there is a version of CAST CAD – the very beginnings of WYSIWYG Version 3 that runs on a Mac.

JM: Really?! You can't do that with Microsoft product anymore, can you?

RB: Then they very quickly came out with Developers Studio 5 (we were doing it all in C++) and all that Mac support, without even a release note, just disappeared. That was it. There were no tools that could do it properly. And at the time, the code was targeted to the 68000 processor, so we knew it wasn't going to be fast enough. Today you would be OK.

JM: Everything is fast enough so you can get away with murder.

RB: I used to have a theory, back in the 80s, that no matter how big your hard drive was, you would always have it 80-90% full. That lasted most of the way through the 90's. Isn't it nice we're now approaching the point where we're not always screaming for speed? We're still wishing, but we're not screaming like we were in the mid 90s.

Lighting Design: David Hersey   GERSHWIN THEATRE, NYC
Associate: Ted Mather
UK Associate: Jenny Kagen   Prod. Elec: Mike Lo Bue

Balcony Rail

Unit#	Inst Type	Watts	Purpose	Ch	Color & Template	Text 4
X	SPARE CIR					
X	SPARE CIR					
1	Ianiro w/BD	2kw	Front Gauze Blue	(146)	R68, HS	
2	Toccata EP w/VSFX w/4" Lens	2kw	DS Gauze Storm Clouds	(409)	L203	
2			DS Gauze Cirrus Cloud Dir			
2			DS Gauze Cirrus Cloud Speed			
2	VSFX HOT	100w				
3	19°S4 w/TH	575w	Rail Corn Gobo Warm	(190)	R13+L138, T:R7833	
4	19°S4 w/TH	575w	Rail Corn Gobo Cold	(184)	R68+R71, T:R7833	
5	Ianiro w/BD	2kw	Front Gauze Blue	(145)	R68, HS	
6	19°S4 w/TH	575w	Rail Corn Gobo Warm	(189)	R13+L138, T:R7833	
7	Toccata EP w/VSFX w/6" Lens	2kw	DS Gauze Cirrus Cloud	(408)	L203	
7			DS Gauze Cirrus Cloud Dir			
7			DS Gauze Cirrus Cloud Speed			
7	VSFX HOT	100w				
8	Ianiro w/BD	2kw	Front Gauze Blue	(144)	R68, HS	
9	19°S4 w/TH	575w	Rail Corn/ Smkhse Gobo Cold	(183)	R68+R71, T:R7833	
10	19°S4 w/TH	575w	Large Glass Moon	(581)	NC, T:Glass Moon	
11	Pani 2500 Halogen w/27cm lens	2500w	Oklahoma Logo	(585)		
12	19°S4 w/TH	575w	Rail Corn Gobo Warm	(188)	R13+L138, T:R7833	
13	19°S4 w/TH	575w	Rail Corn/ Smkhse Gobo Cold	(182)	R68+R71, T:R7833	
14	Ianiro w/BD	2kw	Front Gauze Blue	(143)	R68, HS	

Ted Mather Lighting Design / Lightwright 3   Balcony Rail

Typical printout from Lightwright 3

JM: I would say that is still true. The conspiracy person in me could come out and say as Intel makes the chips faster, Microsoft make the OS slower, so you'll always need a new computer.

RB: It's crazy. Why in the hell are the minimum requirements for an install of Windows 128 meg of RAM now? Maybe somebody is selling RAM.

JM: Mac OS X needs a huge amount of everything. It's beautiful, it's everything, it runs a million miles an hour - but I had to buy a new computer. As an individual developer, how can I afford the time to test on 95, 98, XP, 2000, OS X? I can't afford to buy that many machines, never mind find the room for them.

RB: At CAST Lighting we did. I haven't been there in a while, but until recently we even had a machine running Windows 95. We would only pick it out every three months when we were doing a release.

⊖ ○ ○		Singular Sensations Layouts..lwl		
First Page	Next Page		🗑	

SINGULAR...   **CHANNEL HOOKUP**   Page 1

Working Copy (Verd).lwl   10/30/03
Village Theatre   Lighting by Ken Billington,
New York City   & John McKernon

Channel	Dim	Position	U#	Purpose	Type, Accessories, Watts	Color/Temp
(1)		"B" ELECTRIC	2	Area Stools	Source 4-36° 575w	L-110
(2)		NO 2 ELECTRIC	1	Area Stools	Source 4-36° 575w	L-110
(3)		NO 2 ELECTRIC	8	Area Stools	Source 4-36° 575w	L-110
(4)		"B" ELECTRIC	1	Area Stools	Source 4-36° 575w	L-194
(5)		NO 2 ELECTRIC	2	Area Stools	Source 4-36° 575w	L-194
(6)		NO 2 ELECTRIC	9	Area Stools	Source 4-36° 575w	L-194
(7)		"A" ELECTRIC	1	Star Stool	Source 4-26°w/iris 575w	G-160
(8)		NO 2 ELECTRIC	5	Star Stool	Source 4-26°w/iris 575w	G-160
(11)		NO 2 ELECTRIC	4	Piano Bench	Source 4-26°w/iris 575w	L-110
"		"	12	"	"	"
(12)		NO 4 ELECTRIC	3	Piano Player	Source 4-36°w/iris 575w	L-136
(13)		"B" ELECTRIC	5	Piano Fill	Source 4-26° 575w	R-79
(14)		NO 4 ELECTRIC	6	Music	Source 4-36° 575w	N/C
(21)		"A" ELECTRIC	5	Area L	Source 4-36° 575w	L-110
(22)		NO 1 ELECTRIC	3	Area DC	Source 4-36° 575w	L-110
		"A" ELECTRIC	2	"	"	"
(23)		NO 1 ELECTRIC	6	Area DR/C	Source 4-36° 575w	L-110
(24)		NO 1 ELECTRIC	10	Area DR	Source 4-36° 575w	L-110
(31)		"A" ELECTRIC	6	Area L	Source 4-36° 575w	L-194
(32)		NO 1 ELECTRIC	4	Area DC	Source 4-36° 575w	L-194
		"A" ELECTRIC	3	"	"	"
(33)		NO 1 ELECTRIC	7	Area DR/C	Source 4-36° 575w	L-194
(34)		NO 1 ELECTRIC	11	Area DR	Source 4-36° 575w	L-194
(41)		"C" ELECTRIC	3	Back L	Source 4-Parnel 750w	Apollo D-4100
(42)		"C" ELECTRIC	5	Back L/C	Source 4-Parnel 750w	Apollo D-4100

Worksheet	Focus	Layout

Print Layouts in Lightwright 4.

JM: To see if it worked. For me the installation routine is laborious because the way you install on all those platforms is unique. The new Virtual PC on the Mac can come with any of the Microsoft OS's and you can use all multiple copies of them at the same time.

RB: That's what we're doing with Horizon now. And it's great because you can even route through to the parallel port and all that, natively.

JM: And it has a roll-back feature or don't commit to disk feature where you can spend the whole day playing on it and they you say, OK, go back to where you were this morning. Which means I can test my install routine without having to reformat the hard drive after installing it.

RB: Because once you register all the OCX's and all that it becomes more and more difficult to undo it.

JM: I'm actually thinking of installing Visual Basic on the Mac so I can cut and paste on one machine. There is still virtue in having two separate machines.

RB: Ted Mather and I were working on a museum project were we actually had Horizon running the whole building from his Powerbook.[6]

JM: The big thing now is that Obsession Off-Line won't run under Windows XP.

RB: No – it won't. Neither will the Strand 550 stuff, which is also DOS based. I was visiting during tech week of *Oklahoma* and they're all running around with their Mac AirPorts running 550 remote monitors on Virtual DOS boxes.

JM: I'm just glad that Strand has woken up after so many years.

RB: It's quite amazing isn't it? I think a certain fellow by the name of Richard Lawrence has an awful lot to do with it. We had some hard times at CBC with CD 90 Dimmers and their Supervisory System and the Light Palette 90's.

JM: The dreaded LP90 – 'Attempting to establish communications with tower – dot, dot, dot.'

RB: 'Processor A has gone down, attempting to switch to processor B.'

JM: We get that all the time with the Obsession. 'Tracking backup aborted.' OK fine, whatever, as long as the show is still there.

---

[6] This is a big deal because Horizon has always been, and still is, only Windows based. We could use Virtual PC on his MAC and get the protocol out of his Ethernet port.

RB: For *Starlight Express* we actually got two Horizon Systems running side by side. It took Alan Martello about a day to code the tracking backup. Nowadays you can do all this stuff through the telnet port and you can do a massive query of all the cue structures and submasters, where they are, function buttons, what state they're in, up or down, and about every half second he just asks the master machine "where are we?" I was actually at the theatre programming the show when he coded this. I said that I really wouldn't be comfortable leaving until we had a tracking backup. He did it and e-mailed it to me. I tested it one day when nobody was looking and I left it.

Then about three months later, I called them up and asked how thing were going. They reported that during a recent show, by operator error, they actually closed down the one Horizon and the backup system said "Hello". They actually did a switchover with a full house and stage management never found out about it.

JM: Wow, that's great. That's the way it's supposed to work. That's always been my holy grail; the technology should be invisible, it should just do it - no arguments. I have a designer head. I don't want to know about technology. That's what electricians are for. You guys figure out all the protocols and numbers and whatever.

RB: It's hilarious you're like that and I think that's what makes this interesting. I don't imagine there are a lot of people who think you are like that.

JM: The frustrating part is there are people who think all I do is write software. They haven't a clue that I design lighting. Writing Lightwright has been a double-edged sword, because, if you really want to be a success in a business, you focus on it single mindedly. You want to be a lighting designer; you be a lighting designer. You don't be an electrician, you just be a lighting designer. If you're going to write software, you go and write software. You don't stop and be a lighting designer every other month. I probably haven't got as far in the business as a lighting designer as I could have if I hadn't written Lightwright. But, then again, I have a mind that gets easily bored and I get very frustrated with paperwork and nobody else is going to fix it.

RB: The problem that I find with software is that once you get down to doing it, before you know it, it's 2:00am.

JM: It's all consuming, absolutely. When we got the first Model 1, I gave Campbell a t-shirt one year that said 'Computer Widow'. Because he was.

Lightwright 4 offers many more options for printing.

You get buried in it. You get lost. Computers are very seductive that way. You get in there and you can do anything in the world.

RB: It's better than clay.

JM: It's just as creative, in fact more creative than lighting design. It's all up to you.

RB: We used to apply for National Research Council grants that were tax incentives to perform "Experimental Research and Scientific Development". The key was, it had to be experimental research. What would really qualify is if you took two chemicals and put them into a beaker and they didn't blow up in your face – there had to be a risk involved.

You don't know what the results are going to be before you start the experiment. Then they would credit you the money. All the advisors said that our software applied, but you just have to write the report in such and such a way. I used to write the reports and it was so morally bending for me because I knew that you could do anything with software. It's just time and money. It's not even money. If you're an idiot like me, it's just time.

JM: Right, time, money, imagination – two of the three.

RB: But it's not as if you will never be able to achieve it. If you keep knocking at it you will be able to do it. And that didn't qualify. It had to be inherently risky. Commercial success did not qualify as a risk factor.

JM: Well some things you can't do, at least with certain Microsoft products. The one that is driving me crazy right now is that if you have several edit fields on the screen, Visual Basic will not give me, the programmer, control over the tab key. So, for instance, if you hit tab, Visual Basic advances the focus to the next field. If you get to the field at the bottom of the screen, well my users want it all to scroll up a row. Well, I can't do that.

RB: It will just go back up to the first control in the form.

JM: Visual Basic doesn't even tell me when they hit the tab key. I can't filter it and stop it.

RB: You can specify the tab order, but you can't catch it like a mouse down event?

JM: No, I don't see it. In Future Basic I do.

RB: What about the LoseFocus event on the last control?

JM: Oh, you don't even want to try that. What happens when you switch to another window or another program? It's a zoo. I'm sure I'll find a way to handle the tab key before I finish Lightwright 4, but it certainly isn't obvious today.

RB: Some of the stuff in VB pisses me off. Why do you have to do your own exception handling on disk access errors and things like that? Why can't it be a function that returns good or bad? Like OpenFile(). Good. No Good.

JM: Because I think it's easier for them. One of the virtues of Future Basic is that it has a really good editor. If I do an If-Then-Else thing, it won't intelligently put the end statement in for me, but it will draw coloured lines and indent everything appropriately and it is very easy to see that you've left out an end statement. With Visual Basic, if you want to indent, you have to indent yourself.

I've tried to learn C several times, and I get frustrated as hell because I have to put a semicolon at the end of every line.

RB: I've gone the other way, from C++ to VB and always wondered why it kept bitching at me whenever I put a semicolon at the end. I do like how much VB will type for you and how much context sensitive assistance it gives you on function typecasting and dependencies.

JM: Yes, I do love how you start typing and it will fill in the rest of it.[7] The best part of it is that you can start running it, stop it, edit the code and resume with the edited changes. It makes life so much easier.

RB: That's the beauty of an interpretative language for you.

JM: I understand that VisualBasic.net won't let you do that.

RB: I guess it has to compile and link it each time.

I like in VB how you can edit the watch statements. You can say, yes, I know I said FOR i = 1 to 8, but right now I want i to be 6 again.

JM: Future Basic doesn't really have a good debugger. It's come a long way from what it used to be, but you can't stop and go back and change variables.

RB: So the original Basic that you started with was the old 10 Print "Hello World", 20 Goto 10, sort of thing.

JM: Oh yes, absolutely. Simple times, spaghetti code. Then you figure out assembly code because that doesn't go fast enough.

RB: For your sorts?

JM: Yes.

RB: And that stuff doesn't translate from a Trash 80 to an 8088.

JM: No. And of course I don't know how to do any of this so… I read a lot of magazines.

RB: One of the things I like to ask people is "It all became possible when they made the…?" or "It all fell apart when they stopped making…?"

JM: No! I think the problem boils down to whatever you're thinking, the

---

[7] Anne Valentino talks about this sort of cleverness and how it can get in the way and whether or not it should be used in control desks. Our opinions differ regarding the possibilities. See page 174

```
FCCF FD23   02850 ONAD1  INC   IY          ;TO NEXT PAIR
FCD1 FD23   02860        INC   IY
FCD3 FD23   02870        INC   IY
FCD5 18BB   02880        JR    SLOOP1       ;GO CHECK PAIR
FCD7 D1     02890 SLOOP2 POP   DE           ;GET FLAG
FCD8 CB43   02900        BIT   0,E          ;TEST IT
FCDA 20A8   02910        JR    NZ,SSTART    ;START AT TOP AGAIN
FCDC 181F   02920        JR    CNTG         ;GO COUNT # IN ARRAY
FCDE FDE5   02930 SWAPIT PUSH  IY           ;SAVE PLACE
FCE0 C5     02940        PUSH  BC           ;SAVE NUMBER
FCE1 0603   02950        LD    B,3
FCE3 FD5600 02960 SWPIT1 LD    D,(IY+0)     ;D GETS BYTE
FCE6 FD6603 02970        LD    H,(IY+3)     ;H GETS NEXT BYTE
FCE9 EB     02980        EX    DE,HL        ;SWAP THEM
FCEA FD7200 02990        LD    (IY+0),D     ;PUT THEM BACK
FCED FD7403 03000        LD    (IY+3),H
FCF0 FD23   03010        INC   IY           ;GO TO NEXT
FCF2 10EF   03020        DJNZ  SWPIT1       ;CONTINUE TILL SWAPPED
FCF4 C1     03030        POP   BC           ;RESTORE NUMBER
FCF5 FDE1   03040        POP   IY           ;RESTORE PLACE
FCF7 D1     03050        POP   DE           ;GET FLAG
FCF8 CBC3   03060        SET   0,E          ;SET IT
FCFA D5     03070        PUSH  DE           ;SAVE IT
FCFB 18CD   03080        JR    ONWARD       ;CONTINUE TO NEXT PAIR
FCFD E1     03090 CNTG   POP   HL           ;GET START OF ARRAY          [handwritten: PUSH IX / POP BC]
FCFE 010000 03100        LD    DE,0         ;SET # FOUND TO ZERO         [DE crossed out -> BC]
FD01 7E     03110 CNT1   LD    A,(HL)       ;GET VALUE IN ARRAY
FD02 FE00   03120        CP    0            ;SEE IF IT'S ZERO
FD04 2806   03130        JR    Z,QUIT       ;QUIT IF IT IS
FD06 03     03140        INC   BC           ;ADD ONE TO # FOUND          [handwritten: DEC BC]
FD07 23     03150        INC   HL           ;GO ON TO NEXT
FD08 23     03160        INC   HL
FD09 23     03170        INC   HL           [handwritten: LD A,B or C / JR Z,QUIT]
FD0A 18F5   03180        JR    CNT1
FD0C C5     03190 QUIT   PUSH  BC           ;MOVE TOTAL TO HL            [handwritten: DE]
FD0D E1     03200        POP   HL           ;SO BASIC CAN GET IT
FD0E C39A0A 03210        JP    2714         ;RETURN TO BASIC
            03220 ; COMPARES LIST OF POSSIBLE POSITIONS AGAINST ACTUAL POSITIO
NS - DELETES ANY NO LONGER IN USE
FD11 CD7F0A 03230 COMPAR CALL  0A7FH        ;GET ENTRY POINT OF SOURCE ARRAY
FD14 2B     03240        DEC   HL
FD15 46     03250        LD    B,(HL)
FD16 2B     03260        DEC   HL
FD17 4E     03270        LD    C,(HL)       ;BC NOW HAS DEPTH OF ARRAY
FD18 23     03280        INC   HL
FD19 23     03290        INC   HL           ;HL NOW BACK AT ENTRY POINT
FD1A E5     03300        PUSH  HL
FD1B FDE1   03310        POP   IY           ;IY NOW HAS START
FD1D B7     03320 AA14   OR    A
FD1E 3E00   03330        LD    A,00H
FD20 BE     03340        CP    (HL)         ;SEE IF (HL) IS ZERO
FD21 2003   03350        JR    NZ,AA16
FD23 C5     03360        PUSH  BC
FD24 1827   03370        JR    AA18
FD26 FD6602 03380 AA16   LD    H,(IY+02H)
FD29 FD6E01 03390        LD    L,(IY+01H)
FD2C FD5E00 03400        LD    E,(IY+00H)
FD2F 22C8FD 03410        LD    (AA40),HL    ;STORE SOURCE ELEMENT ADRS
FD32 7B     03420        LD    A,E
FD33 32CAFD 03430        LD    (AA42),A     ;STORE LENGTH OF SOURCE
FD36 ED43CBFD 03440      LD    (AA44),BC    ;STORE REMAINING DEPTH OF SO
URCE
FD3A 3E00   03450        LD    A,00H
FD3C 32D1FD 03460        LD    (AA50),A     ;ZERO MATCH FLAG ADDRESS
FD3F C5     03470        PUSH  BC
FD40 CD67FD 03480        CALL  AA24         ;CALL "CHECK"
```

Examples of John's early assembly code.

hardware or the software can't quite do it yet, but next year it will. And next year it does, but then you think of something better.

It's like when I started Lightwright. It was just enough that it kept the dimmer numbers and the wattages and it kept it all organized in a way that you could actually do it. Now, well, oh my God. Wiggle lights with bazillions of channels and some people want to know all about all those channels and some people don't want to know anything about them at all.

RB: I'm in the latter camp, and don't care.

JM: I don't either, but I know the electricians have to patch all those DMX numbers, or they have to have a console that has a profile of the unit. It's all an order of magnitude bigger. My pet thing for Lightwright 4 is to get focus charts into the program.

RB: Using GIF files or JPG's?

JM: Well, there's all that part. And making them compatible between Mac and Windows.

RB: Well if you're storing it in your own format, you can have issues.[8] Are you starting from scratch?

JM: Eric Cornwell suggested having some primitives that Lightwright would draw so it does circle and ellipses and all those kind of things. In a focus chart, all you have to do is indicate where a light starts and where it falls. There aren't actually very many graphics involved.

The really hard part that everybody runs into when doing focus charts in a database (and people have tried it on File Maker and Access and all those things) is that you can't do it fast enough in the theatre.

RB: Ted Mather tried something new on *Oklahoma*. He got a digital camera and he had them bring up all the groups on the desk and he just took pictures. My God were they telling. I just had a quick scroll through them and they worked better than you would imagine. The funny bit was there was a carpenter working on spike marks on the stage when they did it. They were going to move him, but his shadow really worked to their advantage.

JM: That's a whole other problem with moving lights. How on earth do you

---

[8] Intel chips (and thus the DOS file system) uses little-endian, whereas Motorola chips use big-endian. File conversion and database formats have the potential to be a pain. In big-endian systems, the most-significant bit of data is places in the lowest address, but in little-endian, the least significant bit is places in the lowest address.

document what you've done? Nobody has come up with that one. Conventional lights, I'll get them into Lightwright. Moving lights…?

RB: Do you know what Disney's been doing with WYSIWYG? They bring up position on the console then print the WYSIWYG screen.

JM: That would come close.

RB: Gives you an idea. Is it a fan? Is it downstage?

JM: In *Riverdance*, there are eighty lights doing a full stage wash in templates. How on earth do you tell which one is coming from where?

RB: That was the other cool thing we did with AutoFocus in WYG. You could actually touch the template on the stage, not the light, the footprint of the light, then WYG would choose the light, and if you were hooked to the desk it would choose it there too. So you could touch it here, then wiggle it there.

JM: Perfect. That's the way it ought to work.

RB: Well, we've been doing that since 1996.

JM: I've always wanted to know why you couldn't have a lighting rig over your ice arena or whatever, then today your ice surface is a little bigger or your rig is a little lower and why it doesn't just focus itself to adjust, automatically. It ought to.

RB: The MA Scancommander did that years ago. The Hog can do that with its XYZ space. Great trade show gag, but nobody uses it successfully in practice. You have to be way too careful not to grab pan and tilt and build everything out of XYZ.

JM: There's always a got'cha. Oh, you mean the real world is different? Oh dear.

RB: That's what people would say about WYSIWYG all the time and it would drive me nuts me. They would say WYSIWYG wasn't very accurate. Excuse me? Double precision 32-bit floating-point math. It's hugely accurate. The problem is the lights aren't mechanically accurate. Or the truss is bent, or the c-clamp has some gum on it. Or you're a dolt and either didn't draw it right or you hung it wrong.

JM: Or what you are using WYSIWYG for. This drives me over the edge. It seems to be a coming trend that we're all supposed to light our shows on the computer and not in the theatre.

RB: I'm sorry.

JM: You were just the elephant helping push the door in. WYSIWYG is a tool for figuring out what you can do, ahead of time.

RB: People should know that when I use WYG, I turn on the option called "Stick Beams". A single ray of light, in CMY colour, comes out of the fixture. And I look at it from a wireframe plan view.

JM: Ha – that's funny.

RB: It's fastest that way. It shows you the timing accurately; shows you if the light is on or off; shows you if it's upstage or downstage; shows you if it's red or white. That's all you need.

JM: But there are people that want to light the show, in all 3D glory on the computer, complete with all the fabric swatches and everything. That's just not the point of lighting design.

RB: I use WYSIWYG to do proposals that way.

JM: For an industrial where nobody seems to care what it looks like – sure.

RB: And they won't hold you to the original rendering when all is said and done, if you put forward all the warranties et cetera in the beginning.

JM: If all that matters is that the lights wiggle in time to the music then go for it, but for me serendipity is three quarters of lighting design. I know what I want to do in a scene, but you get there and go, oh, they're facing down left instead of down right. Now what if...? Or you turn to the director and say "Do you suppose they could...". I couldn't design it all on a computer. What's the most important thing on the stage? It's where is the person facing. I'm looking at that face. Maybe one day those computers will give me those faces, but they're not going to be the same face as the actor.

RB: It will take longer anyways. You'll just end up doing it twice.

JM: I go in, create, then out the door. On to the next project.

RB: The other frustrating thing about WYSIWYG is that it always looks better on the screen that it does in real life.

JM: Well of course.

RB: It looks amazing in WYSIWYG – because you fill in the gap.

JM: It's the allure of the computer too.

RB: Perfect smoke. No reflections. Actors always on their spike marks.

JM: No messy lumps on the floor.

RB: When I'm doing rendering for a proposal, I fuss around forever.

JM: Trying to make it a little sloppier.

RB: I do. I put breakups on things that wouldn't normally have them.

JM: WYSIWYG is great because it saves you time in the theatre. Ken Billington did *Footloose* where the first ten minutes of the show was sixty something moves and you don't have time in the theatre for that. And, it is just a light show. So you do the cues, it looks great. Then you get in the theatre and fix it.

RB: As long as you cue using palettes.[9] WYSIWYGing a show was rarely successful before consoles adapted palettes. Let's stop talking about WYG – it was a different chapter of my life.

JM: But the world is all about moving lights these days. I think *One Mo' Time*[10] is the first Broadway musical in I can't think how many years that didn't have any wiggle lights on. "A musical without moving lights? How can you have a show?" I've seen people use moving lights on the revival of a musical where the original production didn't have any moving lights, and it's the same set, we're doing it again. Why do we need moving lights now?

RB: Because the audience demands it.

JM: Do they? They just want a good time. Does that mean the lights have to wiggle. That's why *One Mo' Time* was a flop; we didn't use moving lights. That must be it.

RB: Ted says that it's not a coincidence that since we've added moving lights to productions, shows don't last as long on Broadway. *Cats* didn't have any moving lights and it was on for 20 years.

JM: Moving lights cost a lot of money.

RB: Every week you change out a huge load of expensive bulbs.

JM: I don't know how producers put up with it frankly, except lighting

---

[9] The important thing about pre-programming (with visualizers or not), especially for touring purposes is that you don't use any raw numbers in a cue. Everything must be a reference. That way, you just fix the references and all the cues fall in line.

[10] A Broadway show that John just lit which unfortunately closed shortly after it opened.

All	Pos	Chn	Dim	CktN	C#	ıllı	Pos	Chn	Dim	Pur	CktN	List	Lib	Go Back

| S | F1 - Bookmark 1 | | S | F2 - Bookmark 2 | | S | F3 - Bookmark 3 | | S | F4 - Bookmark 4 |

View: Position Hold:

CEILING TRUSS ☑ Show Work Notes

Sorted By: Position ☐ Append

Position	Unit#	Type	Wattage	Purpose	Color	Template	Channel	Accsry	F	W
CEILING TRUSS	1	S4-19	575w	Warm Wash	R-33+R132		(1)		◇	
CEILING TRUSS	2	S4-19	575w	Cool Templates	L-161	Breakup	(2)	Donut	◇	
CEILING TRUSS	3	S4-19	575w	Warm Wash	R-33+R132		(1)		⊙	⚡
				Focus To Do: Needs refocusing						
CEILING TRUSS	4	S4-19	575w	Cool Templates	L-161	Breakup	(2)	Donut	⊙	
CEILING TRUSS	5	S4-19	575w	Warm Wash	R-33+R132	-----	(1)		⊙	
CEILING TRUSS	6	S4-19	575w	Cool Templates	L-161	Breakup	(2)	Donut	⊙	
CEILING TRUSS	7	S4-19	575w	Warm Wash	R-33+R132	-----	(1)		⊙	⚡
				Work To Do: Burnout						
CEILING TRUSS	8	S4-19	575w	Cool Templates	L-161	Breakup	(2)	Donut	⊙	
CEILING TRUSS	9	S4-19	575w	Warm Wash	R-33+R132		(1)		⊙	
CEILING TRUSS	10	S4-19	575w	Cool Templates	L-161	Breakup	(2)	Donut	⊙	

Cute icons for things like worknotes sex up the Lightwright 4 interface.

designers…

RB: …can't make up their mind before they get there.

JM: That's part of it. You also get musicals that re-write themselves during previews and God help you if you don't have some sort of flexibility.

RB: You say the audience wants to have a good time and maybe they wouldn't notice them or not. Let me give you some insight from a board operator's perspective, not a designer's perspective. When I do a big rock show in a 17,000-seat auditorium, there may be nothing on stage, but when I hit Go (they don't even know where I'm sitting), they go nuts.

JM: Sure – the lights are the show.

RB: Not all of it. Their cheering is in anticipation of something about to happen. They wouldn't cheer if the act never showed up. You're just one cog in the system.

JM: I went and saw *Mama Mia* the other day, and it was lovely. There is nothing wrong with the lighting, but I wanted the lights to move, because it's Abba. I wanted a concert.

RB: Moving lights weren't around when Abba was selling. At least you got the mega-mix at the end.

JM: Where the lights fly in and we get the concert I was expecting two hours before.

RB: *Joseph and the Amazing Technicolor Dreamcoat* started that. It wasn't long enough, so they had to do something at the end.

Tell me about John McKernon.

JM: My father was an electrical engineer so I learned in the third grade how to wire things when he built me a puppet theatre. I never worked in theatre until my senior year of high school, and then I ran publicity. I guess it wasn't until just before my freshman year at William & Mary, I went to a summer institute which included acting classes, and a friend of mine and I did an excerpt from *Waiting for Godot*, which we had a great time doing, but somebody had to light it. I just ended up doing it. Then in a couple of years, I was lighting everything in school and I had to transfer because I ran out of classes. I probably would have been better off staying there because Glen Close was in my class. You know, I might have had connections through being a good friend of hers!

RB: She was at an Eddy Award ceremony I was at, giving out an award to costume designer Ann Roth.

JM: We were on stage together. My first show at William & Mary was also her first show there. She played Olivia in *Twelfth Night* and I was a servant who carried furniture on and off. Two years later she was still playing leads

The production of "Twelfth Night" at William & Mary in 1970. John is on the far right of the picture. People who had lines to speak fill the rest of the picture.

and I was still playing a servant. That's when you figure out you're better at being a lighting designer.

RB: Did you want to act?

JM: No, not really. It was always fun, but I could never learn lines. Just like now, I don't remember channel numbers or gel numbers. I have no mind for it. Generally, I'm a very shy person. The effervescence, bubbly bit does not come easily to me. If I walk into a party and I don't know anybody, I'll normally turn around and leave.

RB: When we do these panels at LDI, for instance, where we sit up there and talk to people about our product, do you find that easier?

JM: Sure, because we've been introduced. They're a known quantity; you're a known quantity. If I'm introduced to somebody at a party, I can talk for hundreds of years on almost any subject, but to introduce myself, that's very scary. I can't do that.

RB: Maybe that's why you write software, because you can reach all those people, but do it from your living room.

JM: I never write software with those people in mind. I really tend to write the software for me. If the rest of the world finds it useful, then that's terrific. And yes, they all scream at me and want something different, and I change it to make it more useful for them.

RB: If you respect them enough.

JM: If I think their opinion is valid, which means it agrees with mine. If I try something, and it doesn't work the way I work, then I really have to have a hard think as to whether it's going to work for anybody else. But it must work, because enough people use it and like it.

One of the problems with the early versions was that it was very idiosyncratic. It's still very idiosyncratic, it's just that everybody has learned how to deal with it. I guess it's one of the virtues of being a standard now. I can do whatever I want to, to a degree.

When I was starting, it was easier because channel numbers didn't have a letter after them or before them or whatever. Now, thank you Strand, we have channel number 20.1, .2, .3, .4. Then we go up to .9 and .10 and .11. It's 'point one zero' as apposed to 'point one' with nothing after it. So, there are all those parts that Lightwright has to start coping with that are weird and strange.

RB: I remember using Lightwright at CBC years ago and we ran out of positions. You had static array that you couldn't dynamically allocate.

JM: I still do and that is something I hope to fix in Version 4. It's always been a real firm principle of mine that if you have a copy of Lightwright you should be able to open any file that any person has made. That is a golden rule. If you use dynamic arrays and base everything on how much memory they have in their computer it would be completely possible for you to write a show that is too big for somebody else to open. To me that would be a disaster. Imagine that a designer does up some show because he has some fancy computer, then sends it off to the electrician who can't read it.

RB: But now it's all running on proper operating systems with virtual memory, doesn't that just go away? Things will just run slower on a pokey machine.

JM: That's part of it, but on the other hand, it just gets more complicated every year. One of the things in Lightwright 4 is collapsible work sheet rows so that if you have a moving light with 26 channels you can collapse it to one row, or three rows, or two rows, or however many rows you want to so you can see whatever you want to see. Well, the data structure to support that, good God, I haven't figured out how to do this. It's going to take memory. I know that.

RB: Eric was talking about Express Track and how he could do that for every channel.[11] His display had one row that had the channels and the second row would be the level. The third row could be its In-time, the fourth row could be its Out-time, and if you wanted, you could have a fifth row showing which cue it has tracked from or another row showing where it's going to change next. It was an exercise in displaying data.

JM: And my eyes glaze over.

RB: It's similar to what we did with WYSIWYG. We had a single database that had all of the information, but you could view it anyway you wanted to. You could view it as a 3D drawing or in a 2D proper plan with symbols. You could look at the data in a spreadsheet view and sort it whichever way you want. Knock out the columns you don't want or add the columns you do. There was none of this synchronization or updating. It was one massive data collection. You just viewed it however you wanted. You changed a record in

---

[11] See Cornwell – page 277

one view; every other window that was open would get a message to re-paint. Then, you have to get clever not to do too much work; don't draw things that aren't visible.

JM: The bear on my back these days is the problem of drafting, with Lightwright or not. I do a light plot and there is nothing but the unit number and a symbol for the instrument. That's it. So there's nothing to exchange back and forth with Lightwright.

RB: In the early days of LXCAD and LXDB, I used AutoCAD 'handles' to uniquely identify the fixtures so I could swap things back and forth.

JM: I use Spotlight. I'm a beta tester for Spotlight – I just never use it for shows. Either there wants to be one program that does it all, or don't even try to get back and forth.

RB: Eric is 180 degrees out from you on this one. He likes lots of little tools that do very specific jobs.[12] He likes the back and forth.

JM: This little brain can't keep it straight. I don't know when I've just exported from Lightwright, and I mustn't make any changes in Lightwright when I'm working in Spotlight.

RB: You've just explained WYG 3. It took all the good stuff from LXCAD, LXDB and LXMOV and put them in one package. It solved the "Who's got the ball?" debate. The Ballet in Toronto uses Lightwright and they have a floppy disk called The Ball. Everybody may have a copy of Lightwright on their machine, but The Ball is passed. You can keep a copy locally if you want – but it's not the real thing.

You work alone, so you've probably never considered using group-ware like Source Safe or Starteam. These are code vaults that keep all the code and all revisions of the code. You must go through a process of checking out the code to work on it. Then it is locked for writing for everybody else. They can read it, but they can't check in changes until you un-lock it. It is absolutely necessary on large projects. We had about six of us writing code when I was at CAST and one day our server went down. We all ended up, quite literally, bumping into each other in the hallway, always asking who was working on what, making sure we weren't both making changes at the same time.

We'd thought of doing the same thing, right inside WYG. Record locking on CAD based data structures gets very tricky. It would be way too easy for

---

[12] See Cornwell – page 275

one user to lock everybody else out from doing anything.

JM: I've been thinking of doing some sort of workgroup features where you could identify yourself as a person and then make changes to the database, then hand it off to the next person and they would make changes and you would get a history of who did what. You would then need an intelligent merge where you would say changes made by John are more important than changes made by Joe

RB: Like Track Changes in Word – "Accept" – "Decline".

JM: Then there's the problem of Trust. Does the designer trust the electrician with the focus charts? Does the electrician trust the designer to not screw with his dimmer and circuit numbers? If one of them locks part of the database, then maybe they're saying they don't trust the other person. Tossing The Ball back and forth is probably more politically acceptable. In Lightwright 4, you can exchange just the changes you make, which makes them more visible, and hopefully more trustworthy!

What I don't want to do is re-invent drafting. I see no point whatsoever in writing a CAD program. There are millions of those out there. I just wish Vectorworks would get their act together and make it possible to exchange data dynamically in real time.

RB: Even before I was doing LXCAD and LXDB at CBC, I was doing Microsoft Dynamic Data Exchange with Excel and AutoCAD for Windows Extension – not even the true Win32 AutoCAD. It was not pretty. It worked, but the Windows Extension was so unstable and generally way too slow. Now with Visual Basic for Applications it's much faster. I can do 10 updates per second on 512 records when I hook AutoCAD and Horizon together. It's LXMOV all over again, but coded in one-hundredth the time.

JM: Problem is, most designers don't use AutoCAD. Vectorworks has gotten to be very popular with the set design crowd. I like Vectorworks. It's the first thing I've tried that made me think I can draft on a computer. AutoCAD for years just made me go "no way". It doesn't think the way I think. But Vectorworks doesn't understand the exchanging of data back and forth bit.

They are on a fifteen-month upgrade cycle now. Every fifteen months there is a new version of software. Lightwright users are lucky if they get one every four years.

RB: That sort of policy puts an awful lot of pressure on the developers and I don't think it serves the public well in any case. Software is too organic to predict when it will be ready. If you're rushing to meet a marketing department enforced deadline, you probably are not getting the prime software out in a timely fashion anyway. It's done when it's done. Once it's done, you can think about how to package it. If all you're concerned about is the wrapper, the users will soon find out what you're up to.

What are your thoughts on charging for updates or subscription?

JM: I thought about this some years ago. If I could get everybody who uses Lightwright to send me $40 a year, I would give them the current version all the time. That would be terrific. There is sort of a problem there and that is that people want some sort of guarantee that they are going to get something. There is also the temptation there for me to go on vacation rather than deliver new stuff.

The other part is, one of the reasons that Lightwright has become a standard is because it has not changed much. We sat in Lightwright 2 for a long long time, about seven years. And everybody shared the data files all the time for seven years and it was a very standard thing and everybody used it. I really think that's what made it the standard that it is now. Lightwright 3 has now been out for three years. There are still people using version 2. But because of that lack of change, you're pretty well assured that you're going to be compatible with everybody else in the business.

If I was on a fifteen month upgrade cycle, the program would have to read and write every conceivable version for the last twenty years. That is fiendishly messy from my standpoint.

RB: It also becomes a tech support nightmare.

JM: It is a nightmare. Then every new version has some feature that the previous version has never even thought about. That happens when you send a Lightwright 3 back to Version 2. There are eight new columns that don't exist in the old format. So you're just going to lose all that.

RB: Alan Martello surprised me the first year I worked with him on Horizon. I kept coming up with all these new features and user options that I was sure were going to change the file format, but he had the foresight to circumvent all of that. He's left all kinds of hiding spots in his file format and just keeps using them up. If older versions of Horizon load newer ones, they just ignore the data – but they don't cough. It will even save data it knows nothing about – just to preserve it. Very clever I thought.

JM: But what do you do in Lightwright? You just lose the data.

RB: Sorry John, you never thought of it all the first time. Those will be the facts of life.

We fought with that with DWG in and out. We finally did DWG in and now I understand CAST are outputing some stuff, but the problem is, WYSICAD was so intelligent of it's environment, and knew so much about the light, it was very hard to dumb it down to Autodesk's level. And once you do, it's very difficult to carbuncle that information into Extended Entity Data[13] so you can bring it back out once they're done editing it.

JM: I don't know what the solution is.

RB: I think some companies think they can insist that people buy maintenance packages, but that is an uphill marketing battle. The automotive CAD industry has been able to get away with it for years – but those are much more expensive packages.

JM: It has become popular among accounting software firms, that in order to buy version 4, you have to have bought the upgrades to 2 and 3 and all of the maintenance packages along the way. And if you haven't, in order to get from say 1 to 4, you have to pay for all those in-between upgrades plus a twenty five percent penalty. Needless to say, customers screamed at this.

RB: When you went from version 2 to 3, how did you charge version 2 users for 3?

JM: There was a discount, naturally. You're rewarding people for being loyal. I think we've put a limit on how many years can go by before you upgrade. I think the cut off from Version 1 was six years. The theory is to reward somebody who is a 'steady customer", so if they didn't upgrade from Lightwright 2 to Lightwright 3 before wanting Lightwright 4, where's the loyalty?

RB: If you've waited that long, you're really somebody new anyway.

JM: This was somebody who wasn't using it, but has now heard that it is good again and wants to get in on it. Sorry.

---

[13] AutoCAD predicted that people would want to store extra data related to their drawing in the DWG file format. They gave you the ability (using AutoLISP or ADS or VBA) to attach whatever you wanted in Extended Entity Data. The DWG would just carry it around even if it didn't know what it was for. Clever.

RB: Did you have a database of users? You didn't have a dongle or anything like that.

JM: No. The smartest thing I've ever done was making it print everybody's name at the bottom of the paperwork. That by itself doesn't prevent piracy, but it certainly keeps it visible and somewhat under control.

We discovered once that the Sydney Opera House had a copy of Lightwright that was from Marcia Madeira in New York. To this day, she doesn't know how on earth it got there, but it's very clear it got there because her name was printed at the bottom of the paperwork! People in the business sort of figure out right away that this is a small business and that everybody knows everybody. I think that the Opera House has a proper copy now. That was ten or fifteen years ago.

RB: When did ALD Pro come out?

JM: When did the PC come out?

RB: I was in high school. 1981 with clones coming from HP as early as '83.

JM: Then that was ALD – the original version. So in some form or another it's been out for almost twenty years now.

RB: And you're only at version 3.

JM: Yes. Well there were the ALD products first.

RB: From a coding standpoint, the major change came when you did the Mac version. That was essentially all new code and everything from that point on has been based on that, correct?

JM: Yes.

RB: With WYSIWYG, our big jump was between Version 2, which was all DOS, to Version 3, which was Win32. Now from a marketing standpoint, with V3 there would have been advantages (and disadvantages) for us to change the name to CAST CAD, rather than WYSIWYG 3, because we charged everybody full price for it.

JM: You had to. It's a hell of a lot of work. But I felt so awful making all those Mac people buy DOS computers for so many years. There were literally Mac users who bought a DOS computer to run Lightwright. That is a horrible thing to do to somebody.

RB: And we were doing it the other way. Working with Tom Thompson during

U2's Popmart tour, I demoed the beginnings of WYG3. He promptly sold his Mac to buy a PC, which he used to start Prelite.

Now you support both platforms, how would you say the sales are split?

JM: I think at this point it's probably between two-thirds and three-quarters Windows. That is significantly higher than the spit between PC's and Mac's in the world.

RB: Oh yes. Only 2% of the world's PC's are Mac, and they're all in the States.

JM: Right, but I would say that in the theatre business it's probably at 30%. Maybe more than that. I figure, why do I want to cut out half the world?

RB: We were frustrated, because we really wanted to support the Mac OS but couldn't find the tools to do it.

JM: You needed completely separate code bases.

RB: We didn't have the money. There were only three of us. And our market was so international. Your 30% is probably only true on Broadway and not so much in Europe and Asia.

JM: People always ask me why I don't hire somebody to help write code. The fact is, the money is just not there. Obviously all these years before the deal with City Theatrical, there was no money for it. If I made $8000 a year, that was a good year. Obviously you don't do that as a career. Now that I'm making enough to pay the rent, that's fine, but it doesn't pay anybody else's rent!

RB: The funny thing is, Lightwright is without a doubt, the most used application in our industry. Much more so than WYSIWYG, Vectorworks, Gelfile or Lightlab.

JM: You're probably right, but you'd be amazed at what a small number that is though.

RB: It shows how small our industry is.

JM: Every now and then, we do those panels at LDI where we are asked how many users we have. Everybody is trying to be very honest about it, but it's hard to say. People get the software, but then they drop off and maybe they come back years later or whatever. If you're only counting current users, you count it one way, and so on. At this point (I haven't looked in years), it's maybe 5000 users. Microlux said six years ago they had 9000 users. I thought, if they had 9000 users, why don't I know any of them?

RB: I think people should know how big the industry isn't. ESTA is trying to get a handle on it.

JM: How many people design all the Broadway shows in one season? It's a lot more than it used to be. It used to be about six people. Now it's maybe twenty. That's a teeny little bit of business.

It's rewarding that Lightwright has taken hold. I think that speaks a lot to the communication value of it, which is why I don't like doing frequent upgrades. It's not just a tool for getting paperwork done, it's how you send your data to somebody and they'll understand it when they get it. That's the important part.

RB: Have any console manufacturers contacted you about incorporating it.

JM: Never.

RB: Would you be willing to?

JM: I would be open to the idea, as long as it were kept non-proprietary. It's just like tying yourself to Windows or the Mac. I don't see the point of restricting yourself.

RB: I worked so hard on developing the WYSIWYG developers program. We had ETC, Strand, Entertainment Technology, Flying Pig Systems, Jands and Compulite all writing DLL's to interface with WYSIWYG.[14]

JM: Oh my God. That's six companies supporting one product as opposed to one. Which is an instructive lesson – Microsoft vs. Apple.[15] It's the same principle. And now ETC has tied it to Expression and not everyone wants to use one of those. Well, perhaps I say that because I come from the land of Obsession.

RB: Anne Foster is still there writing Expression code and Jon Ide, the main Obsession developer isn't. What good is a bunch of code if you don't have the architect?

JM: Or you don't have the code. I've lost the code to Lightwright 2.

---

[14] Since I've left CAST, they have continued the program, calling it RWD (Registered WYSIWYG Developer) and have signed up more developers.

[15] John's talking about how the IBM PC's bus architecture was published so other manufactures could build bits to go inside of the PC. Apple was much more protective about its interface. See Hunt – page 211 and see Howell page 350

Position	#	Type	Watt	Purpose	Color	Dim	Chn
> BOOTH	1	Lycian Long	1200	Follow Spot	Note 1	...	.... →
BOOTH	2	Lycian Long	1200	Follow Spot	Note 1	...	.... →
BALCONY RAIL	A	6x12	1kw	Clouds	L-161,T:R7	144	(109) →
BALCONY RAIL	1	19' Source 4	575	"As You May	N/C,Donut,	54	(144) →
BALCONY RAIL	2	19' Source 4	575	"Six Weeks	N/C,Donut,	53	(145) →
BALCONY RAIL	3	36' Source 4	575	Show Drop	Note 4+R-1	49	(141) →
BALCONY RAIL	3A	Color Ram 4	10	Control		223	(200)*
BALCONY RAIL	4	36' Source 4	575	Drops	L-128,T:R#	50	(142) →
BALCONY RAIL	5	6x12	1kw	Kids Floor	G-106	2	(11)
BALCONY RAIL	6	6x12	1kw	Train Flick	N/C	52	(161) →
BALCONY RAIL	6A	Color Wheel	.....	Train Flick	Mixed	51	(162) →
BALCONY RAIL	7	6x12 w/IRIS	1kw	Logo	R-51+R-119	3	(143)
BALCONY RAIL	8	6x12 w/IRIS	1kw	Logo	R-51+R-119	3	(143)
BALCONY RAIL	9	6x12	1kw	Clouds	L-161,T:R7	144	(109) →
BALCONY RAIL	10	6x12	1kw	Kids Floor	G-106	2	(11)
[							]

```
COMMANDS:  Add              Copy    Delete   Edit    Format   Global   Hold
           If      List     Mark    Note     Print            Stock           Windows
           Press the initial you want, or <Esc> to exit.      F1-Help  F2-Options

 3 6x9      4 6x12     5 6x16      6 5x22      7 PAR 56    8 PAR 64   9 STRIP   10 TEMP
```

Oklahoma-23ml.lw3

| All | Pos | Ch | Dim | .ıl | Pos | Ch | Dim | List | Lib |

View: Ch ▼   Hold:

10-500

Sorted by: Ch ▼   ☐ Append

Ch	Dim	Pos	Unit#	Inst Type	Watts	Purpose	Tmpl	Color
(145)	104	Balco	5	Ianiro w/BD	2kw	Front Gauze Blu		R68,HS
(146)	101	Balco	1	Ianiro w/BD	2kw	Front Gauze Blu		R68,HS
(161)	151	Cove	17	10°S4 w/TH	575w	DS of corn	R7779	NC
(162)	150	Cove	16	10°S4 w/TH	575w	DS of corn	R7779	NC
(163)	149	Cove	15	10°S4 w/TH	575w	DS of corn	R7779	NC

Lightwright 4: Sample Show.lw4

| All | Pos | Chn | Dim | CktN | C# | .ıll | Pos | Chn | Dim | Pur | CktN | List | Lib | Go Back |

| S | F1 – No. 1 ELEC | S | F2 – No. 3 ELEC | S | F3 – Channel 4 | S | F4 – Bookmark 4 |

View: All ▼   Hold: S4-26

S4-26   ☐ Show Work Notes

Sorted By: Position ▼   ☐ Append

Position	Unit#	Instrument Type	Wattage	Purpose	Color	Template	Channel	Accsry	F	W
CEILING TRUSS	1	S4-26	575w	Warm Wash	R-33+R		(1)		◇	
CEILING TRUSS	2	S4-19	575w	Cool Templates	L-161	Breakup	(2)	Donut	◇	
CEILING TRUSS	3	S4-26	575w	Warm Wash	R-33+R		(1)		●	✂
CEILING TRUSS	4	S4-19	575w	Cool Templates	L-161	Breakup	(2)	Donut	⊘	
CEILING TRUSS	5	S4-26	575w	Warm Wash	R-33+R		(1)		⊘	
CEILING TRUSS	6	S4-19	575w	Cool Templates	L-161	Breakup	(2)	Donut	⊘	
CEILING TRUSS	7	S4-26	575w	Warm Wash	R-33+R		(1)		⊘	✂
CEILING TRUSS	8	S4-19	575w	Cool Templates	L-161	Breakup	(2)	Donut	⊘	
CEILING TRUSS	9	S4-26	575w	Warm Wash	R-33+R		(1)		⊘	
CEILING TRUSS	10	S4-19	575w	Cool Templates	L-161	Breakup	(2)	Donut	⊘	
No. 1 ELEC	1	PAR 64 MFL	1kw	Downlight	R-80		(3)		⊘	
No. 1 ELEC	2	PAR 64 MFL	1kw	Downlight	R-21		(4)		⊘	
No. 1 ELEC	3	PAR 64 MFL	1kw	Downlight	R-80		(3)		⊘	
No. 1 ELEC	4	PAR 64 MFL	1kw	Downlight	R-21		(4)		⊘	
No. 1 ELEC	5	S4-26	575w	Color Wash Speci	(30)		(20)		⊘	
No. 1 ELEC	5	ColoRAM		Color Wash Scrol	Note 2		(30)			

| Worksheet | Focus | Layout | 98 items

The evolution over the years.

RB: Wow – how did that happen?

JM: You know, you get new machines and you think you've moved everything over and you haven't.

RB: Eric says he can't run Express Track anymore because he put his own software protection schemes in that had hooks to the OS. So it doesn't run any more and he can't get the code back.

JM: That's frustrating. Every so often I get someone who calls me and says they've lost their disk for Lightwright 2, can I get them new ones. I say, "Honey – that was five years ago." I don't have the code that makes those files anymore.

RB: So that closes the book on Lightwright 2, I guess. What's next?

JM: Once Lightwright 4 is out the door, I'll be back doing some designing, but I do have a few software ideas lurking around in the back of my brain – maybe a followspot tracking program, maybe something that will help make "real" shop orders. Of course, every time I release a major upgrade, I think that's the end of the line, there's nowhere else for Lightwright to go. But as sure as the sun rises in the morning, I know that once people start to use Lightwright 4, the feature list for Lightwright 5 will start. That's good, because I'd like nothing better than some financial security to retire someday. That, and a small swimming pool…

6 ANNE VALENTINO

Introduction

Outside designers, Anne is quite likely the most respected female in our industry. Hopping from manufacturer to manufacturer, she has left a trail of success behind her. She started in systems design, moved on to become a control product manager and is now working in marketing.

Her most acclaimed achievement is the Obsession from ETC (Electronic Theatre Controls). With Jon Ide, this was seen as a two-person effort – and they take the credit. To me the most remarkable thing about the product was the rate upon which it dethroned the Light Palette, which had been the clear and decisive choice for lighting control on Broadway for years. Fred Foster of ETC went after the New York market in a big way and thanks in part to Anne and her work on Obsession, he conquered it in one fowl swoop. Obsession was released at the same trade show (LDI 92) as the Source 4 luminaire and Sensor dimmers (both by David Cunningham), which locked ETC into a continuing success path for the next ten years and through to today.

Nobody will try to tell you that Obsession was an original idea. Wally Russell and Strand released the Light Palette (another Cunningham project) back in 1979. It was the first popular desk to

emulate piano boards, which was all Broadway was using. Richard Pilbrow commissioned Strand to build the Lightboard in 1976 for the National Theatre in London and this was a landmark. It was really the first computer based last-action desk; a control system that could do more than one thing at a time. Obsession rode on the tails of these two desks and makes no apologies for it. They simply did it with 1990's technology while meantime the Light Palette was getting very tired.

Anne's console history started at Kliegl where she supported Gordon Pearlman's Performer and Command Performance before moving on to Strand, where she consulted on Lightboard M and Light Palette 90. She did a quick jaunt at Colortran as a consultant but soon joined ETC as Director of R&D in 1990. It was there she was given the task to create Obsession and take ETC into the lead.

After Obsession, Anne worried she was not riding the wave of technology and needed to get on board the automated lighting bandwagon so she left ETC and joined Vari-Lite. It was there she worked with Charles Reese and Michael Snyder to (again) re-do the Artisan, another desk that was getting tired. During her time with Vari-Lite as Director of Marketing, I visited Anne and Tom Littrell on a number of occasions to try to convince them to integrate WYSIWYG into a console. They were good at keeping a secret at Vari-Lite. Even though I knew they were working on a desk, nobody would tell me that they were re-inventing WYSIWYG to bundle it in the desk. It's the Texan way. In any case, Virtuoso was a great desk and well received by Artisan operators all over the world. It also won an Emmy Award; ironically the same year WYSIWYG won one.

Anne left Vari-Lite in 1999 and briefly joined PRG (now Fourth Phase) as Vice President of Marketing. Since then, Genlyte has purchased Vari-Lite and the Virtuoso has been shelved. (Again – ironically, I'm on a team at Genlyte that is designing the new desk called Marquee.)

Virtuoso has since been revived by VLPS, but Anne is working independently as a marketing guru under the name Quest Comm and has a client list that includes Nautilus Entertainment Design, Schuler Shook, Lightswitch, Electronic Theatre Controls and Prelite.

We did this interview in a bar just off Broadway.

Interview

RB: I was at CBC when we were struggling with a new Strand Light Palette

90, version 1.something. Then an ETC dealer showed up with this big brown Obsession thing and we hid it away in a room where management couldn't see it so we could toy around with it. In playing with it, we found that essentially it was the Version 2 spec that we thought we had bought with the LP90.

AV: Yes, we did that deliberately.

RB: Now, I don't know much about you before that, but I've come to know you since then!

AV: I was raised near New Orleans and have a BA from a small liberal arts college in Louisiana. Got a Masters in lighting from the University of Wyoming. People laugh at the fact you can get an arts degree from the University of Wyoming, but it was actually pretty cool because it was the only four-year college in Wyoming – the state was really rich at that time because of uranium mining – so they had all this money for the arts and no place to put it. The theatre at UW was extremely well equipped and very well funded. Not only that, but they paid me to get my degree – which worked for me.

I started college when I was seventeen. I was in the dorm one night – too young to legally hang out in bars with friends and too naive to know about fake IDs. Out of boredom, I ended up going to the theatre with a girl who lived down the hall from me. It was my first real exposure to that world and I just fell in love. Ironically, the first production I worked on was *One Flew Over the Cuckoo's Nest*. Should have been a leading indicator of the direction my career would take. I got involved in props initially, built scenery, then I sort of fell into lighting when I was in graduate school because I didn't want to write a thesis on Goethe's dramatic interpretation of King Lear #1005, or some such drivel.

RB: Did you ever aspire to be on stage?

AV: Absolutely not. They made us do it, but it was torture for me. Most academic programs make technicians do some sort of stage work so you understand what it's like when the light cue doesn't happen on time or when the prop doesn't work properly or whatever, so they force you into it and I hated it.

My graduate work was actually in theory and criticism. I didn't have any intention to go into the technical side of things. But I wrote my thesis in lighting because I found an interesting topic on the psychology of colour and the impact of colour media on the content of the show – very esoteric, but it was kind of interesting for someone who didn't really know much about the theory of lighting at all.

After graduating, I worked as a technical director for a new road-house built outside Houston – which had been very poorly consulted. This is what got me interested in the supply side of the business.

RB: Was it being built just as you were working there?

AV: No, it was just completing construction. They hired me two months before it opened.

RB: So, they already had all the wrong gear.

AV: Yes. They had a hospital intercom system so only one person could talk at a time, so if your button was held down . . .

RB: It was like a radio.

AV: Exactly. It had electrics that wouldn't fly all the way to the deck because the multis were cut too short because it hadn't been properly specified. There was no cabling of any type. It was a venue built by a private foundation and then given to the city as a gift. It was a 20 million dollar theatre – not insignificant at that time – a 1500-seat road-house. It was a beautiful facility, but technically just awful.

I got really interested in how this situation had occurred. How could these people spend this kind of money and get such a bad installation?

RB: It still happens today.

AV: Hmmm, sadly yes. I was just twenty-three when I got this job and my boss, who was the director of the theatre, started recommending me to go in to other new facilities that had also gone wrong. I learned a lot about how specifications get written: what you can fight for and what you can't fight for; what you can make the contractor fix; what you have to eat. I didn't know any of that stuff; you don't get taught any of that in college. So once the word got out, I started getting hired as a consultant to come into other facilities that had been similarly badly consulted. It was really very interesting.

Then I met Joel Rubin, who was with Kliegl at the time, at a convention in Dallas. I wrote him a letter saying I was really interested to know more about how this whole process worked. How did equipment get designed, developed and installed? Should I go back to school? Should I get an engineering degree?

Well, they flew me to New York, interviewed me and hired me as a technical writer based on this letter I wrote.

So I started writing their operations manuals about the time Performer II was launched and organising training on their Command Performance consoles.

RB: So you actually have quite a history with Gordon [Pearlman].

AV: Oh yes! Gordon and Steve Carlson were my mentors. Poor Steve – the man truly has the patience of Job. I knew nothing about anything technical, really. When I was in college, you didn't get taught a lot about electricity – at least in theory and crit classes. Kliegl had just introduced the K96 dimmer, which was fully digital, Gordon and Steve were in Portland, so I was out there quite a bit.[1] Steve would explain to me over and over again how the system worked. And every time he explained it to me I would understand a little bit more. They were very patient with me and I learned a lot from them.

I started getting involved in product development – or at least began to understand what the process is and some of the issues that the product development team confronts when they are trying to bring a product to market.

I ended up leaving Kliegl after about three years. By that time, I was the Associate Director of Marketing. I had taken over trade shows, all training and pretty much all literature production. In 1983 I took a job with the Strand rep in San Antonio called the CFA Group (Crews Folsom Associates). CFA was owned by Robin Crews – who is now a consultant in Texas and Tom Folsom – who now runs the Katy Group in LA. It was in the days of the mega rep. agencies. Strand pretty much owned the market in the US and there were three or four major rep. organizations that were also dealers. There was CD80 and Light Palette, but no other serious consistent competition out there.[2]

For three years I did system design-build work. My first installation was a television studio in Dallas. I learned (now that I knew a little about the manufacturing end of it) how systems get specified and sold and the whole process of getting the system installed. I thought this was really interesting. I came to the attention of the Strand people at that time because I was doing really well for them – although I don't think I ever won a single bid in my life. I couldn't figure the bidding thing out – all of those side deals and political alignments, but if it was a design-build project done directly with the end

---

[1] See footnote on page 65 for a description of the K96 and the problem it had.

[2] See Cunningham – page 78 on the duel between Strand and Kliegl

user, I could get the job almost every time.

RB: So when you say Strand was getting your attention, it was Strand USA?

AV: Yes, this was the days of Marvin Altman. NAB was in Dallas in 1986 and my clients were just all over the booth. I was running around doing demos and trying to close jobs. Strand were attempting to get a product called Lightboard M to market. The product line was actually Lightboard M and Lightboard XP; they had this idea of a common platform so everything from the very smallest desk to the very biggest desk could be built by expanding the hardware. It's interesting, because in the '90s, the idea of product platforming really came into its own.

RB: I actually started at CBC on a Lightboard M, but we also had Impacts. The Impact was Gordon Pearlman's desk that was a bit strange given the competitiveness between Kliegl and Strand.

AV: Yes, the Impact was based on the Performer concept, with a bit of Strand syntax added.[3]

RB: Impact was DMX whereas Lightboard M was still AMX. So, can we put a name to Lightboard M or was it just done by committee?

AV: I don't know who originally specified it. Susan Dandridge was involved at some point, as was Debbie Garcia. So Strand offered me a job as Dimming and Controls Product Manager. I had never specified a product and I didn't know anything about that – so Lightboard M was my first experience with developing a user interface. The problem was, the hardware had already been developed; it already had a bunch of buttons and displays on it. So it was a matter of taking these buttons and displays and making a product out of it.

RB: They had software?

AV: They had sort of working software – enough to demo the product at trade shows and get a bunch of people to buy the desk. I think by the time we started shipping, we had more than 400 desks on backorder. This was about the time Strand had bought Electro Controls and Jody Good – who was from EC – had taken over all of R&D. We ended up developing this thing with the R&D team in Salt Lake City (EC's headquarters) because by that time, the R&D team in LA was pretty decimated. David Cunningham and his group

---

[3] See Pearlman – page 63 on how Performer III was repackaged for Strand

had left a few years earlier.[4]

RB: The M came along in the late 1980s.

AV: It was designed in Salt Lake, but built in the Strand LA factory. I worked with a couple of software engineers who were really great, but again, I had no idea of how you were supposed to do this stuff.

So I'd fly in and out of Salt Lake, we'd gather around the prototype and make it up as we went along. I

Strand's Lightboard M.

started writing out syntax based on the buttons and faders that were already on the board. We had to design to the feature set that had been published in their catalog and was already included in Section 16 specs. Luckily, the EC engineers had a lot of experience. The syntax was vastly different than the other Strand products, but at least we could make some type of product out of the thing. We completely busked it.

RB: Did you have console experience?

AV: I had console experience as an operator and as a trainer on Command Performances and Performers. Also, as a Strand rep, I'd done training on their product line. That was really the only background I had. I'm very sorry you ended up with a Lightboard M – not one of our finer efforts.

RB: What I loved about it was the four patches.

AV: That was a pretty cool idea wasn't it? It was an interesting learning experience, but it was just an awful time at Strand. Marvin Altman then left and there was a big change in the political structure of the company. I was only there for about a year-and-a-half and just got to the point where I couldn't take any more. But that's a story I'll save for my memoirs. I quit and then ended up contracting myself back to them to help develop the specification for Light Palette 90, which was out-sourced for development to Bill Goddard and Bill Ward. That didn't last very long. Then I went to Colortran as a consultant.

---

[4] See Cunningham regarding Strand firing Wally Russell in 1982 – page 94 Upon Wally's departure, Dave gave Strand two years notice.

RB: I come from Canada where Strand was a different company in the early days so my sense of history is a bit confused. We didn't necessarily get things in the same order you did. Strand in the UK had MMS, Lightboard and the Galaxy. Here they had the Multi Cue and the Light Palette family. Then it was the M, Mantrix, Impact then Light Palette 90's. Out of all of them, the only two-tracking desks were the Lightboard and the Light Palettes.

AV: The first Strand console I ever worked on was a Multi Cue, which was a pre-cursor to the Light Palette. It was very much a computerized multi-scene preset console.

RB: That's what the M was.

AV: Yep. Everything fell into either being a computerized piano board or a computerized preset board. This was, of course, before automation; we're still in the realm of conventional lighting. Automation changes the paradigm totally. In those days, you were either emulating what you did to program a preset console or what you did to program a piano board. The Palette is based on what the operator did to run piano boards – which were used on Broadway.

To understand lighting control – American lighting control at any rate – you really have to understand the origin of both of those concepts. Kliegl's Performer and Command Performance – as well as the whole ETC product line prior to Obsession are really computerized preset consoles. Palette was a computerized piano board. The development of the original Light Palette is very interesting – and I'm sure you cover it with Dave.[5] The North American branch of Strand, under Wally Russell, the president of Strand at the time, developed Light Palette and CD80 as back door projects. Corporate didn't even know they were being done.[6]

David Cunningham was the R&D lead, while Chuck Levy was the guy who sat in the theatre with the designers. Chuck Levy is an unsung hero in the control development world. He sat in the theatre and listened to the way the designer talked to the board operator. He found the common threads in communication. That is the syntax of the Light Palette. It seems an obvious approach today, but nobody had ever done this before.[7]

The original Light Palette is one of the purest lighting consoles I've ever

---

[5] See Cunningham – page 82

[6] See Cunningham – page 79 on how Wally flew the project under the wire

[7] See Cunningham contradict Anne's story on page 83. Dave admits that it was Chuck that had the connections, but he was the one to sit in the theatre.

seen. It's got the cleanest and most unique vocabulary and DNA to it. From my few discussions with Chuck before he died, I think he had an enormous influence on this. He had the ability to really listen to what was being said and to drill down into that to find a language that was so perfect for a theatrical lighting controller.

Beverly Emmons[8] said something to me a few years ago that I've never forgotten, and it is something I think about as I work on desks. If I can ever have someone say this about a desk I've worked on, I'll die happy. She said: "Light Palette helped me understand how I thought about lighting". That's when the tool transcends being a tool and it helps you with your art. It helps you organize yourself in the design process because of the way that it thinks. That's a very powerful statement, and that's the beauty of Light Palette. It's particular logic doesn't apply any more because as you move into automated lighting the very linear thought process – with a single playback – doesn't strictly apply. But at the time it was a stunning piece of work. It's something I strive for all of the time. It's this beautiful simplicity of thought that is stripped back to pure essence. Chuck and Dave did an extremely beautiful job with that. I'm in awe of that product.

RB: I find it hard to believe that preset desks still sell. How often is there just one thing happening on the stage? How often do you want to go from one look, straight on to another? There is always something coming, something going and something else going on stage left. I can't believe people are still settling for a desk that only allows you to run one cue at a time. Every tracking desk to date has followed Light Palettes' lead.

AV: Well, you can do more than one thing at a time on an Expression style desk – you just go about it differently. It's an interesting thing though. A console like Palette doesn't work in the concert/touring world, and it doesn't work in the industrial world. If I were working in that world, a desk like Expression would be my choice. But if you're building a linear production, which is what theatre is, an LTP tracking console is so elegant and so simple.

RB: So did you work on the 90?

AV: Briefly, for about three months. I worked on the specification for it then I left before it got to first prototype. After I left Strand, I did a little consulting for them, then I tried my hand at architectural lighting.

---

[8] Tony award winner for lighting Amadeus. Beverly has received six Tony Nominations.

Light Palette 90.

RB: Actually 'lighting' – like putting photons on . . .

AV: No, no, no. I'm not a designer. I worked for Elliptipar for a short time, but wasn't well suited to the architectural world – how's that for politically correct? Then an opportunity came up to do some consulting for Colortran. I started helping them set up their dealer network, then started acting as ad hoc product manager while the second iteration of Prestige – the Prestige II – was being developed. That was the first time I worked with David Cunningham and Greg Esakoff. This was also during ENR days and ENR was having its problems.[9]

After the USITT convention in Anaheim, I wrote Fred Foster a letter congratulating him on the Expression product line, which was launched at that show. Everyone had talked for a long time about having a family of products that worked together. The Expression product line was the first to actually do that successfully.

I got a call from Fred in late 1989, who told me that ETC were just about to buy LMI[10] and needed a product manager. I'd always thought ETC was a pretty cool company, so I interviewed with them and in between accepting

---

[9] See Cunningham – page 97

[10] Electronic Theatre Controls purchased Lighting Methods Inc. of Rochester, New York in early 1990.

the job and actually moving to Madison, the job somehow morphed from Dimming and Control Product Manager to Manager of R&D.

The idea was to have product management, which had traditionally been in marketing, move closer to R&D. If you follow corporate structure, there are people over here in marketing that say this is what the products need to do. Marketing sends it up their chain of command to their VP, who talks to the VP of engineering, who then talks to these guys over here in R&D. So there is a big disconnect. Our idea was to put all of this together in R&D and close the loop.

When you are looking after product development, you're either very associated with R&D or you're very associated with sales. When you're in marketing, you're very associated with sales, which is good, but there is a disconnect from R&D. When you move those people into R&D, now you don't have a disconnect with R&D, but you do with sales. It's one of those difficult things to figure out. What I've gotten to is that when you're in a heavy development cycle, your product managers should be R&D people. When you're in a maintenance mode and selling it, then they should be in the sales group. I think it's a position that you should be flexible with depending where the company is in selling its product line.

So I started at ETC in January of 1990.

RB: So who was there at this time? Was Jon Ide there?

AV: Jon was there.[11] Tim Nolan, Ann Foster (who is Fred's sister-in-law and one of the core programmers on Expression) and the LMI team was just arriving.

RB: They were buying LMI for dimmers?

AV: That was certainly part of it. It's hard to grow a company just on desk sales. The development and sales overhead on desks is high, and in systems sales, the profit comes from the dimming. LMI was one of the large "regional" companies – primarily east coast; Teatronics was on the west coast, serving a similar market niche.

RB: And CD 80 was omni-present.

AV: CD 80 was everywhere. LMI and Teatronics were just starting to get specified on major projects and often used ETC control. It became apparent if you looked at it that something had to change. Both companies wanted national

---

[11] Jon was the software developer for Obsession, Anne's swan song at ETC.

coverage and both were heavily reliant on ETC and you know the control console is the spec lock. It was a question of who was going to buy whom. Everybody just assumed that one of them would buy ETC and it ended up being the other way around.

When ETC bought LMI, we moved most of the people from Rochester to Madison, including most of the line workers. I thought that was very novel. Usually, when you buy a company and you are going to re-locate it, you bring the management and assume you can pick up the rest of your staff locally.

RB: As Entertainment Technology did to everyone in Portland when it moved Texas.

AV: To ETC's credit, they knew better. They knew that if they were going to stop production on Friday in New York and start production on Monday in Wisconsin, they needed the people who knew how to build the product. So they moved a lot of the company, except some of the senior management people. Bill Florac – Flash – came at that time, as did Bill Smith, who was a phenomenal programmer. So the R&D group went from six or seven people that it had been when I started to nearly a dozen. One of the things they wanted to do was conquer the New York market and they knew to do that they needed something that would compete with the Light Palette.

At that time, this market was so regimented about what they wanted - it was a Light Palette or nothing. Even Prestige didn't manage to make inroads, because it didn't do things exactly the way a Light Palette did them.

RB: Then the tables turned. It was Obsession or nothing.

AV: Yes. But at its core, it is very much the same concept, frankly; just more reliable and more complete. Obsession is a good product and I'm very proud of it. Unlike most new products, it was soup when it went to market. You can either build your desk really flat and wide, which is what most desks are at first release, or you can build them a little narrower and deeper so they give you a more fully functional feature set. We went for that, rather than the flat and wide. We stayed away from flash, and went for a functional workhorse. Having said that, it did introduce some new control ideas and took some existing concepts further than before.

RB: We were having real issues with the LP90 and saw the Version 2 spec. We were hoping and hoping for that, but it never came. Then out of nowhere came this beautiful piece of hardware that had software behind it. At CBC we were doing a live-to-air show every week and it was dying because of the Palette and finally we had to replace them with Expressions. Then we got an Obsession and it did everything, straight out of the box. We ran them like we were at a rave one night; it was an end of season party. We just tried to crash it (by this point we were getting pretty good at crashing things!). It was unbelievable. We would do disastrous things to it – but it just kept working. We hadn't even seen a picture of it before we saw it in real life.

AV: Good to hear! We were trying to keep it a bit quiet. One of the problems people often have with desks is that they launch them too soon. There is so much pressure to bring the product to market and the desk gets launched before it is ready. It's hard to get people's attention back when you blow a launch. We also knew that if were going to take Strand on in this market, Obsession had to come out with people saying 'Yes, this is better' and not 'Oh, come back in a year when you've finished it'. When it came out – it had to be finished and it had to be better. Otherwise it was just going to die on the vine.

That was an interesting process too because, for the first year of development, it was just Jon and me. While I basically wrote the operations manual, Jon started programming. By the time we got the rest of the team involved, we knew totally what we were doing. We knew what the screens were going to look like and we knew what the functions were going to do. We knew exactly

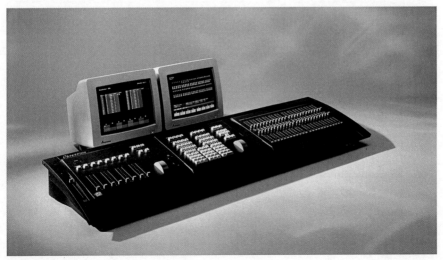

ETC Obsession.

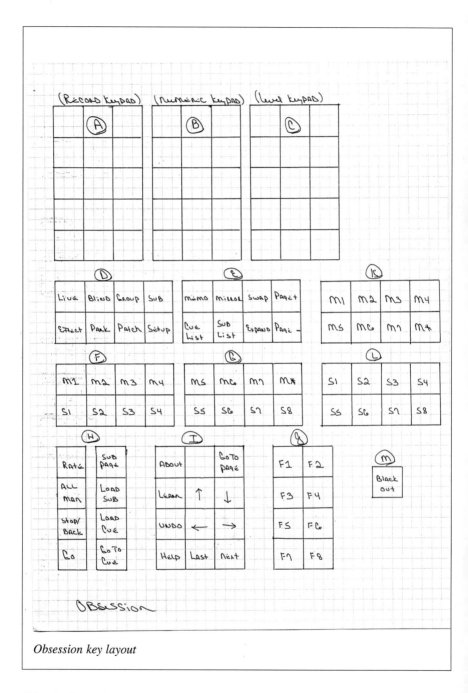

Obsession key layout

where we wanted to take the thing.

RB: You were working from Palette syntax.

AV: Oh yes. That was the market we were going after. We actually tried some features implemented in a way we thought was better – and we were told no, we had to change it, because that's not the way a Palette works. So if the feature set existed in the Light Palette, people wanted it exactly that way. We had a lot of latitude with the new stuff in terms of market acceptance.

One of the things I think is marvellous about the Whole Hog is that it has broken the back of tradition on Broadway. I really credit them being able to create new thinking, even on the conventional side. People are willing to look at new ways of working and say, 'OK, I had to learn something new, but look what I got back for that investment.' I'm forever grateful to Flying Pig.

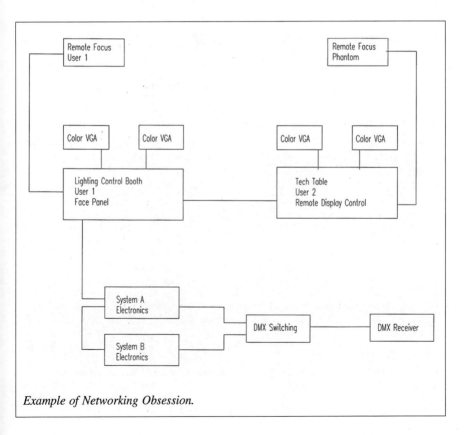

Example of Networking Obsession.

RB: This was the catalyst for me writing this book. A few years ago, I sat people down, like Rob Halliday, Bobby Harrell and Rodd McLaughlin[12] and asked, "Why can't I do a Broadway show with a Hog?" OK, yes, maybe they can't read the keystrokes to me, but tell me what I can do with an Obsession or a Light Palette or a 520i that I can't do with a Hog.

AV: And what did they say?

RB: I never had a tape recorder with me! We would sit over a curry and a pint and they would actually give me real answers. Nothing that would stop the show or necessarily change the look on stage, just silly things like doing functions that would save you two extra key strokes.

AV: Well, two extra keystrokes, if you do them 30 times an hour, are not insubstantial. We always used to refer to what are now programmers – but used to be termed operators – as human macros, because in the days of Light Palette, the designers actually called the keystrokes. They would say, channel one at full, record, cue, enter. They would have a command line on the designer's remote so the moment the guy hit the button wrong they could say, "No, no, clear, clear, clear". There was that level of control over what that operator was doing. Designers fully understood the product and they knew exactly what they were going to get with each button press. The designers totally got Tracking and Cue Only. It was the operators – especially outside of the high-end professional market – who often didn't understand it. They didn't know why the designer said hit the Cue Only button. The designer told them exactly what to do.[13] It's changed a lot.

---

[12] Rob is a hotshot programmer in the West End and made it big doing many shows for David Hersey, including Cats, Les Miserables, Miss Siagon, etc. He also writes for Lighting and Sound International. Bobby is a well-established Strand 500 series programmer in New York and does a bunch of work for Peggy and Jules as well as representing Strand for special functions. Rodd just programmes everything and runs Prelite East in New York.

[13] For the record, it may be worth going through the difference. Terminology often gets confused and that is what hangs a lot of people up. Anne describes it best on page 152 when she talks of the two types of desks: Preset vs. Tracking. I have heard (and this is the confusing bit) people refer to preset desks as Cue Only Desks. More to the point, what confuses people is that if you record all cues on a tracking desk with the Cue Only option, you are emulating a Tracking style console. Not so.
The simplest way I describe it to people is that on Preset desks, each and every channel is recorded in each and every cue. If you dissect the cue on the disk, you will find values recorded for every channel, **even** if they don't change from the previous cue. Tracking desks only write things that are different from the previous cue to memory; similar to how old piano board operators would only make notes on what to change from cue to cue. This is also why Tracking consoles are referred to as Last Action desks, because the desk only gives commands for what to do in the next cue, where all other levels remain unchanged (tracked). (cont...)

Moving lights change that paradigm totally, because there is not enough time in the day to get into that level of verbal detail and frankly, there is no vocabulary for moving lights. There is a lot of "Make it do this wiggly bluey thing down right" and we all know what a ballyhoo is, but it isn't exactly a precise design instruction. Ballyhoo is a general kind of concept.

RB: There are a million different kinds of ballyhoo for the tone of the piece right there. It's up to the programmer to fill in the blanks and try to sell one to the designer.

AV: The designer began to give the programmer more interpretative tasks.

RB: I'm so glad I entered this game at that point in time, because I'm the type of guy who can take that on bit. I would be so insulted if someone started reading keystrokes to me. Go get a monkey!

AV: It's the way it used to work. But I think most programmers feel the way you do. And I think many designers are glad to have the programmer take on the 'man/machine' interface, leaving the designer to design and not worry about how to get data into the desk.

RB: I was visiting *Oklahoma* recently where Ted Mather found himself working with Rob Halliday for the first time. Now Rob has worked a lot for

---

(...cont) Writing a cue on a Tracking console using the Cue Only option means that whatever I change in this cue, please undo for me in the cue that follows. The important thing to remember is, if cue 1, 2 and 3 exist, when you alter cue 2 using Cue Only, there is a bit of magic that happened to the data in cue 3 to put things back to the values cue 2 had before you futzed with it. If you are appending to your cue list, recording with the Cue Only option does nothing. Recording Cue Only does not necessarily record all levels for all channels. (That function is referred to as a Block Cue).

Preset desks may have a function to record a cue as Tracking. This is really a fudge. What it really does is a search and replace in successive cues, changing like values until it sees a change. This is a great idea, but nobody can really tell you why it doesn't work very well. The thing is, it doesn't.

The fundamental difference in the quality of what happens on stage is that Preset desks can only do one thing at a time - that is go from cue A to cue B in a specified amount of time. Tracking desks can have a number of things going on at once (simultaneous fades). That means your first cue, a sunrise, can have a 45 second fade, but while that is going on, a second cue can do a 3 second actor entrance and so on. Obsession allowed for eight different fades happening at once. Although some desks allowed for separate attribute timing, the Whole Hog was the first to allow individual fades for every channel. This is really handy when using moving lights because you often want the lights to come up in one time; others to go down in another; fixtures to move at one rate and gobos to snap at another. It also allows you to do neat things like 'fan' the delay times of a bunch of lights. That means that if your cyc is lit by 24 fixtures, you can have them all fade in 3 seconds, but fan the delay time for the fades in a single cue such that the one stage right starts right away, and the one that is most stage left waits 10 seconds. That way you have a perfect 13 second growth from stage right to stage left on your cyc executed in one cue.

David Hersey and so has Ted, but not together. Ted is from the school of 'read the keystrokes' and was quite amazed to hear David say "What's that?" (they would never say channel numbers). "What are the blue sides at?" "They're around 40ish." "OK, bring them up a bit." Un-heard-of language.

AV: You know, other designers will work with their moving light programmers like that, but not for conventionals.

RB: And that is where the Hog is breaking down the barriers.

AV: I agree, because more and more you are going to run everything off of one desk. It's interesting though, because many designers think about their moving light rig separately from their conventionals. I think that will change when it becomes as easy to program moving lights as it is conventionals.[14]

A lot of designers don't want to know what the syntax of a console is. They want to know enough about the way it works so they are sure they are getting what they need from it, or that they understand the way the show is constructed so they can clearly communicate their editing requirements. But they don't really want to get involved in what buttons do what. Having said that, a greater number of designers do want to know exactly how the desk operates. For them, it's the equivalent to understanding exactly what beam quality will come from different luminaires. The desk is a part of their design kit and they want to know it inside out. Both models – and everything in between – are valid.

This is the challenge in control now, because what do you do to communicate? It was easy when everything was conventional. Everything you did was to communicate intent, about how to build a cue. And one of the most difficult things about lighting control consoles is building the cue in such a way that you can maintain it later. And there is a lot that gets communicated about how this cue is supposed to be constructed. Is it a Cue Only record? In the case of moving lights, is it a full stage record or just what's in the Programmer?

---

[14] I think whether it's one desk or two has a lot to do with politics, the operator's ability and the relationship with the designer. Rob programmed all of *Oklahoma*, wigglies and conventionals, for David Hersey on a Strand 520i. I did the re-light of Starlight Express with David, programming all the moving lights, effects, fog and conventionals on a single Horizon – in just one week! I've done numerous live-to-air television shows where I'm the only guy on a desk and it's always worked out just fine. Rob and I certainly are not the only ones. When it comes down to it – it is probably more the designer's call; whether or not they can work with their rig as one tool, or whether or not they have to separate it into two.

RB: This makes me wonder why the Artisan survived for so long, because that sort of information was so lacking.[15] They had no idea of what was going on. Everything was WYSIWYG[16] – if it's got intensity – it gets recorded. From a documentation point of view, it was horrendous. So much so that they created another position in the theatre just so somebody could track what he was up to.

AV: Recording everything if there was an intensity over 0% was Vari-Lite's way of having a console that did not need a Programmer.

RB: Virtuoso was built based on the Artisan.

AV: Virtuoso is sort of a combination of Artisan and a command line driven, LTP, non-tracking console, which was a challenge to rationalize in a 3D world - although I didn't know that at the time. One of the key problems – still to this day with a lot of desks - is knowing where you are. If your operations get interrupted by someone or something, as they always will, I want a method to know where I am so I can pick it up without having to start over. The beauty

Vari*Lite Virtuoso.

---

[15] See "Where We Are Going" and how Vari-Lite's network lacked the ability to show you where a light was on page 365

[16] What You See Is What You Get

of a command line is that it tells you exactly what you've done so far.

Virtuoso has filtering capabilities, so with the combination of 'does the light have intensity' and a lot of other data filtering, it is going to tell you whether or not the data is going to get recorded in the cue. If it has its intensity, it's going to get recorded because it assumes you want to do something with it. There are a lot of reasons why that is not a bad idea.

RB: But how did it deal with tracking type issues? For instance, at the beginning of a scene the moon is placed on the cyc, but later you decide you don't like it. Do you have to do the Compulite thing – Delta-Store?[17]

AV: In Virtuoso, you could track forward or backwards – just as you can in a tracking console. In this sense, it was supposed to work just like a normal tracking desk, where even though everything was a stage record, if you went back to cue one, which is where you pulled the moon in, and you re-set the moon's level, you should be able to hit Track, and it would look forward through the cue sequence until it saw a new instruction, then it would stop the track. Or if you change the moon's value mid stream – tracking backwards would modify all the way back to cue 1.

RB: Just like Expression does.

AV: Like Expression – and now Emphasis – does.

RB: Expression tried hard to be an Obsession.

AV: That's the thing that moving lights have really done for us; the lines between them are merging. The idea that – here's a computerized piano board – it tracks, or, here's a computerized preset board – it doesn't track, is losing

---

[17] The Compulite Animator was a strange sort of mixture of a preset and tracking style desks. Things did not move unless you asked them to. When you stored cues, only the stuff you changed got stored, so… if you start at the beginning and go on through your show, things would look the same. But, if a number of different things got you to a state, because different playbacks pushed different channels to different levels, you could not guarantee that you could get there again. Their solution to this was the "All If Dim" button, which stored all information for all the attributes for fixtures that had intensity. Not necessarily a true Preset desk, because not all fixtures would be stored. Recording with All If Dim on made it impossible to pile multiple playbacks, each doing specific things, to build a complete look because the Animator did not allow you to filter the playback like the Artisan did.

The difficulty came when you wanted to make a change to a number of different cues. They solved this with a thing they called Delta-Store. It was placing a bunch of stuff in a clipboard, then pasting it into a range of cues. The tricky bit was knowing where to start pasting and where to stop. In Tracking desks, that is all taken care of for you – you just change it where you want it changed and it will change when it needs to again. I have never done a show on an Artisan, but I can only assume it was very similar to the Animator. (Or more correctly, the Animator was similar to it.)

ground. Over the years these things have blended more, hopefully taking the best operational philosophies from both.

Many people thought you made consoles track to save memory. You made it track because it facilitated what you were trying to do at that point during the show and how you were going to edit that data later on. And, it was about what your intent was. It all comes back to intent.

Right now, one of the huge challenges in control is agreeing upon a common designer 'language'. If you look at a Virtuoso or an Artisan, for example, if the designer says 'Kill it', what does that mean? On an Artisan or a Virtuoso, that could mean, take to Inactive, which means that you are to store no data. Take it to Zero, which is a move to Zero. It can mean Mark it, which means store no intensity, but store all other parameter data. So now, instead of just saying Kill It, and understanding what that means, you now have these conditions that you have to describe. And that's true of not just an Artisan, but any control console.

I was talking to John Featherstone[18] recently about this and asked him how he communicates to his programmer what his intent is – and how changes are to impact previous and subsequent cues. He said the programmer he works with just understands what he means – there is no particular discussion about these things. They have worked together long enough that his programmer understands how he designs and how to construct the show. One of the greatest dynamics that exists now is the mind-meld that happens between the designer and the programmer.

RB: So what did you think of the Artisan?

AV: I had so much respect for that desk; so much respect for what they did. They came into this thing – first of all – as a bunch of sound guys, in an entirely new arena of the lighting industry; there was no history to rely on to say how something could work, there were no pre-determined concepts they could accept or reject. They came in from nowhere, and they developed a control system to run these lights. So much of the Artisan was spot on. Fifteen years ago, and spot on! The whole filtering capability, the way timing is handled, the way the playbacks worked – they just nailed so much of it.

The problem with it was, as you moved outside the Artisan programmers, it didn't have a syntax that made any sense to the rest of us.

---

[18] John is partners with Norm Schwab and Howard Werner in Lightswitch.

RB: You couldn't instruct Artisan programmers.

AV: No. And you know what? That was a big thing for them because the desk was a big mystery. They liked the fact that you didn't understand what buttons to press to get a light up. That was their mystery and I don't fault them for that. Because they weren't just driving the desk – they were a key part of the design team. In many ways, the Artisan programmer was a precursor to exactly the production model we know today – where the programmer is part of the design team. The early programmers set the standard for what that job was to become. Just because you can wiggle a light around with the pan and tilt knobs doesn't mean you know jack about programming moving lights or that you are qualified to sit at the tech table. I know a little bit about how to drive these desks myself and I'm sure as hell not qualified to be a programmer. Having said that, mystery works when you are completely controlling your product and completely controlling where it goes. If you want to develop something that you can sell, you have to develop a user interface where people can at least walk up to the board and see there are buttons on it that make sense.

RB: At Full.

AV: My litmus test on a desk is: "Can I bring a light up? Can I get intensity, and can I wiggle it around?" That gives me a comfort level. And I know I'm going to be able to figure things out; there is something here that has a little seed that I know something about. One of the things that was really shocking to me when we started Virtuoso was how little I knew about moving light control. We had done Obsession and it was very successful, and I thought, what's this moving light stuff? A few more parameters with some time – big deal. I got straight on that soon enough. The Artisan programmers made sure they got me clear on how different it was. But, although it might have been frustrating for them, it was good that I entered the development as such a novice. I questioned *everything*.

RB: I've always described moving light control to conventional control in the same way I've described to people the differences between 2D drafting and 3D modeling. I've said, 3D is not 2D plus one. It is a huge paradigm shift. That's why Gordon Pearlman hired me because they did a pretty good copy of Obsession in Horizon. Then they decided to just add some parameters and do some moving lights.

AV: It just doesn't work the same way.

RB: Well, Obsession II is a testament to that. And that's why, as you say, it's so surprising that Artisan got it so right. But they didn't even try to control dimmers. They didn't start there.

AV: They didn't care about that stuff at that time. It was a completely self-contained system.

RB: Wouldn't you love to get in a time machine and go back there then?

AV: What a phenomenal time that must have been. I've learned so much from Artisan – or maybe I should say I learned so much from the Vari-Lite programmers and the designers who used those programmers.

RB: When you went to Vari-Lite to do Virtuoso, did you go do a show on an Artisan?

AV: I couldn't run an Artisan to save my life. I wanted to know enough about it to make sure that I could make Artisan programmers happy. But I didn't want to get so comfortable with the desk that it became the blueprint for Virtuoso. We had the whole base of Artisan programmers that we were going to be transitioning to Virtuoso and we needed to make sure their needs had been accommodated. The Artisan is a lovely desk, from standpoint of muscle memory. That hundred button array – I remember when I first saw it I thought it was an antiquated piece of garbage. I said, put me on a desk and put an Artisan programmer over there, and I guarantee you I can get stuff just as fast as he can. Well, you know what? When someone is calling you channel numbers, absolutely, give me a keypad, I can bring it up just as fast as a hundred button array. But moving lights don't work that way. Nobody is calling you channel numbers. So the beauty of that hundred-button array is pattern recognition; it gets to the point of doing what everybody wants, which is liberation from numbers. The hundred-button array gets you really close to not having to think about numbers. It's all about patterns. It's muscle memory. Those guys don't even think; it's totally instinctive to them. They get so proficient on the tool, cognisant thought never enters into it.[19]

One of the problems we have as things become more powerful is that now the desk is very modal. We give it all these soft surfaces because soft surfaces are more flexible. Now you constantly have to remember, "Where am I? What display am I in?" This slows down the whole programming process to the

---

[19] The funny thing is, a button array is how Gordon addressed fixtures on LS-8 ten years earlier – then conventional control system dropped the concept. See Pearlman page 46

point where you can no longer blindly reach out, with complete confidence, without having to stop and ask yourself, "what mode am I in?"[20] That's one of the complex parts about design now – you need that soft flexibility but it also hammers you in terms of speed of programming.

RB: You know where I learned that? I've been operating Hogs (I's and II's) for years but have never operated the Hog 500 series desk made by Jands until this summer when I programmed Ringo Starr's tour using one. The 500 only has one CRT. I spent all my damn time getting up what I wanted on the display. It had nothing to do with getting stuff on stage. It was: 'Give me the display so I can see what I want to do.' On the Hog II, you have four monitors and you always have what you need. I rarely change them around. During programming I may open up a Contents window and during playback set them up slightly differently, but in general they stay pretty static.

I've asked Strand 500 operators if they are as fast on the 300 series as the 500. After things are set up and they're reading numbers to you, they thought it was. Which must be tough on sales for the 550.

AV: I would think so. If you do this long enough, you make certain assumptions about what you know. One of the things I've learned from my Virtuoso experience is that you should go in without any preconceived notions of how things are supposed to work. I try to go into everything with a completely open mind – because I'm highly opinionated and pretty stubborn, I struggle with this concept a lot – and fail as often as not – but I do try.

RB: It must have been tough to do Obsession under those constraints.

AV: We were given the model and told to go. One of the things that was really interesting on Obsession – and this is something Fred asked Jon and me to do – was to go back and find the thesis statement of the Light Palette. We didn't want to copy a Light Palette, we wanted to really understand it. What is the one reason, the one underlying thing about that desk that made everyone want to use it? Every product should have that thesis statement. And we found it. This is what I call the DNA of the desk. There should be something that is true to the desk that runs through the entire development of it and keeps it consistent, keeps it true to itself. It is very much like language. I probably over romanticize this a lot, but it's like Spanish. Spanish is very easy to learn.

RB: It sounds like it's spelt.

---

[20] See Hunt on why operators want buttons, not displays on page 209

AV: Yes, and it's got a very definitive instructions set about how the language should be used. It's very easy to teach, it's very easy learn, very easy to pronounce. It lacks nuance though. French, on the other hand, I find very difficult. It's hard to get the accent right. It also has a rule set that says this is how it works – unless it sounds better this way. It's feminine, unless it sounds better masculine, then it's masculine. But it has a lot of nuance to it. The vocabulary of a desk is very similar to this. You have to find the line between easy to teach, easy to learn, easy to remember, and having nuance. And what happens to a desk over time is that is becomes too complex and it loses that core structure, because you're trying to make everybody happy and you pile too much stuff in there.

I've thought a lot about this because I'm at the point in my career where I'm tending to pass the baton a little bit. The people who are good at console development are very linear thinkers, they have to be able to deconstruct very well; they have to be able to strip away everything and get to the core of the issue. It's almost like an archaeological dig. Then you have to stay true to that. I see so many consoles where they say: "Oh, this guy wants that, OK, we'll write it in this way, and this guy wants that, OK, we'll write it that way". When probably – they were trying to do exactly the same thing, but just framed the request slightly differently. What people tell you they want to be able to do is often not the problem they are actually trying to solve. And you have to be able to dig deep enough to tell the difference. It's a tough line to walk.

RB: Have you learned the grandMA yet? There's a hundred ways to do anything.

AV: I've had some time on the grandMA. There are some very interesting ideas. But this thing about user defaults – I think as developers you're just being lazy.[21] You can't decide how the desk is supposed to work so you say, OK, let's leave that up to the user. Whenever I'm in a UI discussion and someone says "Let's just make that a user default" I swear to God the hair

---

[21] I have done some shows on the grandMA and other users will say what I do. The first few hours (or days – depending on how bright you are) can be frustrating, but once you get over the hump – it's wickedly powerful. Anne is referring to the fact that earlier version of MA's software would boot up the desk and there wasn't a button on it. Not even the Intensity, Colour, Beam and Focus buttons. You had to build the desk before you could use it. The defaults are much more sensible now. We're now facing these issues when designing Marquee. I ask myself daily whether or not we should make it a user option, or just put the foot down and state "This is the way it is going to be because we say so." Tough choices and sometimes you lose functionality to gain clarity.

stands up on the back of my neck. There are reasons why you want to have user defaults, but you have to be very careful with them. They should be things that facilitate the preferences of the designer or programmer, but don't violate the core personality – the DNA – of the desk. Above anything else, a lighting control console must be predictable. There should be no surprises when you hit the go button or edit a cue. Too much capricious customisation makes it difficult to reliably predict behaviour.

Whenever I went on this rant at Vari-Lite, Lindsey Glover would quote to me from Ralph Waldo Emerson . . . "Consistency is the hobgoblin of little minds . . . "Sometimes, I'd really let this get to me. "God, maybe he's right, maybe I'm too rigid and restricted in my thinking. OH NO! I'm NARROW!" Years later I discovered the complete quote was "A *foolish* consistency is the hobgoblin of little minds, adored by little statesmen and philosophers and devines." I rested much easier after that . . . but Michael [Snyder] and Charles [Reese] certainly lived through my user default phobia.

RB: Feature creep can be dangerous. You can ask some manufacturers for the ability to hold your elbow down, hit that buttons and spin this thing and they would do it for you. Before too long, you would have software versions that had four decimal places and a 'b' at the end of it. It can be a nightmare of trying to maintain the same code base. The Obsession has fallen victim to that. As an end user, that sort of close interaction with the development team is very satisfying (immediately), but has nothing to do with the 'product'. At some point you have to drop a product line and start again fresh. We did that between WYG 2 and WYG 3.

They also did that with the Hog II – dropping Hog I code and starting new. During the development of Hog II, I had the ear of the development guys, as they wanted opinions on how things were done in TV. They needed no help in concert touring and were doing brilliant research on theatre shows, but I was close to them and happened to do a lot of TV. I would say: 'This is what we need.' They would say, 'Awesome idea Rob. Fit it into our syntax and you can have it, but we're not going to give you a Shift-Left-Button-3 menu option to do it.' That is why it was a success. Anybody can walk up to a Hog and bring up a light.

AV: That's one of the tricks of developing desks. You have to look through the five million responses you get about what people want to do, and you have to drill that down into something common, that can actually be implemented and taught. They've done that really well. I hope Obsession and Virtuoso did that really well.

The other advantage the Hog has had, and this is also one of the advantages of the Expression product line, is the same group of engineers working on it throughout its life.[22] Part of the problem you get with control consoles is when the engineering team changes, the personality then starts to change, because there is no one who knows what that underlying language is. Hog and Expression have had the kind of longevity . . . hell, Expression is almost 20 years old, and it's still got original code from the Epcot days in it. But the same programmer has worked on it consistently. That is an advantage that few companies have.

RB: Given that both you and Jon have left ETC, do you think Obsession will survive?

AV: Well, Obsession is 13 years old – it's been around a long time. And increasingly, you can't make a high end desk that is primarily conventional in operation any more. A hybrid desk is more than gluing some encoders onto conventional controls, in the same way that putting a part button on a moving light desk doesn't address the needs of conventional lighting. The programming process is always easy – anybody can do it. And that's the reason it's hard to tell from a product demonstration on a trade show floor how good a desk it. It's in the editing process where desks don't follow through on their promise.

RB: If you're always building the next cue, it is really easy.

AV: It's very easy. But eighty percent of the time you're editing. People don't often think about that. What tools do you need for editing? Can you make those edits seamlessly while cues are in transition with total confidence of the outcome? When you make a change, how easy is it to communicate what it is that you want to happen?

RB: Is that one of the things that you would attribute to Artisan's success? There was only one rule.

AV: That - and the fact that they had a very select group of programmers who

---

[22] At the time of this interview, Anne was correct, but things have changes since then. Not long after the aquisition of Flying Pig by High End Systems, one of the original three FPS partners Nils Thorjussen, then acting as VP of marketing for HES, quit. Shortly after this interview was conducted, Tom Thorne was relieved of his duties as software architect for the Whole Hog range of consoles (see page 183). As of December 8, 2003, Nick Archdale, the last surviving founder, also left and the lion's share of the senior software developers, including product manager Richard Mead followed him.

completely understood their tool. The only people who could put their hands on Artisan were certified programmers, and Vari-Lite was guaranteed this particular person understood everything they need to know. And even with that, you saw that only a few programmers could work here on Broadway, because only a few of them ever made the transition from rock and roll to theatre. The theatre programming environment is something totally different. The shows have to be constructed differently, they are maintained differently. This is the most nuanced programming you will ever encounter. The amount of detail and concern that goes into the art here puts such a high demand on the product that if you can make it work for them here, you have a product that can work anywhere.

RB: You've just quoted a song I know.

AV: Lucky for you, I didn't break into song. In this instance though, it's very true, because there is more time on Broadway, to work and work and work something. Interestingly, opera is one of the most complex production environments, with very little time typically for lighting. If you work in corporate theatre - you have limited time, limited staff and at the end of the day, the CEO of the company doesn't really know or care. At some level, he's probably aware that things feel better with a certain designer, but he couldn't begin to tell you why. Which is sad, because I've actually seen some stunning lighting in the corporate world.

RB: After the keynote, he's gone back to his hotel room for cocktails and not around to criticize it.

AV: Exactly. Television, live-to-air, you get one shot at it then it's over. You're not going to fix it for tomorrow night because you're not doing tomorrow night. It is only this community, and rock and roll, to some degree . . .

RB: It's a different audience.

AV: And it's about maintenance and about turning the show over too, because Broadway shows generally run for such a long time – and then hopefully they tour. Consoles are subject to the 80:20% rule. It's the first 80% that determines if the desk is going to be any good at all. It's the last 20% that makes a good desk a great desk or a good desk a mediocre desk. A lot of companies never get that last 20%, because by that time, they are trying to get the desk to market, rather than making the product right. And the mantra is true – the devil is in the details.

There are so many things you focus on when you're trying to figure out how the thing is going to work that you don't think about what the displays are going to look like or how you're going to navigate the displays. Well, you know what – that is what the guy is spending fourteen or fifteen hours a day looking at. So while you're really concerned about how the thing works, the way the data is represented is hugely important. It sounds so stupid because it sounds so obvious, but people don't really think about that very much. Or, they give you any number of ways to do it.

RB: I have a topic here on my notes that I thought I might cover called "Displaying data structures – the Great Debate over 20 vs. 25 across".

AV: Oh please! It is a non-issue. I believe – I hope – this is a complete non-issue now, given the options now available. It used to be such a thing when displays were DOS based. Working in a Windows-type world, you should be able to set things up any way you want – this may seem contradictory to what I just said, but the way the data is displayed doesn't impact the output of the console. It's a good candidate for customisation – but the defaults have to be really good!

The designer and programmer are a team and the tools you design have to work for both of them. But we have to be careful not to swing so far that we facilitate the programmer at the expense of what the designer needs. Because at the end of the day, it is all about the show and the designer is the one who represents that vision.

RB: Have you read Crossing the Chasm, by Geoffrey Moore?[23]

AV: I have it. I haven't read it yet.

RB: The basis of this book is how to market high tech products so that they become mainstream. The author talks of the four groups of people that buy things: the Early Adoptors, the Early Majority, the Late Majority and the Laggards. The gap between the early and late majority is the chasm and if you don't clear it, you will never be truly successful. It's similar to your 80%:20% rule. You can sell anything to Early Adoptors. These are the guys willing to try the new stuff. I think, to some extent, Richard Pilbrow is one of these guys. For example, he was the first to use WYSIWYG and a Hog for conventionals on Broadway. These guys are not where the money is at; you only sell 15-

[23] ISBN 0-06-662002-3

20% to these people. Then there are the laggards, the guys at the other end of the spectrum, the last 10%. You'll never sell computers to these guys until they don't have a choice; like the computer that runs their anti-lock brakes. The money is in the middle 70% of the market, and that market is not the manager who writes the cheques. It is the actual people who use the gear. They will fight the battle for you on their own turf. They know the battleground there much better than you do. You just have to make something they want.

AV: That is what ETC did pretty well. They made their product line very well accepted, to the point where it was users going in fighting for them.

This is also where ACN[24] is interesting. You will sell more lights once you can get the rigs up faster. So the sooner we move to a plug-and-play environment so you're not spending all day setting things up, the moving light manufactures will sell more products. People will have bigger rigs if they can talk to their rig faster, and spend more time programming rather than spending the time getting the rig up and running. That's why I think the whole communications protocol thing is so important. That's why VLPS is still the preferred supplier on these large live-to-air television specials, because the Series 300 system can just plug it together and come up, pretty reliably, without having to look at five thousand dip switches and who's talking to who. That's always been a big advantage to that system. The sooner we get that out to the market, across all product lines, the better for the users... and I would think moving light manufacturers would be way interested in making that happen. It benefits them at the end of the day. The same is true with control. The faster we can get it all in the desk . . .

RB: I'm a big fan of predictive text messaging. I had grand schemes of how to use all of WYG's data in combination with a control desk. Unlike any other product in the industry in its time, WYSIWYG was hyper-aware of the environment. Not only did we know what type of light it was and what mode it was in, but we actually knew how many pieces of the set it could hit and were it could be useful. You would never use a Cyberlight to hit the ceiling because you can't. It could make intelligent decisions for you. Predictive cueing.

AV: We've talked a lot about that kind of stuff and I think it has a lot of value. However, I don't know about you, but I hate Microsoft Word. Word thinks it's

---

[24] Advanced Control Network – ESTA's proposed replacement for control protocols in the theatre, including automatic device discovery and patching.

smarter than I am. I spend a lot of time reversing the work Word is trying to help me out with. But, in general, I agree with you. I think we're at a point where the system knows a lot of what's going on. It's OK when software says here are some common threads and as you extend your input, the choices get narrow and narrower, or makes suggestions to you, as opposed to Word which makes decisions for you.

RB: That is what I want to extend to wiggle light control: to suggest sensible options given certain parameters.

AV: It's great to make it smart, but not so smart that you spend all your time undoing how smart it thinks it is.

RB: Some console's "Move While Dark" didn't work so well first time around.[25]

AV: Rob Hailliday wants things to be really smart so the desk automatically creates groups for you upon selection and so on.[26] There is a core concept here that has a lot of value – it's a matter of an implementation that doesn't result in you cursing at it.

RB: Have you ever operated the Icon desk? You can't record a cue without recording a palette first. It doesn't let you put raw numbers for pan and tilt into a cue.

AV: That would make me nuts.

RB: A lot of it is hidden from the user.

I would like to talk to you about how, in the early days, vigorously protecting intellectual property served LSD (Icon) and Vari-Lite – how they built protocols and control desks that only talks amongst themselves. Was that their own arrogance or their own R&D idiom that allowed them to do that and how did

---

[25] The complaint I've heard is that you could not adjust, on a cue-by-cue basis, how quickly the marking cue would execute (subtle scroller moves in quiet places) and you didn't know when it was going to occur as it had to guess when you were going to need it. It could set up the lights in the dark just before you need them, but it doesn't know how quickly you are going to jump on the GO button. It could also set them up, one by one, after they were last used. Then they could be sitting in the dark, in a relatively funny place for a very long time. When you go to edit cues you wonder why it's not where you left it.

[26] Rob wants the console to remember your "intent" when you select lights to build a cue. For instance, when you selected lamps 2 & 4 & 6 & 8, why was it those four? Were they the ones that hit the main actor? Where they the ones that made good-looking shafts of light? Where they just the ones that were working at the time you recorded the cue. Documenting and recalling this information for a later point when you are editing the cue would tell you that if you want to make a change to lamp 2, you should also change 4 & 6 & 8 for the same reasons.

that work for them then, and maybe how that doesn't work for them now.

I recently did a show with VL2C's and a Hog[27]. What a gorgeous light! Working with it on DMX was beautiful. Why people were denied a way of doing that during the 90's is a shame. Did that protectionism serve them well then, or was it a mistake and they are just correcting it now? Or, is it an evolution of the times that allowed them to correct it now?

AV: Hindsight is always 20/20. I think when you look at Vari-Lite's approach in the early days of controlling their technology you have to put yourself back twenty years and remember that at that point in time, the technology was so fragile and it was so new. The moment you sell a product, how it's perceived and how it works is out of your control. It's now somebody else's and whether the designer thinks the desk can do what it can do is up to the guy that is sitting behind the desk. Or the perceived reliability of the luminaire is up to someone else. You have no control over that any more.

One of the things that made sense for Vari-Lite in the early days when the technology was so fragile was to protect their own name. They needed to have control over how the products were used. I think it made tremendous sense for them to do that. I don't think they would have been nearly as successful, nor would automated lighting be where it is today, if the mass market been able to buy those products and try to deal with the failures and complexities of the technology. The fact that they held that so closely to them, I think moved the industry forward faster.[28]

There was something really interesting happening between Morpheus and Vari-Lite, and later LSD. In those really early days where there was a huge belief in intellectual property, there was respect for intellectual property, and the industry moved really quickly because Vari-Lite came out with something and then Morpheus needed to top it – they couldn't clone it – they had to come up with a better idea. LSD got in the mix; they wanted to play too. They couldn't clone it either – and they had to come up with an even better idea. There was a huge amount of respect for what the other company had done. [29]

Having said that, we're now in a state of creeping featurism with regard to moving light technology. There don't seem to be any great new ideas out

---

[27] Until very recently, VL2C's only listened to Vari-Lite's Artisan control desk. It now can talk DMX, which is the only protocol that the Hog speaks.

[28] For instance, the Icon desk didn't have any sort of printed manual for eons.

[29] See Mark Hunt's ideas why working with and around patents is a good thing on page 217/218. Also see Wayne Howell's thoughts on page 352

there anymore – excepting video projection and such. We're now into sort of one-upmanship of 'I can move my shutter with this many motors rather than this many'. When that's going to change and how I don't know and I'm not close enough to the products to understand. All I know is that everyone is just duplicating what everyone else is trying to do and do it cheaper and more reliably. This is a totally predictable pattern as markets mature. We have come a long way in that respect in the past few years. I think holding on to their technology served Vari-Lite very well – and the industry in general. When should they have let go of that? I don't know. Sooner than they did, for sure. I really wish things work out for them in this new business model of theirs.[30]

The industry really needs Vari-Lite, in the same way it needs High End. I don't think it would serve this industry at all well if something happened to either of them. I really hope that both of them see their way through their present struggles.

RB: I always thought that if Vari-Lite sold the VL5 when they first came out, you never would have seen a Wash Light or a Studio Color. Well, maybe you would have seen them, but not to the huge saturation you see them now. VL5 was such an amazing product. If only they'd sold that thing . . . and they could have. When it came out of the box – it worked.

AV: It was a perfect product and I think if you told that to Rusty Brustché[31] today he would probably agree with you. Again, hindsight is 20/20. And would that we could all go back and relive aspects of our lives in light of what we know today. They hung on to that model a little too long. But when your whole company is based on renting proprietary technology – and you have built a successful 100M company on the back of a controversial business model – changing to not having proprietary technology when your entire income stream is based on the fact that you have it - that's a really hard thing to change. And it wasn't just about the product – it was the service – they came to do a gig, and they did the gig. You were guaranteed of that – it wasn't just a rental shop.

RB: They knew how unreliable the VL1 technology was, and I think they

---

[30] Anne is talking about the recent change in practice where they are only making 'For Sale' units. When this interview was conducted, Genlyte had not yet purchased Vari-Lite's sales and manufacturing division. It was a little awkward for me because Genlyte had just purchased Entertainment Technology. I knew Genlyte wanted to get into the business; I knew they had cash; I knew Genlyte and Vari-Lite were in the same city and I knew that Vari-Lite had financial troubles. Fill in the gap.

[31] Founder and former CEO of Vari-Lite, Inc.

were a little gun shy out of the gate when they created such an amazing product like the 300 series lights.

AV: It's always very easy to say now, long after the event, that they should have done this or that at a particular time.

It's come to the point now that almost anybody can sell a moving light – just like they sell a Leko. Selling software intensive products is a little more difficult – especially control consoles. The sales guys really have to know how it works.

RB: This is the analogy I always use. My brother-in-law sells CAT diesel engines for transport trucks. Since he is the head of the power train, he has to understand how transmissions work, how drive shafts differ, how differentials work, how treads on tires make a difference, how airfoils on the cab change things. The guy who sells tires doesn't have to know about anything but tires. The people that sell consoles have to know about everything downstream.

AV: And they should. Not to inflate your head, but one of the things that blew me away about WYSIWYG is the amount of knowledge that WYG has about what's out there and what it's doing; the libraries… Products that integrate with WYSIWYG will benefit from that knowledge of what those systems are capable of doing. What kind of colours you can really get from it; how fast it really can move, regardless of what you're asking it to do. The fact is that WYSIWYG knows all of that stuff and it shows you that – I think that is just astounding. I never knew that the libraries were that in-depth. I didn't know that when you ask a VL5 and a VL6 to move at full speed, you would actually see on screen this is how fast the VL5 can go (not very) and this is how fast the VL6 can go (wow!). I hear that sometimes manufactures would call you to find out what their own products were capable of.

RB: I've been sitting in on ACN task group meeting and involved in proofing the documents on the Device Description Language. That is going to go a long way towards publicizing information about fixtures that nobody has had, never mind collected, before.

Nobody modelled lights with the accuracy that we did at CAST Lighting. By the time we got to version 3 of the libraries – we had a pretty good idea of what was needed. Doing batch photo quality renderings to create real-time movies really showed us what was needed – in a big hurry. It can tell you that a mark cue doesn't have enough time to do what it needs to do. This is the sort of information that people will demand in control products of the future.

AV: I love that. This world has moved forward at such a clip. That's why I left ETC. I knew I had to get direct experience in this market. I couldn't keep up with the technology if I didn't have my hands on it. Some people can – but I'm not one of them.

RB: It's difficult to move on. I wasn't happy about leaving CAST, but at least I have closure. If I had had to leave WYSIWYG twelve months or twenty-four months before I did, I don't think it would have been a 'whole product'. But when I left it, it was as done as far as software gets in my opinion. My wish list was almost nil. The only natural thing for it to do was to become a control desk. Now I'm designing control desks and really enjoying it.

You left ETC before Obsession II was launched?

AV: I left before Obsession I started shipping. I have this great habit. I like to help develop lighting control consoles and put them into beta test, and then leave the company I'm working for. I've done that on three separate occasions now. I joke about it, but it is really an uncomfortable thing for me. And actually, only Dave [Cunningham] and Dennis Varian are permitted to kid me about it. On the other hand, every move has propelled me forward in a way I couldn't have achieved had I stayed stationary.

7 TOM THORNE

Introduction

When my contract at CBC ended in December 1993 after developing LXMOV,[1] I went for a self-directed pub tour of England to contemplate what I should do with my life. On my return home, I started to write letters to every manufacturer in the industry who I thought would be interested in my idea. Tom Thorne's name was listed as the contact for Flying Pig Systems in the PLASA Industry Yearbook.

Nils Thorjussen, one of Tom's original partners, has since told me that Tom completely ignored my letter. It was only on one of Nils' visits to the UK office that he found it filed away and said, "What the hell – when did we get this?" It was not long after that that Nils, not Tom, flew to Toronto for a visit to talk about developing what would ultimately be WYSIWYG. Using monies supplied by FPS, CAST Lighting was incorporated in April 1994.

It wasn't until two days before the PLASA Show in September of 1994 that I met Tom at the Flying Pig office. I was to demo to him and Nick Archdale, Nils' other partner, that their investment was about to prove itself. I was a tad nervous because the software was very shaky and

---

[1] See WYSIWYG Seeds – page 27

I too had only seen it work for the first time a few days earlier.

I managed to doctor our ISA DMX reception cards into one of their 486 computers and hooked it up to a Hog I – the first I had ever seen, let alone operated. They had a demo room downstairs at The Spot Co. in which this presentation was to be made, complete with real moving lights to prove that we were doing it right. There were a few tense moments where I wished I could just jump back on a plane and try again at LDI in November, but I did get it working.

Nick and Tom came downstairs when it was all ready. Nils and I were tensely hoping the software would hold together. It did. And Nick kissed me. It was then that I knew I would be OK. It worked out great for us, because they had the Hog II hardware done and were going to show it at PLASA, but there was no software to go in it. WYSIWYG, hooked to a Hog I, ended up being a main attraction at the booth, while the Hog II sat alongside in the dark.

Since then, Tom and I have obviously had a close relationship as Flying Pig remained involved in the marketing of WYSIWYG and I was a fearless beta tester for the Hog II. I was doing an awful lot of live TV at the time and always had the respect of Tom and quite often got my way with introducing particular features.

A number of years later, when both WYSIWYG and Hog II were mature products, Tom and I were standing on our booth at LDI. A customer walked up and proceeded to ask Tom questions on some of the finer points of operating the desk. He eventually gave up and asked me to do the demo for him because, "I knew the product so much better than him anyhow."

I conducted this interview at Tom's house in Lincolnshire, about two hours north east of London. After Tom and Steph's second boy was born, they moved to the huge manor house with lovely gardens. I ended up rototilling the gardens as Tom burned the leaves. This was about a year before Hog III was to be released.

During the development of Hog III, Tom was in a severe skiing accident; he broke his back and ended up being taken off the mountain by a helicopter. For months he lay on his back in bed and headed his development team via e-mail and the telephone. After his recovery, he opted not to take the trip to the Flying Pig offices in London as often, but continued to lead the team from a distance.

As is typical with all software projects, development on Hog III code took much longer than anticipated and the result was that Tom was relieved of his post. This interview was conducted before Tom's departure, and before the release of the Hog III. Tom has since left the industry and is writing financial software. I've always asked software developers in our industry why they didn't write financial software as they'd most likely be better off. Maybe Tom has the right idea after all!

Interview

RB: You are as comfortable in a suit as you are in the theatre. How did you decide this is what you wanted to do?

TT: I started at school. I can remember the day quite specifically. I just arrived at what is called a Public School in England, which is actually a private school. I was boarding there and you had to pick an activity to do every Wednesday. Stage lighting sounded groovy and I liked the theatre.

RB: How old were you?

TT: Thirteen. Two years later I was doing all the lights for all the shows at the school, and since I was technically minded, I wanted to combine that with some of my science courses and I started trying to develop special effects controls. It was a way of triggering the lighting in the show off the sound track, which was quite cool. I also started working on an electronic control console with a common computer that was available in those days, called the BBC Micro. But then again – I never finished it as I had left school by that point.

RB: A BBC what?

TT: The BBC, as in television, had sponsored a computer from Acorn, to design a computer in the early 80s that they could then use on their TV programs and such. It was a huge hit.[2]

RB: It had its own language and such?

TT: You used BASIC and assembler code. You had access to the I/O bus so it was quite good.

BBC Micro Computer. Photograph courtesy Acorn Computer Museum.

---

[2] The 1981 television program was called "The Computer Programme". BBC specified what they wanted in a machine and asked for bidders to build it. Acorn (now defunct) built them the BBC Micro, which used a 2 MHz 6502 processor with 32 KB of ROM and 32 KB of RAM

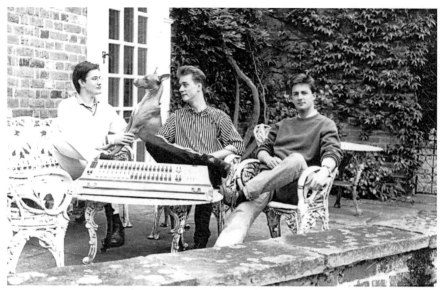

Early publicity shot for the DLD 6502 console (left to right: Tom, Nick Archdale, Simon England.

When I left school and went to college, a friend from my school went to a different university and met Simon England. He and Nick Archdale had been trying to do the same thing at a different school.

Simon didn't have much time and wanted to find someone to do the software programming; my friend said he knew someone who was doing that at his school. We drove over to Simon's house in Yorkshire. I remember it quite clearly. There they had their Compulight, funnily enough[3], and some work they were doing and I thought it sounded cool. So during my university term I started writing software for it, again on the BBC Micro in Assembler, and that eventually lead to the DLD 6502 console. I don't remember why we changed the name to the Digital Lighting Desk from Compulight – perhaps we thought t was a bit crap.

RB: Was Compulite building the Telescan Controller by then?

TT: We'd never even heard of Compulite.

RB: So this would have been . . .

---

[3] This is humorous as Compulite, the popular control and dimming manufacture from Israel, was quite likely Flying Pig's greatest competitor in the early days of generic moving light control desks. They built the Animator, a spin off of the custom Telescan Controller for Cameleon.

TT: This would have been 1985. Then in the summer of 1985, I went down to stay at Simon England's place in London and Nick Archdale was also staying there, having dropped out of Imperial[4]. He was doing a circuit board for the front panel, which he was doing by a hand stencil. He was laying out all the buttons and spending an enormous amount of money on photography in order to have this circuit board done. Not only that, we found out that we'd have to spend even more money having the photography corrected as it didn't come out quite right because the acetates had shrunk or something like that. It was a complete nightmare, as we didn't have an enormous amount of money. Nick wasn't earning money from anything else, we didn't have a proper business plan and Simon was working for, at that time, I think it was Dunn and Bradstreet's financial software division. So it was a bit stressful. I was still at university at that point, and so was Simon.

RB: Which university?

TT: Cambridge – doing physics.

RB: It was after that you went to Stanford for business?

TT: No – it was three years after. I graduated in 1986 and it was the year after my graduation that we did our first PLASA[5] show with the DLD desk at Olympia in Hammersmith..

RB: You paid for a booth?

TT: This is really vague now. I think we did actually. Well Nick was in touch with a group called the Last Horizon Discothèque and they had a big Tri-Lite rig with a bunch of pinspots. We were setting up our booth at Simon England's garage in Paddington with this rig with all the lights on and everything happening and it was at that point that we realized that you couldn't take an inductive load and put it on a dimmer. We couldn't figure out why we were blowing the Avo rack so frequently. But it was quite amazing because you would open the garage door and there'd be all this smoke pouring out with the pinspots and so on – this wild lighting rig in this garage in the middle of London. It was rather like something out of Close Encounters.

RB: You were feeding the Avo racks analogue at that point?

---

[4] Imperial College London – one of the UK's leading universities and heavily into technology.

[5] PLASA (Professional Lighting and Sound Association) – a popular industry show held annually in London.

TT: Yes, we hadn't heard of DMX then (1986). Then we started advertising on the run up to PLASA and Simon England took his girlfriend out to the Caribbean and left Nick and myself desperately trying to get this thing ready to go to the show.

RB: You had just one of them?

TT: Yes, we had one working. So we got to the show and we had *some* interest. Funnily enough the main interest we got was from Holland and also Ralph Jörg Wezorke of Light Power and MA Lighting[6]. He must have thought that we were barking mad – but it might generate money. So he buys a console!

The console that was actually sold was not the one I had actually written, which was a straight… I don't know what you'd call it, but you weren't able to have different levels for fixtures on a playback. If you brought up a playback, every single channel was at the same level. It wasn't what we'd call a real level memory console. We'd decided to sell a real level memory console, and that's what these guys had bought, even though we didn't actually have one.

At this point, I'd started work for a "suit" company called SPA and I didn't have the time to write the software, so I told the guys that they would have to do it. I'm a bit unclear what actually happened, but Simon, through his engineering contacts at Durham, had got this 68000 board, which they grafted onto this BBC Micro, to do all the real level memory calculation. The thing is, we should have spent the time and sat down and worked it all out, it wasn't at all necessary, but we didn't know that at the time, and they were committed down this route to get it done. It was very expensive and very stressful for Simon because he was also still at university and they had bills to pay. He got it working (roughly) and I had enough time to come in and fix a few bugs.

We shipped a console out to Jansen and Jansen and to MA Lighting. At this point John Offord, having taken a whole bunch of orders for back page advertising for Lighting and Sound International magazine was suing for payment. His lawyers were going to get Simon and Nick's company wound up. At that point, I was always just a hired hand. Eventually Nick borrowed money off his mum and Simon's dad pumped in a bunch of cash and they

---

[6] Michael Adenau founded MA Lighting three years earlier and Light Power was doing all their distribution. It was just about when the DLD was being shown that Michael hired Ernst Ebrecht, the code architect responsible for almost all of their control products since. He started with the Lightcommander (1992), an inexpensive and widely successful console that could control up to 48 lights and most recently the successful grandMA line.

managed to pay off all the creditors. And that was it – the company was dead. Simon went off to get a proper job somewhere. I was a full time suit and Nick just floated about and then started a production company called DLD Productions.

RB: Doing raves?

TT: Raves actually hadn't occurred at that point – we're looking 1987-88.

RB: He'd bought equipment?

TT: No – he rented it. He and Simon were the first people to persuade Vari-Lite in the UK to hire equipment for one-night stands – as against long-term leases. Simon always had an ambition to do college balls, because that was what we were focusing on in those days. They wanted an articulated lorry to turn up with the gear. He finally achieved his ambition at Durham University. He had all the gear and Super Towers, but they forgot to bring the forks. The whole thing was held up by loading straps.

We had a bunch of fire works on Durham Hill, and one malfunctioned and knocked Simon clean off his feet as it blew up at ground level. It threw him back about five yards. He landed on the ground yelling, "I'm hit – I'm hit!" Meanwhile, all these embers are flying in the case where we had all the fireworks we hadn't yet loaded into the tubes. One guy, Andy Neal, who was our mentor at the time, took one look at this situation and said "Fuck'n Hell - I'm out'a here!" - and he legged it out the door while I'm trying to put out all these embers before the whole things goes up. Needless to say, the audience said it was the most dramatic firework display they had ever seen!

RB: You weren't actually trying to control them with anything clever, were you?

TT: No, no. You see, the whole key with fireworks is that it's much more fun to let them off by hand. This whole electric thing is garbage. You want feel the concussion as it leaves the tube. Yes, we used to get royally shit-faced and do firework shows. It was absolutely insane.

RB: So how do we get from there to Stanford and Nils and back to the UK?

TT: Basically, I moved to the States. I stopped working as a suit because I didn't want to do it forever. Nick had got in with Andy Neal doing DLD Productions and was turning around his business life into cash flow positive rather than no cash flow at all. They got to know Peter Miles and Tim Baylis

Early Hog I days in the uninsulated loft above The Spot Co.

of The Spot Co.[7] and got good contacts. Nick was the premier rave lighting guy at the time.

RB: Spot Co. were making a living doing that at the time?

TT: Spot Co. were renting gear to Nick. They had a whole batch of Strobeflowers, which were the "rave light". They strobed and rotated and the ravers really loved it. Every so often I would go and help Nick and Andy, lugging kit and that sort of thing. Nick was using his prototype DLD 6502 to control the light. Then we saw these Golden Scans come in and they were great. Much better than nodding-buckets.[8] We added on a module controller-wise and he'd use that.

RB: So what was Clay Paky using at the time to attempt to control their lights?

TT: Dimmer desks, I guess?

RB: Highest Take Precedence …

TT: Highest Take Precedence dimmers desks – yes. But they also had, before the Pulsar Masterpiece came out, this huge console with touch-faders and a whopping great screen. It was manufactured by Pulsar and called the Oskar. I think they were going to use that to control them, but I don't know that happened to that system.

RB: It was quite simple back then from a control standpoint – everything was 8-bit, no 16-bit fades.

---

[7] Peter eventually becomes the fourth partner in Flying Pig Systems and the Spot Co. rents loft space to the Pig boys. Now, Flying Pig, or more correctly, High End UK, occupies the whole building and The Spot Co is defunct, having been sold to Production Resource Group (Fourth Phase) in 1999. Peter was an investor and Director in FPS, but FPS was generally viewed by the public as a trio consisting of Nick, Tom and Nils as they were the active employees. After selling Spot Co. and trading in his shares of FPS to High End Systems, Peter moved on to Coemar UK. My favourite story of Peter involves him turning a mate upside-down at a pub to shake loose change out of his pocket to pay for a pint.

[8] Clay Paky introduced the Golden Scan family in 1989 and retired it in 1996. Mirrors moved much faster than the Vari*Lite heads (nodding-buckets) and thus were more suitable for raves.

TT: Yes – there were no 16-bit parameters at that time. Then we move forward two years. I had moved off to California, but I'd still come back to London on breaks, and I'd see everyone, including Nick and I'd even do some electronics work and software programming. I did an interface for Spot Co's Strobeflowers so they could control them from a DMX desk. I got to know Pete Miles that way.

When I came to the end of Stanford, I couldn't find a job that really interested me. It was also a bit of a recession. I didn't want to go back to what I was doing because I had really done this course to get away from that. I was talking to Nils, who had also worked at the same company. I had known him for two years at this point and he was gung-ho for doing something on his own. He was looking at doing business record storage or something like that. I said maybe we should do something together. Maybe we should do stage lighting because I know something about it. I did a huge musical show at Stanford Auditorium. I hung every single light they had and more - and every single bit of cable. The technical support guy (they had a professional) thought it was so funny that he actually hung a kitchen sink.

RB: His name wasn't Dak Harris was it? I did an industrial with him where we had over 200 LSD Washlights, 96 Icons, 48 Cybers, 100 8-light scrollers and 800k of dimming. All for a dinner party! He did the same sort of thing. He hung a toilet brush in the truss and it was our task to find it.

TT: No no. This guy's name was Michael Ramsaur and he was head of department for drama and taught lighting. I had done the advanced lighting course and it counted toward my credit. It was actually a credit-worthy course for masters students. So I got to know Michael quite well. He'd actually been working on a visualization program. I wonder what every happened to that!

So Nick realized I was up for doing something. And he had money from Pete Miles. Pete Miles had money at that point, so Nick came out trying to persuade me to set up a company with him to control systems to do all these new waggly lights. He'd realized by that time that I had already signed up with Nils and Nils would have to come along too if we were going to do something together.

RB: Did you and Nils have notions of doing something in the States or was Nils committed to coming to London?

TT: I can't remember. I don't think it mattered but we settled on a plan and it made perfect sense. Nick was going to do the hardware, I was going to do the

Nick and Tom at the Grand Canyon on the infamous cross-America road trip on which the FPS business plan was formed.

software and we needed someone else to run the business and that what Nils was going to do. It suited Nils' perfectly as he didn't want to be a suit – he wanted to be in a wacky industry and this looked like a wacky enough industry to get into. I think we agreed to do it in San Francisco.

We were sitting in my apartment in Mountain View when Nils came in one afternoon and said: "I've got a great idea. Nick you've got to go visit these people in Miami – Let's DRIVE there!" It made total sense. So we thought, cool, we'll drive there and visit all these people on the way and we'll think about what we want to do.

We had the coolest road trip you could imagine. Oh, God, it's all coming back to me now – it was really ghastly. We drive down to LA and we get completely rat assed and go to Magic Mountain. (It was my car so I wasn't drinking). Nils and Nick were so pissed they didn't even notice they were on a roller coaster.

Before we left, someone had offered Nils a place to stay, but he wasn't actually there. We then arrive at this person's apartment and his flat mate was there and he had forgotten to tell his flat mate that we were turning up. So, in the middle of the night, a whole bunch of drunks invade this poor woman's apartment. It was very embarrassing. Oh well, we got over that.

We cruised on down to the Grand Canyon and the Hoover Dam. We did a flight over the Grand Canyon and I was nearly sick. Nils and Nick thought it was the funniest thing ever.

RB: Nils wasn't piloting the plane, was he?

TT: Luckily, no.

We then visited Morpheus in San Francisco.[9] There we heard about the Celco Navigator and got very nervous. We

Three FPS partners with their first product.

then went down to LA and we actually starred in a movie. We were in Future Kick with Don The Dragon Neilson. Nick and I ended up on the cutting room floor, but if you get the video out Nils is clearly visible in one scene for about a half a second.

We then headed out east. We went through New Mexico; went to Santa Fe, got absolutely drunk there and went white-water rafting. Then we went off to Texas and got to Dallas and as you can imagine drove past the Grassy Knoll. We went to talk to Vari-Lite, as I was trying to get a job with them. Jim Clark, one of the owners of Vari-Lite is a Stanford alumni, so I got in touch with him and they were trying to set up Irideon[10] at the time and they were looking for someone to do that. They were moderately interested in me and I was interested in them. We did meet, but at this point I had already decided to do Flying Pig.

RB: The name had been decided by then?

TT: Flying Pig was decided a little later. We definitely had that idea during that trip. we wanted to call it Flying Pig Designs instead of Flying Pig Systems. At Vari-Lite we met both Jim Clark and Rusty Brustché. We saw the VL5, which looked very cool. I remember sitting in Rusty's office telling him what we were going to do, and Rusty just looked at us, very sceptically, and perhaps understandably so. When three complete strangers turn up, with no money,

---

[9] See Pearlman on the Morpheus Commander – page 63

[10] This was an attempt at an architectural division. The first produced the AR500, an outdoor version of the VL5, then the AR5, a tiny, indoor colour changing yoke and the AR6, a gobo projecting mirror that could recess-mount in ceiling tile. ETC bought the division in 1998.

and say they were going to make a lighting console you'd probably think they're barking mad.

He just said to us, "Watch out, we're the gorillas in this market!" In any case, we didn't take that too seriously and went on to Austin and met High End's Larry Cotten, Lowell Fowler and Bob Schacherl[11] and they were incredibly nice guys. They showed us around and gave us all their protocols and said best of luck and keep in touch.

We then went down to Galveston Bay and had a bit of a break sailing with Nils' two cousins.

RB: I'm sure that kept Nick occupied.

TT: Oh yes, Archdale was in total heaven. Famous occasion. It was was just one of those sentinel moments of hilarity. Nils – 'Mr. Captain Extraordinaire' - who knows what he's doing on a sailing boat, manages to run us aground. Not only does he run us aground, but he does it at high tide! He runs us aground having failed to bring a radio to be able to call for help and also without any flares on the boat. And he runs us aground because he failed to turn on the depth sounder. So, there we were, desperately trying to get off this sand bar and we have this great idea that we're going to blow up this inflatable dingy and row out with the anchor and try to haul ourselves off by winching it in. So poor Nick, being the smoker at the time, gets to blow up the dingy. Nils climbs down into the dingy and we pass him the anchor and he gets blown the wrong way and it starts to foul the line. Then Nick jumps in to help him and the water only comes up to his chest!

RB: Well, that would have been above Nils' head!

TT: So we really had no need for the dingy at all. So we're busy trying to shove this boat off and eventually we had this grand scheme that we were going to drape the two girls over the edge in hopes that every powerboat from miles around would rush up and try to rescue them. And, funnily enough, one did! This big powerboat come up and pulls us off and we sail away and moor in the middle of the bay.

In the middle of the night we go swimming. Nick jumps in and they have this weird photochemical, whatever you call, plankton in the bay and when

---

[11] I am now working closely with Bob as he is VP Sales for Vari-Lite and Entertainment Technology and we're developing the Marquee console for them. Back in the early 1990's, it would have been unheard of to think Bob would be at Vari-Lite, as it would have been unheard of that Tom was NOT with Flying Pig. Many things have changed and we all have to adjust.

he jumped in and the whole thing went "booph" in a huge green light. And Nick, with the same movement as jumping in, literally leaped six foot clean out of the water back onto the deck again he was so shocked. It was really strange watching this whole thing.

In any case – the road trip continued to Miami, did all the Miami things, and then drop Nick off. That's it, road trip over. On that trip, most of FPS and how it was going to work and what we were going to do and our first product were formed in our minds. They weren't totally specified, but the rough aims were all mapped out on that trip.

Whole Hog console, now called Whole Hog I.

RB: When did Peter Miles become involved?

TT: He had £45,000 to pay for two layouts of circuit boards and things.

RB: That was figured out when you got home?

TT: Well, what happened was I went to work for a company for the summer. Nils moved to England. Nick also moved back to England and we started the company in September or October of 1991.

RB: The name Flying Pig came from an English saying meaning things that could never happen.

TT: The name came from the idea back in the DLD days of a console that would be so powerful that we'd never have to design another console again!

RB: Funny that.When I met Nils pre Hog II days he told me the very same thing.

TT: In the DLD days we had this idea with the DLD 68000. We even had it mapped out, what it was going to look like and what it was going to do. Following on those ideas, we had this concept of a lighting console that was so powerful it would detect whether you were doing something unfeasibly large (like the Olympics or something like that), and little explosive bolts would fly off and this panel would open up and the flying pig would float out to say: "This is it – you've gone beyond the realms of normality". And that's where the Flying Pig, the ludicrous power and over the top design and the name came from. Whole Hog – the name – I think we coined during the trip. I don't know – Whole Hog, a piggy kind of thingy – going the whole way?

RB: Did Beaky have his name by then?

TT: Yes. Nick had been named Captain Beaky by Andy Neal during DLD Productions days. I think it comes from a children's show or something.

So that's when Flying Pig started. And in October '91 Nick and I went to stay out of London for a week to get away from phone calls and we sat down and mapped out the Whole Hog I. We took our computers with us. It was the first time either of had used IBM PC's and the first time either of us had used DOS – and the first time I had used C++. Nick was going to do the design electronically, and it was the first time he'd ever done that. He used CAD Star, and it was the first time he'd used a schematic capture program or an automatic router.

We had no idea of how much computing power we'd need to do what we wanted to do. We though we'd need a computer backstage to do things, a computer at FOH. At one point I think we thought we'd need about five

Tom at Hog 1 on stand at PLASA.

different computers to do the system. Then when I got my first 386 computer, which was a 25 MHz or 40 MHz computer, I wrote up a little program just to see how fast it could do multiplications. I ran the program and it sort of did 2,000,000 multiplications in a second and I thought, this is amazing, we don't need all these computers, we can do this whole thing off this one 386 chip. Thank God we did because it made the whole design a whole lot simpler.

Nick had actually drawn out what the front panel was going to look like and he mapped out a lot of the syntax that week based on his experiences and based on what I thought I could write. Then I set to work, writing the software. Not that there was much of a GUI on the Hog I – just the playback engine and the editor. I got that done in seven months.

RB: Built that hardware in seven months?

TT: Yes.

RB: Very ambitious.

TT: Well, we were only bashing metal you see. We had a very a very hot summer in the warehouse trying to get it to work. Then we went to PLASA and won best product and we thought all we needed to do was sit back and let the money roll in. But no one called.

RB: You sold two.

TT: Yes, but at a big discount. We were desperate for cash and Nils went back to the States because he was in trouble with his travel visa.

Nils:[12] I went off to find perspective buyers. I took a booth at the back of LDI 92. Then on the last hour of the last day Candice Brightman and Arnold Seramie came over.

RB: That was in '92 and I met you in '93 because we released WYSIWYG in '94. So in '93 you still had that tiny booth at the back of LDI?

Nils: Yes, in Orlando we still had our booth, but by '94 we had AC Lighting selling it. But you know what, you don't really need anything more than a small booth, no matter how big your company is. Trade shows are a big waste of money.[13]

TT: You really just need a place to meet people and that's sufficient I think - and show gear.

RB: You shipped the desk with a version of DOS.

TT: Every Hog I console was shipped with a copy of DOS. It was designed with a compiler called Zortech; written with a 32 bit DOS extender. I learned a lot then because the only other compiler around then was Borland and that was 16 bit and I knew that that wasn't good enough – I needed 32-bit of

---

[12] Nils had walked the room at this point carrying a glass of wine and warning me it was time to catch our train. We were up visiting Tom after PLASA 2001 as we were both stuck in the country due to the 9/11 disaster.

[13] At the time, Nils was VP Marketing of High End Systems. Since this interview took place, he's left High End and now heads Element Labs that manufactures LED based video displays.

precision. I knew this was a 32-bit processor and I was stunned to find there were no compilers that supported it and you had to have special gizmos in order to actually run it in 32-bit mode. We had no money to go out and buy whopping great OS packages and compilers and it was a total godsend when I discovered this Zortech compiler that you could buy for around £500 and it came with everything you needed and it had a 32 bit extender.

RB: Watcom was around then too. That's what I was using.

TT: Watcom was more money and it was slower.

RB: You knew you needed to do 32 bit math because at that time you were attempting 16 bit fades and you wanted to add a rate to that.

TT: Yes, I had 8 or 16 bit values, but at that time they were just 8 bit parameters. But then I had 32 bit intermediate results because the way the Hog did its refreshes in order to keep up with its 6000 channels was unusual. Not the way any other console had done it. I needed to multiply a 32-bit number by an 8 or 16-bit number and with 386 you could do 32 by 32.

RB: You had a hardware device that outputted DMX at the full baud rate regard-less of the refresh rate. That caused problems with some lights. You ended up putting in a switch to back it off.

Whole Hog II with wing.

TT: Yes, the DMX came out at the same speed regardless of whether the packets were different or not, which was dependent on the software. Now to tell you the truth, I have no idea how fast that was. It was sufficiently fast that no one noticed.

RB: What was the first big system that may have noticed it?

TT: Those first tours: The Grateful Dead and Sting. Nils did Lenny Kravitz's award winning video 'Are you gonna go my way'. That was 4000 channels.

RB: Four thousand channels was a lot then. Not so much now.
   Where do you think the world of control is headed?

TT: I think consoles will all disappear and we'll all be using PC's. No one will bother buying desks. Moving lights will become generic. Moving light manufactures will concentrate on architectural stuff. Architectural jobs rather than professional lighting will drive the development of a lot of control systems.

RB: And to deal with the obscene number of channels we're talking about nowadays, will the software be distributed or scalar?

TT: Difficult . . . I haven't thought about it much because having just gestated Hog III I've been focused on that. Ask me again in two or three years time. If you had asked me four years ago I would have described the Hog III to you. But I can't describe the Hog IV, should there ever be such a thing. I can't think what it would be because I can't see past the III right now.

Flying Pig Systems' Whole Hog III.

8 MARK HUNT

Mark is one of the happiest people I know in the industry. If you ask him how things are, he will always say they're manic, but that he's enjoying himself. Generally, we all do, but if you look at Mark, he's always got a smile on his face. He has been working at Light and Sound Design for many years now, and frankly, in my opinion, their entire R&D department would be sunk if anything ever happened to him. And I've told the management that on more than one occasion.

Mark is passionately Mac. He admires the simplicity of the Mac's design and what you can do with it with software. He is a self-proclaimed hardware-dude, but as any one would tell you, the silicon doesn't do much without bits running around in them. Software, to him, is a means to an end. He likes his soldering gun and his breadboard, but found analog hardware design was inevitably going the way of the Dodo and if he were going to survive in the electronics world, he would have to understand processors. To him the Mac made sense, and somehow, unlike so many others, he could bend it to make it do what he wanted it to do.

His love for electricity started at an early age - similar to mine. We both had a passion for model railways. While Mark went on to be a sound engineer, I graduated

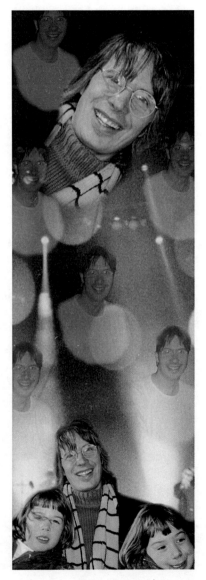

from toy trains to real ones getting a job at an electric railway museum. Through his key involvement on the Icon project at LDS, Mark has worked with more famous rock bands than anybody else in this book. Most of us stay a little closer to the more traditional theatre, while LSD has supplied kit to every major act that has ever toured. Mark knows better than most the saying 'The show must go on'.

Cutting his teeth on the old monster 'ego' desks, Mark tried desperately to make the archaic analog beasts remember cues - in a way, forcing technology into a part of the industry that was fiercely hands-on. His comments on his passion for computers and his belief that they don't make for good human interface, particularly in a live show situation, are very insightful. He says we can't ignore computers in our designs, but we shouldn't have to know about them. The Rock & Roll industry, in some ways, is more traditional than you may think and Mark has been able to design products that are quite at home with people who live on the road.

Mark was key to one of the most highly anticipated products in our industry; but unfortunately, the Icon M project turned out to be a bit of a white elephant. Icon M was the first automated luminaire to provide electronic imaging at the gate of the fixture using the Texas Instruments Digital Micromirror Device. This allows the fixture to do amazing things with images never before dreamed of, such as additive gobo mixing, custom shutter cuts and shadowless followspots. When it was first shown at LDI '99 you heard people saying things like "heart stopping", "jaw dropping", "fabulous", "amazing" and "awesome". Unfortunately, the major issue they have with the fixture is that it is not bright enough.

Mark designed the light so that all the clever image manipulation is done in the unit's head using parallel digital signal processing. Other manufacturers are currently using multiple PC's with dedicated video serving hardware to send NTSC signals to video projectors. Mark has taken all he's learned building the Icon M and turned it into their own video server called the MBox for use with conventional projectors. Although the light did not see any commercial success, I have to admire LSD for wanting to build a 'proper' light rather than adapting commercially available consumer products into our industry.

I was grateful that Mark made an unscheduled stop in Las Vegas to do this interview. He met me while I was staying at the Luxor Hotel where we were both fascinated by the 'inclinators'.

Interview

RB: You were saying that you think your story might not be interesting. I think that's nonsense. I think many people have an interesting story, but it's never told. If it's not documented and read by you and me or our peers, it may at least be read by people like Kille and Drew![1]

MH: ...to try to understand these mad men who create the tools they use.

RB: Through your work and your products, you have touched a lot of people, even if you don't get to meet them every day.

MH: I have met loads of people to whom I'm famous, and that is weird.

RB: What got you into this crazy business? Why didn't you go off and write financial software?

MH: Well the thing is, I never set out to write software. I got involved in electronics quite early - the late 60's, early 70's. I am also a model railroad enthusiast; I like my trains. As a kid, I was probably maybe thirteen, fourteen, I had this amazing bit of kit called a Codar Controller that made your trains accelerate and it had brakes.

RB: Because a lot of the engines were worm gears, you had to emulate all those dynamics.

MH: Right. So you needed this electronic controller to control these movements. I was fascinated by this and I took it apart to find out how it worked, because I'm that kind of guy. There were all these things called transistors inside.

From there on, electronics were really cool because it could do these magic things. I taught myself. I was at school at the time so I spent a lot of time in the physics lab, building my own stereo system (couldn't really call it a high-fi) with valves, vacuum tubes, and that sort of stuff. I was enjoying myself with electronics. Then I started to take an interest in music and thought I would like to work in the music industry, although I'm not an artist of any description; I can't play or really sing or anything like that. But I thought there were a lot of electronics in the music world and maybe I could get into that.

One of the first jobs I got was as a service technician at a back-line[2] hire

---

[1] Kille Knobel and Drew Findley are two of the very best Icon operators and have worked very closely with Mark throughout the years.

[2] The back-line consists of the guitar amps and effects racks, plus other gear on stage that is used to support the musicians.

company in London and that was my first rock and roll gig. I got in because I was the only applicant for the job who wasn't a burned out roadie. I actually knew some electronics by then because I had been studying for several years - not formally, I was just buying magazines and building things and designing, figuring out how everything worked. That kind of application goes right through to the present day. I don't know what I'm doing, but I'll somehow bloody well find out.

RB: Guitar players like Joey Satriani would have so much kit in their back-line that they were like mini analogue computers. Was that the sort of thing you were doing?

MH: If you wanted to be in electronics in those days, the way to go was via the military. as they were the only people that had the money. But there was this other business that wasn't military where people had money to throw away, and they would buy anything that you could design for them. They're still like that to a degree.

RB: I think the real surge was in the seventies Mega-Rock days.

MH: Yes, and if you had something new, you could design it. I went through back-line hire, back-line servicing and then I went into recording studio servicing to learn another side of the business. Then I became a sound engineer for a few years. I did front-of-house sound for Joe Jackson, when they were a proper band with guitar, bass and drums.

There was a period of my life where I learned to break things, which is quite good for a designer. You learn how these things get treated on tour and what sort of mishaps can happen to portable equipment because it can be quite badly used. I used to have this adage that roadies are a bit like the military, except the military knows their life may depend on the equipment working. It's quite a hard life for equipment being on the road.

Then, in '85, I had just done a nursemaid gig for the Thompson Twins in New York. It was as technical support for the start of a tour. Rather than have them find problems during rehearsals and have to send for someone, they brought me in just to be there.

RB: Sound or lights?

MH: Sound. I was still doing sound for a friend, Steve Sunderland from Audio Lease. The whole sound business was going digital. I remember that it was going away from being analog to becoming very corporate, in the sense that as a small systems designer you were really out of the league of people like Yamaha or all the other companies that were coming into the market. And I wanted to find something else to do that was a bit more fun.

Sometime in the year before that, I had a really bad experience (quite a lot of my life is rather embarrassing actually) doing a gig for a band called Sky (Francis Monkman was the keyboard player) and he wanted to automate the mix down of all his keyboards using an Apple II computer. He wanted somebody to do the audio mixing side - the analog bit of controlling of levels and stuff, where somebody else was doing the digital bit. I said sure. I kind of messed that job up quite a lot because I didn't really get what the interface between digital and analog was going to be like and how to avoid problems with it.

At that point I thought that these computer things were not going to go away. The Apple II was quite new at that point,[3] and I was going to have to deal with it or I wasn't going to have a job in the future. So I bought myself a kit, which was a computer, called the Compukit UK-101,[4] which was a single board a bit like the American KIM 1 using the 6502 processor with a few K of RAM on it, BASIC in ROM - that kind of thing. You got a power supply and plugged it into a television and you had yourself a computer. I built this thing from the kit, and it didn't work, which was probably the best thing that could have happened because then I had to find out why it didn't work.

RB: You spent your eighty quid on it and you weren't going to let it go.[5]

MH: That's right. So having got it working, I wasn't seen for about a month because I was just working with this thing all the time, getting to understand it. Because I had to fix it, I got down to the machine level in it and I began to understand what the processor was doing. I still like to know that; I still like to be in control of the machine.

RB: I think you're one of a unique brand of people that actually understand that stuff. There are a lot more punters like myself around that have only written assembly code as university projects, and just got through it. Many don't have an appreciation for it as they normally jump into programming with

---

[3] The Apple II was manufactured from 1977 to 1993 which is a remarkable life for a computer – especially a consumer based model. The sad bit that no Mac-head would like to admit is that the 6502 floating point version of BASIC on the Apple II was written by Microsoft.

[4] Released in 1979, again using Microsoft BASIC. It had 4 KB of RAM and ran at a speed of 1 MHz.

[5] It actually cost £249 in kit form.

high-level development tools like VB or Java. I have a little grasp of it from school, but starting out with Fortran, Pascal then C, you don't really understand the electrons going down the data bus. By the time I got involved, they were all moving too fast.

MH: I used to have problems with this one guy at a recording studio I worked at, because he had no idea what was happening inside the console when he turned a control - no conception of what it did with the electronics. I couldn't work out how anybody could work at a sound desk and not know what it did when he turned it on. But he was a good sound engineer. It worked for him.

RB: Think of all of the people who have gone up that elevator we used tonight who never thought that it runs on rails like a train. I'm always like that...

MH: ...how does it work. Exactly. So, I had this computer working, I spent a lot of time programming it and I discovered that you could do things like read a keyboard with a computer and how it was done, because I actually disassembled the code that was in there and worked out how it did it – how it knew which key I pressed. It was fundamental stuff that nobody really bothers to look at. So I got really at home with microprocessors.

Around that time, I was working alongside the people at Chameleon Lighting in Acton. The first proper job I did with them was design a thing I called the Washboard, which was an add-on memory system for an analog lighting console. This was the first lighting thing I did. It probably wasn't a great success, but it did work and I wrote all the code for that in Hex in 6502 machine language. It was about 2k of code that captured the analog outputs of the console through an A-to-D, into memory, then, when you hit the same button again, it would actually re-play those outputs through a D-to-A onto the same analog lines. So you had this memory snapshot system that you added to an analog console when memory console were pretty new at the time.

RB: So what was the human interface to it? Was it an array of buttons?

MH: It was like a memory sequencer. I think we had sixteen buttons, and you pressed one of the buttons and you could record into it or play it back. It was a pretty good idea until digital desks came along and took away all of that.

A friend of mine, George Cound, said I should get someone to market it because it was quite a neat idea. So, I spoke to Steve at Audio Lease and he suggested I get in touch with the guys at Light and Sound Design. This was about '85 or '86.

So, on Steve's advice, I went to Light and Sound and told them they needed me and this sort of thing should be done. I needed a lighting company that was going to fund the development of this product. It was to be great; we would share in the profits and everybody would be happy.

Then along came the ColourMag, which is probably one of the best products I've ever done. It's a colour scroller as you are probably aware.

RB: Oh yes, I've used them a lot doing shows around Europe.

MH: I was quite proud of the product. We did a prototype with servomotors and about twenty logic circuits in it – it was all hardware. We actually made it with stripes on the gel. There was an up/down counter and things like that. We could get it so that sometimes it would actually find the right colour. There were feedback mechanisms behind the servos to park on the right colour. It kind of worked, but it kept burning the motors out and was pretty unreliable.

RB: At the same time, who was doing scrollers? Wybron?

MH: Yes and Colour Max, because that's where we got the name ColourMag from, as in Colour Magazine. I don't remember who did Colour Max. It had a stepper motor and quite a lot of logic in it as I recall, plus a power supply and a spring roller assembly. It was quite a complicated thing.

RB: Did you deal with hardware?

MH: I didn't actually design the metal, but I did mock up the original mechanics to show how simple I thought the thing could be. I put two rollers into a frame that was held together with bits of threaded rod and put a motor on the bottom with a belt drive and I showed how you didn't need tension in the gel; you could let the gel flop and you could

MegaMags in use on the Rolling Stones 'Steel Wheels' tour.

MegaMag colourchanger, with (left to right) Mark Hunt, Keith Owen, Ian Clarke, Chris Millard, Simon Carus-Wilson.

park the gel just by moving the rollers in a particular way.

RB: Two motors?

MH: One motor. I showed the people who were looking at this thing that it would actually work even if you twisted the whole thing out of shape. Because there was no tension on the gel, it would just find its route through the whole thing.

The Colour Mags worked quite well when they were built properly. I did all that with a single Motorola 6805 micro controller that didn't have a serial port. I had to emulate a serial port in software. I was very pleased, because there was almost nothing in it. The power came down the four-pin cable, there was the Motorola, a few transistors to drive the stepper and a stepper motor and virtually nothing else. They were quite successful for a while. People have made better scrollers since, but I don't think any of them have been quite that simple. That's what I liked about it, the fact that there was almost nothing in it.

I was always fond of the acoustical manufacturing company that made the Quad amplifiers. They said that the perfect amplifier would have no components. It would be a straight piece of wire with gain. I like the concept that a good design has very little in it. Software allows you to do that. This is where the software project started to take control.

RB: Did you do the ColourMag controller, the thing with twenty-four buttons and the LED display?

MH: Well nobody else was going to do it. This is the problem - as an electronics engineer, you slowly realized that you couldn't go forward in electronics without dealing with computers. It just wasn't going to happen. You had this realization that no matter how much you know about logic gates, it just wasn't going to happen unless you knew about computers.

The situation is that you then have a product where you have a complete concept in your head as to how the thing is going to work. You feel you know how it's going to work. You can design the hardware and you know how that is going to work. And you also know how to run that hardware, so you can write the software. And obviously I started in assembler because the level of the things I was working with, like a micro controller driving a stepper motor, you don't do with high-level languages. You certainly didn't then.

RB: No, you had to build your own bootstrap.

MH: That's right. Every machine I have written for, I have written the boot code. That's the Icon Console, the Icon M, and obviously all the micro stuff. It all boots under my code.

RB: So, you've gone to LSD and made the ColourMag. Who said that you needed to make a scroller?

MH: LSD – it rather side-tracked me from what I was supposed to be there for. It was good; it was a good product and it was good to do, but it was not what I was supposed to be there for.

RB: You wanted to write this thing for the analog desks.

MH: That's right, but events made that an unnecessary product anyway, so the fact that the ColourMag was there and that was a success was good. I didn't regret that at all.

RB: So, in 1985, the Artisan would have been out.[6]

MH: The first time I saw Vari*Lites was on the Thompson Twins rehearsals. I was impressed. Actually, more impressed that I should have been, because I thought they were better than they were, being quite naïve at the time.

RB: We were all fooled. No one knew any better. That's the beauty of having dedicated techs taking care of them. They weren't trying to sell them; they were just maintaining them.

So then after the ColourMag, did LSD just say can you hang around for a bit?

MH: Not really, just like most products, they can be never ending if you let them. That is the great thing about working at LSD, it's always the case, but... there is always a show to do. You have a concrete deadline where it *must* work. It doesn't have to be finished, but it must work.

RB: The show must go on.

MH: Failure is not an option. You have to have something working for a show. We have come close, very close, on occasion.

RB: That's what I enjoyed so much about WYSIWYG development. Once it got to the audience being there, it didn't matter if it crashed. It was a very comfortable position to be in because I was very closely watching Flying Pig putting together the Whole Hog II. I was often one of their beta testers (if not alpha tester) on real life shows. A different sort of pressure – but ultimately, not my responsibility.

I now write code that does automated testing of the Horizon code. I've actually built scripts and an interpreter to go through every bit of code and all of its functions. So as Alan Martello sends me code, I just run the routine again to see if I get the same results again. It gives me a comfort level.

MH: The thing is with a micro controller, the ways in which you can make it crash are pretty limited, because it is normally a pretty small program. The scope for having show-critical bugs is pretty small.

RB: You don't have to worry about other people's device drivers and all of that.

MH: Thankfully. It's rather nice in that way. The ColourMag controller was

---

[6] Vari-Lites first appeared on Genesis' Abacab tour in September 1981. The Artisan was not released until 1986.

a 6809 with battery backed up RAM to hold the program. Originally we used a Tandy Colour Computer with a command line interface. That didn't go down at all well. That's where I started to get into console user-interfaces. That's why the ColourMag desk ended up looking the way it did. It just looked like hardware.

RB: The command line interface didn't go over well with the people that were using it.

MH: I took notice that they didn't think it was the way it needed to work. The people that were going to use this thing don't want to see all of that. They want buttons to push. The kind of interface where they are just operating something, they don't want to be typing crap. I've always been open to people telling me what they need from something, because they are the ones that use the gear. It's always been a wonderful pleasure to see what people do with the stuff I design. After seeing the first show with a hundred ColourMags and the way they could be used with colour changes rippling backwards and forwards, I knew why they wanted it like this.

RB: And it's important that you go to those shows. A lot of products are developed that the engineers never get to see.[7]

MH: It is great having the feedback from the users and trying to understand what they want. A lot of the time, what they ask you for isn't what they actually need. They'll come up to you and say I'll want this. That doesn't make sense. Why do you think you want that? And they'll tell you and you'll say, wouldn't this do what you want in a better way? You can actually give them the tools they need rather than what they are asking for. You need to try and understand their problem and what they are trying to achieve.

RB: Another method of product development, which I believe is the wrong way to go, happens when a power user comes to a sales person and tells them this is what they need. If the bureaucracy of the organisation is set up so that the marketing people determine what the R&D people do, they will determine what is needed. "Don't think about it; just implement it." You then end up with a code structure that is a disaster.

MH: I'm quite argumentative. If I think something is wrong, I really fight against it. I used to have great fun with Bill Hewlett. He had a different approach and I really won't do what I believe is wrong. I don't avoid things I don't

---

[7] See Tom Grimes' feelings on this subject on page 263

want to do because they may be hard. If they need to be done, I'll do them, but if I don't believe in them, that's a different story.

RB: So let's move on from ColourMag and discuss what you did next with Icon. Or was there something in between?

MH: There was quite a lot actually. Around the time of the ColourMag, I thought the computer would be a good tool to drive a ColourMag rig. Around that time, Apple were doing the promotion where they would lend you a Macintosh and they try to get it back off you.[8] They called it Test Drive a Macintosh, where they would lend you one for a week and people would pay for it rather than give it back. We had a Mac Plus for a few days and I figured it was cool.

RB: The Mac Plus was with a GUI?

MH: Yes.

RB: The Apple II was like a PET computer.[9]

MH: Yes. The Classic is what the Mac Plus became. It was totally GUI and there was something friendly about it. Just the Welcome to Macintosh and the smiling face; this computer just wanted to be friends with you. It worked. Even on me. Being a technical kind of person, I understood the approach to the user that this machine had, and that it was something to learn from. Also, as I began to write programs for it, I began to realize how elegant the event driven loop was and in the Icon console now, you will find a dramatic similarity to how the Apple Macintosh works because it's such a good way of doing things.

I originally thought of the Mac as being a tool for control, but it never will be that without external console hardware because a screen interface isn't something a user can really get into.

RB: This is my current fight with Horizon. It was my first day on the job as Product Manager for Horizon I said to Gordon Pearlman that we needed to make 'furniture'.[10] They had already been having the fight for four years before I came there. He said all I had to do was design it and they would build it. I have now designed four variations for them over two years, and they still

---

[8] The test drive campaign was launched in 1984, and unfortunately failed. Many people returned them.

[9] The PET was built by Commodore and was the first thing I had at school. It was also built on the 6502.

[10] See introduction to Pearlman – page 36

haven't built one.[11]

MH: It's very depressing when you do the work and it doesn't become a product.

RB: As we talk about this, we will get into Mac Icon, where it is a complete GUI emulation of your hardware and people do use it contrary to what you just said.

MH: We'll get to that. The Mac was a bit of an inspiration. I still love Apple to pieces because it's a nice place to work. It's like working in a really nice office instead of a dingy little dungeon. There's something about how Microsoft software works that is just not right.

RB: I'm glad you explained your madness. I was going to ask you why. There are so many tools available for the ISA bus and the x86 instruction set and the number of compilers for Microsoft's OS's. Why would you ever corner yourself by working with a tool that I find so inaccessible? I used to find it so hard just to find a phone number for Apple. I remember the first ones, you just couldn't get inside them. They didn't want you to get in to see that there was actually a PCB in there with ugly green busses on it and a hard drive.

MH: You really want to take the back off your Macintosh because it has all the names of all the people that worked on it engraved inside the plastic case. They actually signed the moulding tool. It's a really nice touch. I still have one.

RB: I've always said (I don't say it so much nowadays) that having a Mac was like having a Porsche, but they wouldn't let you pop the hood.

MH: That's not strictly true, but you had to buy the developer tools to get in there. It was after many years of working with Macintosh Programmer's Workshop - which is a beautiful command line development environment I found where you can actually script and design your own tools - you can actually extend the environment and add things to it that work the way you want. It didn't occur to me until I started to study things like Unix, that actually I had been using something like it for a very long time and hadn't known it. The whole thing was based on the C shell of Unix. I thought, hang on, all

---

[11] The fact that Rosco sold ET to Genlyte; the plant was moved from Portland to Dallas; Genlyte purchased Vari-Lite and then proceeded to move two buildings into one delayed the release date for Marquee – the console built upon Horizon's fade engine. At the time of this interview, I could not talk to Mark about Marquee.

these commands look very familiar.

That environment took quite a lot of understanding. It wasn't something a naïve user or someone who was used to writing C programs from the start would have found very intuitive. But as an assembler programmer, I was used to taking things to bits to understand them. In fact, there is an awful lot of Macintosh code that I've disassembled and taken inspiration from. Of course, you almost never copy someone's code because it doesn't quite apply to what you are doing, but you actually get an idea of how things can be done from looking at it. "Ah, yes, brilliant idea. I could use that here." I know all programmers do this. It's a kind of plagiarism, but everybody does it, but if they are good ideas, they deserve to be used.

RB: The View Source option in Internet Explorer is good for that. Where would the World Wide Web be without that?

MH: The Mac was in my blood so to speak, a few projects on from the ColourMag. We did things like motor control systems based around the 68000. We did this 68000 board, which is actually in use now. It's the same circuit on a different PCB, which is in the Icon lamp. That board has a 68000 and a Zilog 8530 serial port chip, which is the same one they used in the original Macintosh and a Rockwell 6522 VIA which is the same chip they used in the original Mac and some static RAM and a set of ROMs. Apart from things like the address mapping and the fact that there is no video hardware, it's a Mac. It's a 68000 board with the minimal stuff and the same chips that Apple chose. They are actually quite superb chips. That Zilog serial chip is brilliant.

Because it was almost a Mac in terms of what hardware was in it, it was easy to use Macintosh tools to write software for it and I have a platform to run this stuff on that was almost identical to what it had been written on in terms of the available facilities.

So that board had been around for a long time before the Icon was developed, and we were using it in consoles to control motors. We did our own hoist control system which is what Ian Clarke was working on. We said, here's a 68K computer card that does pretty much everything we want, it's our own design, so we'll just use this in everything we do.

We did another product that was a 2k xenon searchlights including pan and tilt and control, which we used on a Tina Turner tour in 1990. That was really our first moving light. It wasn't particularly successful, but we learned a great deal from it as you usually do. The console side of that was very much based

The first Icon gig was the Madness tour of 1992.

on Avolites styling where you select lights and store cues. It wasn't a very important product except for the fact that it showed us how not to do things. You have to learn from these mistakes.

We did try to do a moving light, well moving head, or moving mirror. It was similar to the Coemar NAT, but although we could make it work, we never actually got any light out of it. It got nicknamed the 'Moving Dark'. Clearly a disaster.

Then Simon Austin came up and decided he wanted a light that would blow Vari-Lite out of the water. Simon didn't get on very well with them.

RB: This was around the time of the VL2B's or 2C's?

MH: It was 1991. The lamp and console project was the Icon project and it was entirely Simon Austin's baby. Without him it wouldn't have happened. You needed an extrovert with enthusiasm to push a project like that along and he was just that type of guy.

We had all kinds of issues that made it difficult. The console hardware layout was designed before we knew what it was going to do, which in some ways proved a problem later on. It's amazing that things happened at all, really.

We were given a panel and there were loads of buttons on it, and we really had no idea how it was to work at the start of the project.[12] This was probably a little out of sequence. Originally, the Icon console was going to talk to the

---

[12] This is similar to what happened to Anne Valentino with the Strand Lightboard M – page 150

lights through a network, which was based on Apple Talk, of course.

RB: What sort of length can you go with Apple Talk?

MH: One hundred metres is no problem. We were going to have repeater stations as well.

We decided on a 68020 console with about 4 MB of static RAM for the cue memory, 16 MHz processor and the serial chip to talk to the lights and a SCSI hard-drive inside. It all sounds very familiar if you're a Mac person.

So we had this hardware design for the console and then 'The Big Event' threw a spanner in the works. At that time, we were owned by Christian Salvesen. They had just bought Aggreko, the generator company, and they were looking at getting into the entertainment business. They wanted to buy a lighting company and a venue and a staging company and that sort of thing. They really didn't know much about the business so I don't think they enjoyed it very much. They were a logistics company fundamentally.

Bill Hewlett was involved at this stage, as a consultant, and he discovered that Vari-Lite had patents on networks communications controlling lights. He said, "You can't do this. You can't control moving lights with a network."

RB: Serial Network.

MH: In fact, any kind of network. If all the lights are on a network, this patent clearly states that that is patented. You can't get around this. If you take this to America, you are in serious trouble and they can take tens of millions of dollars from your company for infringing this patent. We would be at war with Vari-Lite on this and they would not be nice to us. This was serious stuff.

There were various meetings with the Salvesen board and Bill and the design team on this issue and after several weeks of discussion, it became apparent that the product wasn't going to get built if we were going to use a network to control the lights. We had a patent attorney and I said it strikes me that the only way that the lights are not going to be on a network is if we send a separate serial line to each light. I asked if we do that, do we infringe this patent. They said no, you'd be fine. You wouldn't infringe.

RB: Wasn't the VL2, at the same time, doing the same thing? They had a separate line going to each light. Well at least they didn't have the cable go from light to light to light.

MH: Yes, they didn't do that, but the network traffic that left the console was the same traffic that arrived at each light. So every light saw every packet on the network. That's the basis of network communication. It doesn't matter what the topology of the network is. If there is a point on the network where all the data appears, and it gets to the lights and the lights choose what they want, then that infringes their patent. This is a problem. It has all to do with addressing and all the data arriving at all the fixtures.

I gave an off-the-wall idea. I didn't know if it would work out, but if we could say that only the data for a light would appear at that light, and none of the other lights would ever see it, would we be OK? They said "yes". So I said, if we had something like an audio multi-core with thirty pairs in it and we sent a separate pair to each light, then we wouldn't infringe their patent? They said "yes". I said that that cable would cost us a couple of thousand pounds to make, but that sounds like peanuts compared to the ten million dollars you're talking about losing to Vari-Lite if we don't do it.

RB: So, coming off of the SCSI?... SCSI is considered parallel.

MH: It is. The key to the SCSI thing is that we argued that SCSI link was part of the console because the console can't control lights without it. And, you can't put a light onto the SCSI cable because that data is meaningless to the fixture. It's only when it leaves the distribution that it is in separate wires. And you can't put more than one lamp on one wire because you can't control them separately. That was fine by the patent attorney, which was OK by me and it was a relatively small price to pay for all the triple damages and all that patent talk. We found a way that didn't infringe and it solved the problem.

RB: What was the data-com cable you found?

MH: It's actually audio multi-core. We knew that SSE, the audio company next door, could manufacture a multi-core at a certain price and this price was nothing compared to the money we would risk losing in law suits. So we went that way. I could see that this was not going to get solved. The product was not going to go on because Salvesen wouldn't have let it out.

It meant fairly radical re-design of certain parts of the system as you can imagine.

The Icon console 365 back-lit LCD buttons – one for each day of the year.

RB: I understood it because I have done some Icon gigs in the UK. I thought it was ludicrous, but I knew what you were doing. Then I worked on the U2 Pop Mart Tour where you had the UGLI[13] boxes and every single Studio Color was addressed at 1. I just saw all these Mexicans soldering DMX cable. That's when the silliness really hit home. Think of the money being thrown into this just to avoid this law suit. At that point, 99% of the industry was using things like Hogs and Animators to do shows anyways.

MH: We weren't permitted to do this. Light and Sound's attitude would have normally been 'OK, we'll go ahead and do it anyway'. But Salvesen wouldn't let us do it. They were very cautious and in quite a lot of ways they were right to be so because we were head to head with Vari-Lite at the time and I don't think they would have let us get away with it.

So, full steam ahead. We already had a SCSI port because we had a SCSI hard-drive in the console. So that seemed the obvious alternative output. We had to build our own distribution network, which had a Texas Instruments DSP in it, strangely enough[14]. It was the only processor I could find that had Harvard architecture.[15] The problem was that we had to fetch data from the SCSI port and get it into the distribution units at as high a rate as possible with a fairly low clock speed. The DSP technology that Texas had would allow you to run the program in internal RAM in the processor, then your bus was completely free for data transfer. So, you could get pretty high data transfers through this chip. We weren't doing any DSP stuff with it, it just that it happened to be quite cheap and it would transfer data between ports really quickly.

There was also a DMA[16] clause in that patent as well. DMA was a bad word. We weren't allowed to DMA anything. You can have incredible fights with patent attorneys. I don't know if you've been through this.

RB: A little bit when I left CBC. The attorneys basically said don't take a

---

[13] LSD's Universal Guest Luminaire Interface

[14] A Texas Instruments TMS32C80 Digital Signal Processor would later become the heart of the Icon M.

[15] A processor that uses Harvard architecture has separate buses for the instructions and data. The instruction fetch is sent along with the data access of the operand executed in the previous cycle. The term originated from the Harvard Mark I computer. It stored instruction on punched tape and data in the relay latches.

[16] Direct Memory Access systems allow peripherals to read and write data without involving the main CPU. See page 252 regarding performance of DMA DMX devices verses pure UART FIFOs serviced by the processor.

thing with you except what's in your head. Luckily. CBC didn't have any patents on what I did there.

MH: You can have incredible arguments because it seems you're not allowed to do anything if there is a patent. Of course, that's the point of a patent. But there is usually another way.[17] This is one of the things that I think is one of my strong points because I do not know that something can't be done. I've never been taught. I've learned things as I've gone along. So I have no sense that things cannot be done. So I don't start from a defeatist point of view and if I can't do something, it's only because I don't know how to do it. It's because I haven't found out how to do it. It's not because it can't be done. So I will not give up. If something doesn't work the way I'm trying to do it, it's not because it will never work, it's because I'm trying to do it the wrong way. There is nothing that can't appear to be done. The trick with software is that you can often fail to achieve something, but make it look like you've succeeded.

I get a laugh out of every time I do it because it is cheating in a way, because you're not doing it the right way but you're getting the results and it's kind of cheeky.

RB: As long as you don't make yourself a carbuncle. That's what I call a bit of code you put into a system that you regret for the rest of you life – but you just have to live with it because it's out there.

So you were respectful of Vari-Lite's patents, but with a smile on your face. I think it was because you were still making money and you could be smug that you were not violating any patents. I'm now just starting to understand you. I never got it before. It is because you were…

MH: … naughty. It was a game – how can you make a moving light without using any of the obvious technologies?

RB: "Here's a problem. They set the rules. I will now use these rules to make a living where nobody else can."

For example, Whole Hog could not get onto the U2 tour because LSD waved somebody else's patent in the face of U2 management. They knew that Willie Williams wanted to use HES kit and LSD had the solution.

MH: It is being naughty, because the whole idea of the Vari-Lite patent was to stop anyone else from doing a moving light system. They thought they had got it sewn up. But! There is always a way. And, by not knowing you can't do

---

[17] See Wayne's alternate development success forced by other patent holders on page 352

it the other way, you get round it.

There are advantages to the way the Icon system works. We can lose a serial data link in our system, and we only lose one light. It's far more serious in a DMX system.

RB: In a DMX system, it can be very serious, and I remember watching Pink Floyd's Division Bell performance. It essentially changed my whole perspective on moving light programming. I got to sit in the lighting booth with the six board ops. I got a real appreciation for good programming and good execution there, wow! In the middle of one of the songs they lost a VL Smart Repeater. Nobody in the audience knew what was going on (why would they, there were a ton of lights), but I saw six lights go skywards, do a little recal, then come back to the show. With you, you obviously just lose one.

MH: It's hardware intensive in the cabling, but you have to send power to each light anyway. If your power cable has data in it anyway it doesn't really add much to the rigger's work. For a professional application, it actually makes quite a lot of sense.

RB: Anne Valentino made a good point to why Vari-Lite's and your kit always gets spec'd on the 'big' shows like the Grammys and the Emmys and MTV Music Awards and so on. She says that when you don't have much time to set up a rig, and you want to make sure it's going to be set up flawlessly, there is nothing like having a system that just goes and does it. You don't want to be fiddling around with binary dipswitches and why is that one is not talking to that one and so on.[18] Yours is very true. There is a line of sight between the console and the light.

MH: You know where the fault is. You also tend to have spare lines in your system. We actually have a patch system at the stage end where you can take any line in the multi-core and we could reassign a console channel to any channel in the software, so we could patch around dead lines in the cable as well. That worked really well. For what we needed, it actually fitted very well – once you step back from the sheer cost of it, and said OK we'll swallow this cost because it prevents us getting into legal problems. Was it the time that Vari-Lite was suing High End Systems?

RB: They had already taken action against Summa and Syncrolite.

MH: I think they were on to High End by that point. The figures they were

---

18 Valentino – page 174

talking about in law suits and legal costs were astronomical compared to implementing our system.

RB: And LSD has never been in court with them. Think of companies that have fought for so long, like High End, and how much money it must have cost both parties. Nobody was making money doing this. Vari-Lite has some wonderful products but I think they did spend too much money protecting their IP rather than using it.

MH: ...when perhaps they should have been licensing it.

RB: Like the VL5. It could have made the Studio Color so much better.

MH: We have our own attitude within Light and Sound, because we have our own IP now and from seeing what Vari-Lite has done, we've learned that the thing to do is license. I really believe that. It hasn't happened yet. Obviously there is IP protecting Icon M and all things like that. And rather than saying you can't do that and we'll take you to court to sue you, we'll say we 'could' take you to court and sue you and it will cost us both huge amounts of money. Let's do a nice sensible licensing deal, and forget all about it because that way we're both happy. We're making money from our IP and you're making money from your product. That's the way it should be done. This aggressive Vari-Lite thing was just a huge mistake I think, apart from the fact that it alienates much of the industry, which is not something you can afford to do in this business.

RB: Wayne Howell from Artistic Licence makes DMX widget products. He's now making a DMX-Ethernet box that fills the gap while we wait for ACN. His philosophy is completely different from Vari-Lite's. He says I've got an idea on how to do this, but I'm not going to protect it from anybody. I'm actually just going to make it public domain. I could license it, but it really involves too much paper work to make it worth my while.[19]

MH: The Linux approach.

RB: Exactly. At the end of the day, Wayne wants to move boxes. So the more people that can talk to his stuff allows him to move more boxes. Somebody else could (and is) make a product exactly like his taking the protocol that he's developed, but he's cool with that. He'll still sell plenty of his boxes.

MH: It's a very healthy attitude. Almost everything Apple has done has

---

[19] See Howell – page 342

increased my respect for the company. OS X and the Darwin code base and all their Unix code is public domain. That is an incredible step to take for a big computer company. Could you imagine Microsoft making the source code for Windows public domain? They are the Vari-Lite in the computer world.

RB: There is so much stuff Microsoft protect from us. People find (or leak) all these back door commands – undocumented system calls. We are using one of those to get to the parallel port drivers in Windows XP for Horizon's legacy DMX interface. It's called AllowIO and takes advantage of an undocumented MFC call.

We've actually debated opening up all the source code for Horizon, for the two people who would actually play with it. It sends a message.

MH: It does. Apple have been so good to people over the OS X thing. The support's incredible. You join one of the user groups and send in a request for help and you get a couple of users helping you. Then people who write the code come back and tell you how to do it, people I really respect that have helped me with networking problem on OS X. These guys are like serious gods. It's kind of like having Steve Wozniak[20] answering your questions. You think why? I'm not really important at all. I don't pay Apple anything for this. This is free. I just asked a question about how to do this and someone who is costing Apple a lot of money has taken five or ten minutes of his day to answer my question. I really respect that.

RB: It helps if you ask intelligent questions.

MH: It also helps if you've already really tried to solve the problem yourself. You say I don't know if I'm being stupid, but I've tried all this stuff and it still doesn't work. The guy comes back and says that it actually doesn't work. He gave me some sample code that I needed to bolt some stuff in and told me I would need the new version because it didn't work in the one I had. You then say to yourself, I'm not being stupid. These people are obviously very busy writing code to make things work but they still have time to help people who aren't paying for extra support to write code. It's really nice.

RB: You are also helping them.

I have always viewed the Icon as a real classy light. The motor control is so tight, the colours are beautiful and the optics are damn bright for a 600 watt

---

[20] Steve Jobs and Steve Wozniak founded Apple Computers in 1976.

light. It just seems to be a nice package right out of the gate. I was just surprised that there was never a 200 watt version or another wiggly light that preceded it. The light seems to be so well designed and so tight and punchy.

The Icon fixture.

MH: I dispute that. It was damn hard work and it wasn't pretty in the early days!

RB: Then I'm lucky I wasn't there in the early days!

MH: Roger Harvey, who worked for Tasco on the Starlight in the early days, did the optics for the Icon, which in some ways were poor, in my opinion, but it is very bright. When you get the flare out, and you focus it down, to get a decent image it's no brighter then than any other light, but certainly when you say I want all the light you can give me, you get an awful lot of light. Some of the mechanical stuff is a nightmare because of all the gear wheels. I fought desperately to use belt drives, but it's all metal gears.

RB: Did you do the motor control code?

MH: Not initially, no. I had to take it over to make it work properly. I don't like slagging off my own product, but it is a miracle that it works at all!

The motor control processor is a TMS 77C82 micro. It's quite a small micro about the same power as an 8051. It's quite a nice chip. One of those does pan, another does tilt, and two more of them do twelve motor functions all together (six each). Those two are seriously overloaded microprocessors. They really don't have the processing time to service six channels of motor control.[21] The guy who designed the circuit board with all this on with all these pulse width modulation chips and encoder reading chips, etc. said that it didn't really work and could I sort it out? It was a horrible situation to be in.

I managed to get the PID[22] control loop from a time of five or six milliseconds to service each of the six motor (which is a pretty appalling loop time – it's hard to get any kind of control or response out of that) down to 1.8 milliseconds at a clock rate of about 7 MHz. I did all kinds of horrible things like self modifying code in RAM and things like that just to get those few instruction

---

[21] See Grimes – page 251 on servicing motors efficiently

[22] Proportional/Integral/Differential

cycles off. But it works. I would like to make some of the servos tighter, but the stability issues become appalling, especially when you have sloppy gear drives between the motor and the load. You have this disconnection between the motor and the load and it makes the stability of the system really difficult.

But having taken over the software for that board, I was then in the nice position of having both ends of the serial link – with my 68000 board sending commands to this motor control. I did one of the things I really enjoy doing, which is to make my slave a parametric system that accepts parameters from the master. You program the slave just by changing values in master program. So when the system is set up, the master tells the slave this is what you are doing and here are the parameters of controlling this motor. So once you've programmed all that in, you don't need to change the code in the slave – it's burned in. You can actually reconfigure the servos in the Icon lamp by changing the program in the 68k. I love that kind of stuff because it gives you control over all kinds of things.

RB: You gave me insight here where you would never expect it. I knew that you were a different thinker when we first put the Icon into WYSIYWG. Everybody has lamp head code that does things and services motors. It was a bit of a pain in the ass for us during WYSIWYG 1 and 2 because we never had a very complex state machine for all the virtual motors like we do in 3. We basically took the DMX frame and drew the pictures as quickly as we could and as soon as we could we would go grab the next DMX frame and draw the next picture. When we got to WYSIWYG 3 we started to emulate the things we never could in WYG2, like High End System's MSpeed.[23]

I knew the profile of your lamp and I knew that the gobo control channel had a section that did index and another section that rotated it at various speeds in different directions. So I wrote the profile so that when DMX levels were right, I would start a state machine that would rotate it, just like everybody else's lights.

Then you started sending us data and we hooked it all up together. I couldn't understand why the gobo control channel, which was pegged to a specific rotation speed, kept changing. You then said no, no, I control the motors from the main processor. You did the rotations for us.

MH: All I did for you was to make the DMX channel a virtual motor.

---

[23] MSpeed is either Motor Speed or Mirror Speed. The debate continues. See Grimes page 248

RB: It came out of nowhere. It was such a gift.[24]

MH: It was easier for me to do that because that's the way the Icon works. The motor control channels just obey what they're told to do by the main processor. The main processor keeps the state machines for all the motors

---

[24] You can see what I mean when you compare the definitions of a Cyberlight gobo rotator to that of the Icon's in the WYSIWYG 2 library format.

```
        *** Cyberlight definition **************
        GOBOROTATOR:
                OPTIONAL: FALSE
                EDITABLE: FALSE
                DIR:
                        DMX: 10 255
                        RANGES: 7
                                0 56 STAT
                                57 94 RIGHT
                                95 132 LEFT
                                133 179 STAT
                                180 217 RIGHT
                                218 254 LEFT
                                255 255 STAT
                        END
                SPEED:
                        DMX: 11 255
                        RANGES: 4
                                0 10 STOP
                                11 85 SLOW
                                86 170 MEDIUM
                                171 255 FAST
                        END
                INDEX:
                        DMX: 11 255 0 ; OFFSET MAXVAL MINVAL
                        ANGLES: 0 360 ; MIN, MAX
                        END
        END
        *** Mock Icon definition ***************
        GOBOROTATOR:
                OPTIONAL: FALSE
                EDITABLE: FALSE
                INDEX:
                        DMX: 11 255 0 ; OFFSET MAXVAL MINVAL
                        ANGLES: 0 360 ; MIN, MAX
                        END
        END
```

going inside it. They are actually driven in real-time. This is a time-driven system.

I really get annoyed about DMX and how it's used to control moving lights because of the motor speed thing. That is not the way to control a show. The Icon console was designed from the ground up with a show control basis, which is why we have two point fields in our cue numbers. It was always designed as MIDI show control as a driving force and time as the basis for the show. You can only really spec something in time. In fact, we have a little stopwatch built into the console. If you hit the time button to enter a time on our console, then hit it again at the end of the time that you want, it automatically enters the time between the two key presses. Whenever you are entering a time, you can say that you want it to go from here… to here.

RB: Do you have to learn timing on chases?

MH: If you have an auto-running chase, you can step the advance key and every time you tap it, the console remembers the interval between the taps. Then on the last tap you hold it down and hit the Retrieve key and it goes back to the timing you've already set. I can't remember how to work the console these days, but there is a way of actually writing that back into the original chase definition so you can permanently update the chase. I have to ask operators how to do things on my desk! There are loads of things on the console where I would have to look at the code to figure out how to work them.

RB: You never had a manual?

MH: People who use the console all the time know the tricks. I just have to deal with the new stuff and it's been ten years since I started it.

RB: It helps when there is one person who maintains the code base.

MH: It does, but sometimes it's a bit lonely. I wish that there was someone else, sometimes, as it's nice to explain things to people who understand what you are saying, because quite often when you have a problem, all you really need to do is tell someone about it. The mere act of talking it through helps you solve it. It doesn't really matter if they understand.

RB: And it doesn't help if you talk to yourself in a dark room.

MH: One thing I've learned over the years, particularly during the Icon project – and quite early on I was starting to realize this – was that we did 36-hour work sessions to get things done for deadlines. You start to recognize a pattern where if you keep on plugging away at something and getting more and more tired; you do more damage than good. You end up with something worse than what you have started with.

RB: You can fall out of the truss.

MH: Especially with software where you can do an awful lot of damage in a short period of time, you need to learn to recognise the point where you are not getting anywhere. If you are actually following a path through a problem and you can see it progressing towards somewhere you want it to be, then you carry on, because that is a good flow and you follow that.

RB: That takes discipline because I get so involved and I sometimes can't even think about my wife or my family.

MH: Family helps a lot.

RB: But sometimes you can't relax until you get the splinter out.

MH: There was a famous incident, just before the first Icon tour, where I had the console software running, I had the lamp software running, and it was all going pretty well. It was Depeche Mode, and we were in rehearsals at the NEC in Birmingham. The thing that was missing from the console was the patch. I could not think of a way of re-patching console channels to different distribution channels so we could swap things around. Tom Nolty who was the guy we hired, an ex-Vari-Lite technician, was our guru in how touring moving light systems were going to work from a technical-keeping-them-going point of view. He was a pretty cool guy and he said this 'has' to be there - you cannot run a moving light system without this. But I couldn't figure out how to do it. I had been working really late and long for a couple of weeks and I was pretty shattered.

That particular night, the day before rehearsals were due to start, I couldn't think how to do this and I promised to take my wife and children to her parents for the weekend. I was going to be working so the idea was she was going to have a nice weekend with her parents. I knew I had to do that family thing which was useful because it was a good excuse for me to say I cannot do this now. I knew that I could sit there all night, and still not solve the problem. I had this other thing I had to do and so I was going to go and do it. I didn't even have the mental capacity to explain things very well and I just left. It caused enormous eruptions at Light and Sound - in fact the guy who was managing the project resigned that night. It was pretty scary stuff. I was sorry, it's just the way you get when you're messed up. Tired people do irrational things.

I knew I couldn't solve that problem then and in fact I couldn't promise to solve it the next day, but I knew there was a better chance the next day. I had a better idea of what to do by the next morning, but my walking away scared a lot of people. I have a lot of confidence in my ability to fix these things, but sometimes they don't happen to order and sometimes you have to have a little patience. I've learned to recognize those symptoms and have confidence they will solve themselves, and also to give myself time in the project to make sure those things are solved before they become critical. Sometimes things will not work to order and you have to be aware that you will probably need three or four days where a very important thread in what you are doing is stalled. No amount of working on it will unlock it. You have to leave it alone and do something else. Go to a theme park – anything – but don't work on it.

RB: It takes a huge leap of faith because if you keep banging your head against the wall, at least people can see that you are trying.

MH: I don't think there has been an occasion where it hasn't worked. Quite often, you will find that when you walk away from a problem of this kind, it is that you were trying to do it the wrong way. That's normally what it is; you've lacked the perspective you need. It takes an enormous amount of courage but you have to have faith. It scares me more than other people.

There is the one bug I've been looking for three months. I found it yesterday. You never learn all the ways you can mess things up. You often forget the ones you've solved before.

RB: I remember when we were developing WYG 1. It was a very hot summer and we were working in my living room. I had this list on the wall that I would add to whenever I need to. It was called 'Bugs that bug me'.

We had this one memory leak that just about drove me around the bend. Rick Szijarto at that point was back at school in Kingston and I was alone in Toronto. I was spending hours of testing each day looking for this thing. Weeks later I finally found it, but it was a whole combination of things that made it go wrong.

MH: You have to lay traps for them. We have a little issue on the Icon console at the moment. We've made some dramatic changes in the last couple of months, and we can't expect it to be bug free, but one of them is setting the menu panel to an illegal mode and the menu panel stops working until you change mode on it. It's quite irritating. I can't find it, but what I've done is put some code into the console that every time through the loop it checks the menu panel mode and if it's illegal, it will put up a dialog on the console that says you have a bad menu panel mode and it will switch it back to the cue launching mode which is the mode it's supposed to be in most of the time. Not only does it always make sure that it's working, but it tells the operator when it's just gone wrong. Then he know the thing he's done before probably triggered it.

RB: We had another one that I remember fondly. It was quite early in the project and it was my code that was screwing things up. A certain sequence of events that the user would do would put it in this mode where a bunch of stuff would stop working. In fact, I think it was that the keyboard mnemonics for the menus. At the time we didn't have a keystroke recorder – it was DOS and we didn't have the multi-threaded tools we have now. The way I solved it was to get a video recorder and tape myself using the software. It ended up that as I was ALT-Tabbing between the compiler and the application, I would turn on Cap-Locks in the compiler to edit some bit of code we had formatted like that. It was something you would never find, because it wasn't in the code. There really wasn't anything wrong with it except the fact that I wasn't scanning for the cap-lock flag.

MH: It's hard sometimes. One of my greatest assets I think, and the quite frightening thing about my whole career, is that I don't know what I'm doing.

RB: And you're afraid to let people find out.

MH: My whole career has been based on saying "Yes" to people. People say to me, do you think you can do this gig? My first PA gig was Sonia Kristina gig at Eastbourne in the UK. Can you do front of house sound for this gig? Yes, sure. Never done it before. There's a PA in the warehouse somewhere - you find it and put it in a truck, put it together, make it work, and do a concert with it. I had never done anything like that before in my life. But I got away with it. Just. I've done that all the time and very rarely have I been a complete failure. Sometimes it's been a bit marginal but most of the time you get away with it.

RB: I lack that confidence early on. If I get pushed, I soon find that once I get into it that I'm all right. Then near the end of it I figure that I can do it and I often think that I do it quite well.

MH: I have the advantage of being technically more knowledgeable about the equipment I'm using than most of the people that use it for a living. So having fixed it and got to the stage of seeing how the design of it could have been better, because as a service engineer you find out an awful lot about other people's gear, you get the confidence in that you know how to make it work. You may not have the artistic requirements required for being a sound engineer or whatever, but you will be able to get the rig up and running and everything will come up on the fader and work. That's a given. So you go in with that confidence.

RB: That bit's done. You just worry that someone's going to come up and point to you and say you don't know what you're doing. Then you say, "You're right. I've got to run. Bye."

MH: There is a lot of difference between being that and a guy who has never seen a microphone before.

RB: When I started developing LXMOV at CBC (the predecessor to WYSIWYG) I had already done a load of code in LISP…

MH: Brave man.

RB: Well, it was the only thing you could do in AutoCAD (before Release 11). At school I had done Pascal and working for Dad I did Fortran, but I had never done C. Then CBC said the project was a go and I knew that LISP wasn't going to be fast enough so I had to do it in C. "Alright, we'll figure this out. It can't be that difficult." You do jump into it and you have to realize that nobody is going to do it for you.

MH: You do what everybody else does: you just get some sample code and change it.

RB: Then you find that by dinner you've grafted so much onto it that you can call it your own.

MH: I don't know about Microsoft, but on Apple's web site they say that is what sample code is for. This can be the basis of your application. You're free to use it. What you're not allowed to do is modify it and ship it as Apple's own.

RB: What I've found now is the AutoCAD code examples are really really good. In the early days it was very thin and poorly documented and the Internet didn't exist.

MH: It's such a wonderful thing.

RB: Thank God they're not too big on AutoLISP now days. They now have VBA (Visual Basic for Applications) and they have oodles of sample code. They say this is how you do this, then literally say highlight from here to here then copy and paste into your VB editor. You then hit F5 and it runs. It's beautiful because you can just graft on and you're half way there.

So, enormous success with the Icon, then... the Washlight?

MH: It wasn't really my project. It was Bill's baby. I don't think I wrote anything for that. He's like me in that he likes to control things and that was his product. We had to do things in Washlight that emulated Icon so I had to port bits of the Icon code onto an 8051.

RB: Was the colour system in the Washlight an idea from LSD?[25]

MH: No, it was Bill's and he patented it.

RB: Morpheus built a system with three colour scrolls with perforations, which is very nice. You can get some lovely colours and you can really beat them up. You can bump through the colour very quickly. I did a tour with them and I was amazed how fast you could run them.

MH: Having holes in the gel really helps. You don't get air cushions between the gels. It's like having tread on a tire that lets the water out.

RB: We had to build a new widget in WYSIWYG so we could model the Washlight.

Then years later Wybron came out with their CXi and they had a client that wanted to program a gig with them in WYSIWYG. They told Wybron to call me up to have it profiled for them so they could go off and do that. I remember the guy on the phone getting all prepared to share with me this new technology that was so radically different. Before he could speak, I had explained the whole mechanism to him. He was quite frightened because he thought he had the secret. I warned him that LSD had done it three years earlier, but he had

---

[25] Many fixtures that use the subtractive colour systems of cyan, yellow and magenta use three flags or three gel strings to remove red, green or blue from the white light. Washlight uses only two strings, the first going from full saturation of cyan toward open white then to full saturation of magenta. The second similarly goes from full saturation of yellow towards white to full magenta again. The 'home' position for the strings is in the centre and you achieve colour mixing by moving each of the gels off centre. The advantage of this system is that you can crossfade between colours that you can't do under a CYM fixture. Where a VL5 might crossfade through black, a Washlight may crossfade through white, if it does at all.

just never heard of the Washlight. I then talked to Keny Whitright to make sure he was cool. The deal is, they use spliced gel where you use pure graduated gel.

So that was the Washlight. I've been meaning to ask you about who and how did you decide to use those backlight LCD switches on the console.[26]

MH: That was Simon. He loved them.

RB: But $25 each!

MH: A huge quantity of money.

RB: You even used them for the '10 key' - zero through nine. You never even change the background on those.

MH: Once you have them all over the console, what do a few more matter? It gives you the power to do all kinds of things. You can tell when the console is in reset because all the keys are blank.

RB: Come on. A single blinking LED can tell you that.

MH: It's a sort of diagnostic tool. It lets us dynamically change things – it's so nice.

RB: They do have a nice feel with good travel. How many are there on it?

MH: 365 – one for every day of the year. It's not a cheap console. It's not a console for the average market. It's supposed to look expensive. Beaten up, but expensive. They're getting a bit long in the tooth these days, but they're pretty impressive machines. It's supposed to be an expensive console for top-flight tours. Expense really is no object. I mean people pay $100,000 for a sound console, why not for a lighting console?

RB: Well if you're renting the whole system, why not?

MH: The Icon console is cool.

RB: It's very cool. There's no debate there. But for those of us trying to make money selling things…

MH: It wouldn't be a product you would want to sell. It had to go up against the Artisan. Once again, you had to take it in context of where we were and the Artisan is a fairly impressive machine and the Icon console had to be better because that was Simon's mission.

---

[26] The Icon desk has these beautiful liquid crystal square buttons that are cabable or re-labling themselves on the fly and can be backlit in either red, green or yellow.

RB: Luckily you found the money.

MH: That's where Salvesen came in.

RB: They made their money back?

MH: No. I don't think they did.

RB: So then, do we get to M?

MH: Yes, but there was also quite a lot of console stuff that went on before that. It's never actually stood still for very long.

RB: You did Mock Icon.

MH: We did do Mock Icon, which was just a toy. I was told about WYSIWYG and I thought that would be quite a cool thing to do. I'm not even sure it was called WYSIWYG then.

RB: I must have been still at CBC and you had heard about LXMOV. Lighting and Sound International wrote it up.

MH: I thought that that was a nice idea. We could do something like that as a programming tool. So I did something that just drew the centre lines of beams, which is Mock Icon. The brilliant aspect of that, as it turned out for us, was that instead of emulating the lights and how they would respond to the commands from the console, I actually ran the light code in a shell. Because it was running on a 68000 processor on a Macintosh, you could actually encapsulate the code from the light in an operating system shell and run multiple instances of the same code for each channel.

What you're actually seeing run in Mock Icon is a lamp, which is how you can get all the outputs from that process to drive a DMX channel. That is what we ended up doing to interface to WYSIWYG. That's where that actually comes from. You're actually running Icon lamp code many many times on a fairly fast processor and looking at the results on a DMX stream, which is why it behaved just like a lamp, because that's what it is.

Haven written all that code once, it seemed pointless to try to write something that tried to be that code. It was much easier just to run it. So, that became the basis of what we call the UGLI. The UGLI is basically the Mock Icon in a box with DMX serial outs. That's all it is. It's kind of a freebee, based on what Mock Icon was, which is just the Icon lamp code running on a Mac.

RB: So I can take a small bit of credit for the UGLI boxes.

MH: I guess so. You can also take credit for the fact that it never got beyond that stage.

RB: That was a very satisfying day for me. I remember the date. It was PLASA '94, the year we launched WYSIWYG. You and Nick Archdale were quite good friends and I was nobody. It was my first year to PLASA and we were showing a very shaky version of WYG 1. It was impressive enough though. It was in 3D, in perspective and it had hidden line removal and gobos and all. Nick took me over to your booth, which had lovely black leather couches and draught beer and I sat down with you and him (it was the day I met you). We sat for about forty minutes and talked. Then you showed me what you had done on Mock Icon and I politely went, "yes". The setup of how you got the fixtures in 3-space and orient them all was really horrific at the time.

MH: Yes, it wasn't...

RB: . . . developed yet. Then Nick finally sat up and said, "Come on then, let's have a look at what he's done." We took you about two aisles over and we showed you WYSIWYG working with a Hog I. You saw about ten lights working in full perspective moving about and you said, "Right, well I'm done with that then!"

MH: Yes. There was just no point. We didn't need Mock Icon. I had a plan to do 3D movement[27] on lights and in fact there is still 3D code in the Icon lamps. We don't use it. We did actually get it working once because we built an interface to Wybron's AutoPilot, which would allow us to look at what AutoPilot said, translate it to 3D commands and send it to the Icons. We got that working once but never used it.

For what we wanted to do, I knew that we would never develop anything as good as WYSIWYG because we didn't have the time or the manpower, which is me. So it was never going to happen. Your product deserved to have the market anyway. It was never worth putting all our R&D into a competitor. We'll just use it. It is much better than our product. It's pointless trying to do something that would be the same.

RB: Then you built Mac Icon – the thing that looks just like the console on the Mac.

---

[27] 3D movement allows you to position a light by mapping three encoders on the console to absolute X, Y and Z coordinates on the stage, rather than local pan and tilt to each and every light. It gives you the ability to recalibrate your stage by updating only four palettes, and then all other positions and cues are updated automatically. The MA Scancommander was the first desk I knew of that did this.

MH: That came first, because I was aware from previous things we had done that if you start designing the control system after you have the product, then you're lost. I was aware that the console development was going to be an extremely long project, and we were going to have lights in 9-12 months. We would maybe have a prototype console ten months into that.

RB: It actually existed before the desk did? Interesting.

I tried to convince Flying Pig to output DMX from their Hog Mimic well before they released Hog PC. Their justification for not doing it was that they didn't want to kill sales of a very expensive certain piece of furniture they were producing. After they had made the money on that, they made the Hog Widget to output DMX using a PC.

MH: The problem with product development is that you have hardware that you know is going to be ten months away and you have a eighteen month software project before you have anything that's really usable. That doesn't really work out. You have to start your software project 'now' and ten months away, you may have some hardware to run it on.

The first thing I wrote was the virtual shell, which was a complete front

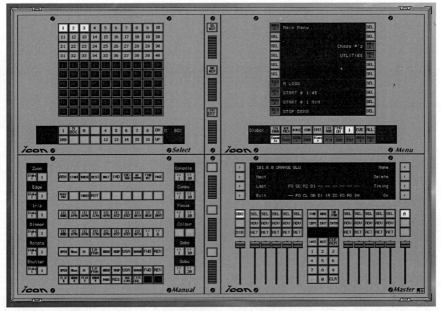

Mac Icon.

panel shell emulation. We knew what the buttons were going to look like so I drew them all in by making resources for the Mac and actually taught it how to operate a front panel and every control on there actually works, and all the displays do the same as they do on the console. I had drawings from the drawing office of what the console was going to look like. I have actually modified it in light of what the console actually is, in the sense that I've gone back and changed the graphics so that it looks more like a real console than what the original one was. But it had to exist before the console because the software had to be working and in development months before there was any hardware.

As I was getting to understand how this thing was going to work, then I got to the point where some hardware came along and I would just write device drivers for that hardware that emulated what I was already using for my virtual front panel. It was an iterative process where I would find things with the hardware that the emulation wouldn't quite do and I would have to rewrite it, but generally it worked really well. The virtual console is a very powerful tool and we still run shows with it.

RB: Doing big industrials in Europe, we would always have an Icon desk in the hall running the rig, but the lobby, which had six or eight fixtures, would just be run off a Powerbook.

MH: It's very reassuring that you have an emulation that runs on a commercial product you can buy almost anywhere that will run your show. It was the perfect console replacement and it was because of the parallels between what Apple was doing and what I was doing.

RB: Well, I'm only giving Apple the time of day now. I love the Titanium and OSX looks very promising. I loathed the previous stuff. I guess I just wasn't very left-handed thinking. I find that most people that use a Mac are left-handed.

MH: Very true. I am.

I knew that those parallelisms between a Mac and the console design were going to be very helpful and because of them I was going to be able to emulate it very successfully. The code it actually runs is the same instruction sequence, so when you get to debugging and finding problems, it's great being able to step through your code on a real computer because the debugging tools on custom hardware are never very good. Being able to find problems on that platform, where it is so helpful is that it allows you to fix it there and it will work on the console 99 times out of 100. Very, very seldom do I have a problem on the desk that I don't see on the Mac.

RB: Is it just timing things?

MH: There are little issues where the desk is subtly different from the Mac. They bite you occasionally, but most of the time you are OK. If someone says they do this, then they do this, then they get a bus error then you go back and do it on the Mac and you get a bus error. It's great because you're in the debugger and you go, well OK...

RB: ...forgot to initialize that pointer and...

MH: Especially where you are doing stack frames in assembler, which can be a bit tricky. One of the problems with the Icon console is that, at the time, we didn't have much money to spend on the processor board so we had 2 MB's of static RAM for the cues, and a completely separate bank of 512K of memory for the code to run in. So everything ran in RAM and the code was copied from ROM so you could run the console code at full speed with no wait states on the processor. It was running as fast as it could go. But that code space was quite limited and compilers tend to think they have as much memory as they want. If you want to write something compact and fast you are driven into assembler. The coding tools are much better now, but in those days, you couldn't afford to write something that small in C.[28]

It annoys me that there is no way to get a carry flag out of a shift in C - things you take for granted in assembler. You shift a bit out of the end of the register and it goes into carry so you can branch in a state. Having to do proper bit tests on stuff to see if the bit's a 1 before you shift

Icon M.

---

[28] See Grimes on embedded systems and using Assembler vs. C on page 259

it out. I've got used to C now. Quite a lot of the Icon M code is written in C. Once again, there are things you do with a DSP that just don't work in C and you have to write in assembler. I'd say 90% of it is C.

RB: The Icon M is actually doing the processing in the head.

MH: Yes. It's a TMS 320C80 DSP, which is now getting to be obsolete. It was new when we first started using it. It was called the Multimedia Video Processor. It has a RISC processor similar to the Power PC's, running every instruction in a single clock cycle at 50 MHz and four digital signal processors, each of which can execute four instructions in the same clock cycle. They are the things you need to hand code because you have to get them so they do all kinds of efficient things. DSP programming is quite fun. I don't know if you've ever done any.

RB: Heaven's no. I'm not that clever.

MH: These chips can do two or three things in a single cycle at the same time without losing any time. So you can do things like fetch data from where something is pointing, operate on some other data and increment a pointer to point to the next bit of data, all at the same time. That's how they manage to process all the multiplication and other things they do really quickly.

I was going over some of the code somebody had written for the Icon distribution system and it was working in a way, but I had to go back and put a new feature into this distro and had to take someone's code and go through it, which is always fun. This guy wasn't really a programmer. He was an engineer and he designed the board and he had been given the task of making the thing work, which meant he had to write the code for it. Although it worked, almost every instruction that he had written was a missed opportunity. There wasn't actually anything wrong with it, but it completely ignored all the parallelism built into the processor.

RB: He just built it like a linear one.

MH: We do this, then we do this, then we do this. We could have done those three things in one instruction then you would have managed the loop time we were trying to get. It was running really slowly and it wasn't until I actually measured loop times in the system that I asked why it was running so slow. It should have been four times that speed. I went over it, and although it was right, it wasn't what you should have been doing on this processor.

RB: So why are you, on a device that is designed to accept NTSC, doing all the manual work of bitmapping via a DSP rather than just sending a video signal to it? People are now looking at the Catalyst and thinking this is where it is obviously all going. Why don't they just do it like that?[29]

MH: Because it's not a video projector. It's a light. Icon M is not a video projector. It's Bill's baby and it's a pretty cool idea. It nearly killed him; he was that passionately involved in it. That may be a bit dramatic, but it did have a bad effect on his health. When Bill was around, the "V" word was not allowed.

RB: It wasn't TI saying, "You can have this chip but don't dare put NTSC on it."

MH: No, not at all. They thought what we were doing was pretty cool. The idea was that we would have a lamp with an almost infinite number of gobos in it that could do all these cool things that no lamp could ever do – like additive gobos. It took Bill a little while to explain to me what he was on about. There would be things like we would never show a square beam out of the light – it would always be round because lights produced round beams. These things were to stop people perceiving Icon M in the wrong way. It was really important in the early days that it was not a video projector. There is a video cable in the multi-core, because we knew that in the long term we wanted to put a live feed into the light, but that had to be a secondary thing.

RB: It would be a black and white video projection.

MH: Yes, at least by the time it came out. It could be a colour image going in, but the lamp is monochrome so you couldn't get a colour image out of it.

I can see his point now because by making it a luminaire in concept, and trying to avoid people seeing it as a video projector, the control becomes more natural for a lighting designer and they understand it better.[30] And putting

---

[29] The Catalyst is made by High End Systems and is basically an interface between DMX and a MAC, which is doing lots of real-time AVI manipulation. You can control video frame-rate, zoom, crop, colour etc, all by using a DMX console. You then ship the image up to a projector and can even pan and tilt the image around using a head. The TI micro mirror device and DSP that LSD is using in the Icon M are basically the main components in many commercially available video projects.

[30] My how time flies. Since this interview we've had another season of trade shows and the world has changed. At LDI 2003 there were at least five DMX Video Servers being shown (including LDS's M-Box). This is the year that the world of video and lighting collide. To put Icon M in context, it was first shown four years earlier and what LSD was doing was quite revolutionary stuff: putting the world of image manipulation in the hands of a lighting board operator.

the DSP inside of it was pretty easy. Apart from the five processors, it also has a complete video syncing and video controller. So, there's the DSP chip and some RAM and some Flash and there's little else on there, apart from the gate array. I'm a big fan of gate arrays these days.

RB: Explain to me a gate array.

MH: It's called a Field Programmable Gate Array. Basically it's a piece of silicon that's empty when you start up and the first thing you do when you start it up is that the CPU teaches the gate array what it is supposed to do. It loads some data into the gate array that configures all this logic. It's just sitting around waiting for something to do. It kind of wires it up under software control. Once you've done that, the gate array comes out of its initialization mode and becomes whatever piece of logic you told it to be.

So what you do is solder one of these chips onto your board and join everything up with it. It doesn't really mater how you do it.

RB: How many bus pins on it.

MH: There is a 64-bit data bus, 32 bit address bus and all the I/O on that board is in the gate array. So there are the serial ports that receive data from the console and output data to the motors, there is the digital multiplier for the fade, because all the fading in Icon M is done in the gate array so we don't have to redraw all the graphics to fade the lamp so even when the drawing rate slows down, this lamp can still fade out smoothly. The multiplier on the gate array does it.

The beauty of these gate array things is that because they are uncommitted logic when they start up, you don't have to commit to what your design is at any point. You can impose limitation by how many pins you hook up and what you wire them to, but if you do as much as you can at the design stage, then you can change your mind at any moment by reconfiguring the gate array.

There is this wonderful language called VHDL, which is a VHSIC Hardware Description Language. It's a sort of reverse programming. What I felt was so cool about this language is that I spent a lot of my life following Apple's example of emulating hardware with software. The Mac had almost no hardware in it and most of the things that make it so nice are in the software. So it's a minimal hardware base, with this excellent software layer that makes everything work. Which means of course you can change your mind about how it works just by changing the software.

Before, you'd write software that emulates how you would like the hardware to work, i.e. it makes the hardware appear to work in a different way by changing how it's accessed. With VHDL you write code that describes how something works, which is like the software you would write before, but what it does is generate the hardware that produces those results. It's really backwards programming. You write a program that describes how a job is done, then this amazing bit of software, the VHDL compiler, turns that into the wiring diagram for the gate array. That's amazing stuff. We use these things in every product we do because it's so nice to say here is the hardware design, were going to need these I/O chips to do this interface, and we'll need the CPU to do the working out and we'll just put a gate array in the middle of the board and glue everything together with it. Once we got the gate array configuration system working, because you need special pins to load the stuff in, we can change our minds at any point about how this is going to work. You're not committed at any point – even after manufacture.

The whole point about the M was that it was a 'magic' light, but it didn't pretend to be video. It panned and tilted and did CMY, but it had these magic gobos that didn't behave like gobos you had seen before. We put all of DHA's catalogue into the light.

RB: What was the resolution of it?

MH: The chip was 1024x768, so you see a 768 diameter circle.

Early in 2002, some of LSD's clients started ordering Catalyst. This gave our in-house operators some first-hand experience of High End's product, and caused Drew Findley to ask: "Why don't we put a video output on the Icon M DSP board?"

This idea couldn't work for two reasons: the Icon M DSP is now obsolete (time was when silicon had a 20 year lifespan – now it's two), and the icon-M design was monochrome. So I started investigating a port of the Icon-M software onto the Mac – anticipating the request that was obviously coming. This allowed me to explore the graphics accelerators that have exploded onto the market

LSD's Mbox.

since we designed Icon M – I'm sure we'd have used one if they'd been around at the beginning.

Mbox has become much more than a port of the original Icon M code. It's been an opportunity to rewrite with the benefit of hindsight – always a joy. It isn't just a software product – there's custom hardware in there too. We've used all our experience to produce a really professional product.

It's interesting to hear what clients actually want from these media server products. A lot of the really "clever" features of competing products don't seem to be important to our users. Their focus is always reliability, and doing the simple stuff really well.

The name was Dave Keighley's idea – "let's put an 'M' in a box – we'll call it Mbox".

I'm still a hardware designer at heart. It's nice to be in the position where you're working on hardware and software and know how they are going to give and take. Rather than having a hardware designer who gives you this bit of kit, then you have to write software for it, which can be a nightmare because he hasn't thought ahead about what you are going to do.

RB: I don't have an appreciation of that. I can see your point, but it's not my world.

MH: When you're starting with a design for something, it helps to know what aspects of your design are going to benefit from a hardware solution verses a software solution. Then you can make those decisions very early in the design stage. You then end up with a leaner product that works better and costs less.

RB: Are you happy where you're at now?

MH: I am happy, but I'm good at it. Happiness is learning to want what you've got rather than get what you want. I have a lot to be grateful for. I'm a very lucky man. I always have been, and I always appreciate that and I've enjoyed my life and I enjoy my family and I enjoy my work. I get paid to do what I enjoy.

RB: There is a new ad campaign by a recruiting company in Canada, the people who collect résumés and find people jobs. It says "LOVE what you do". If somebody is actually in the job market and you're giving that advice, that's a pretty tall order. I speak to so many people in our industry and they say just what you have said. We get paid to do this. A 36-hour day in the venue trying to get something to work can sometimes be pretty high stress, but at the end of the day, we create magic.

MH: I used to have this thing when I was a touring sound engineer. You would get to the venue and it's empty. You set the gear up and do sound check and all that tedium, then you do the show and thousands of people come in and have a really good time, and at the end of night, you would take all the gear down and put it in the truck and you would look back in the venue and it's as almost you've never been there. But loads of people had a great time that night. It gives me a really strange sort of magical feeling.

9 TOM GRIMES

Introduction

Tom and I have always shared a chuckle or two at trade shows. I was managing all of the library development at CAST while he was writing micro-code for the High End fixtures. Some of the newer fixtures have all these extra channels that make the fixture do all these wacky things like pulse the iris in a certain way, or ballyhoo the lights in some random fashion. From a guy trying to emulate a whole rig of lights on one processor, this was a royal pain in the backside. I was used to the Hog's Effects Engine and it did all these nice things, but it did it via DMX. WYSIWYG would just receive this data and draw the pictures. Reverse engineering and then emulating Tom's micro-code was a real challenge. But like all of the hard things in life, what doesn't kill us makes us stronger.

Tom is always a joy to talk to, even if I don't understand half of what he says. He lives in a different world. He is the sort of guy that can see the electrons going down the wire and wonders what he can achieve while he waits for them. I don't work at that scale. I can appreciate it, but I will never understand it.

I'm the sort of person who feels sympathy for my computer. I always feel sorry for it when I send it off on a difficult mission. It makes no sense and maybe

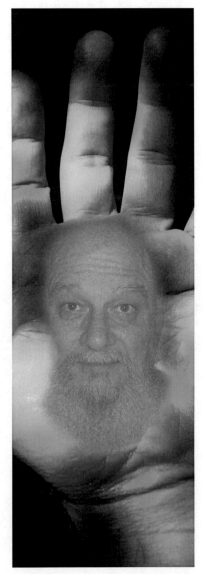

that's why I've never been a really good code guy. People like Tom can dissect a problem and break it into little pieces, and never worry that a processor might get confused when trying to juggle them all at once.

People who write micro code think in a different time zone than us. They see things like the DMX refresh rate of 44 frames a second (512 bytes per frame) and figure out how much they can do in between bytes. I look at a problem like that and just wonder where the hell I'm going to put all that data, never mind what I could do with it.

Read this interview and appreciate what it means to service a three-phase stepper motor. I bet you've never known what sort of influence people like Tom have had on your life. We are all too concerned about what font is used on the screen, or whether or not the Little Lites are casting a shadow on your book. Sure, we've all addressed fixtures using the LED display and had to decipher all the silly hieroglyphics, but I bet you didn't know that the same chip that draws those hieroglyphics also receives the DMX and drives all the motors and while we're trying to figure out Tom's hieroglyphics, Tom is still trying to figure out how to write the micro-code to make his toaster toast faster.

Interview

RB: I know you've been with High End for about ten years, but you've mentioned an oil rig. What the hell was that?

TG: Aside from electronics, I've also done welding and carpentry. I used the GI Bill[1] and moved away from electronics for a while. Welding was neat so I did welding for a while for US Steel and I've done some welding out in the oil patch. That's where the oil rigs come in. I got tired of getting burned and shocked and breathing bad noxious things.

RB: Can you do big arc welding with a beard like yours?

TG: It helps to keep it trimmed!

RB: You grew up in Austin?

TG: I was born in Austin and my family moved to San Antonio when I was about five. I was raised in San Antonio, went to school there, and went off to the navy when I was about nineteen, moving back to San Antonio after that.

---

[1] Tom served in the U.S. Navy from October '67 to October '73. At this time, the government provided 45 months of tuition assistance to people who completed their military service in an acceptable manner.

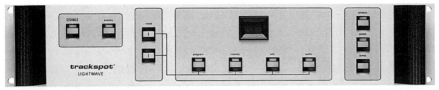

Trackspot Controller.

Now I oscillate between Austin and San Antonio as the work is available. I've been in Austin, fortunately, for the last fifteen years.

RB: What did you know about the entertainment industry before High End?

TG: I was working with three guys: William Moore, Mark Scurrah and Rico Morales. We had a company that did programming for laser shows. We used Pangolin, which is a package put together by Patrick Murphy from Virginia and William Benner from Florida. We did that for a while and it caught the eye of Steve Tulk and Steve introduced me to Richard Belliveau.[2]

RB: Steve, by that point, had already done DataFlash and Intellabeam? And maybe Emulator?

TG: By the time I got to High End, Trackspot was just about completed.[3]

RB: So who did the firmware for those original products?

TG: Scott Ingham did the electronics design and firmware for the Trackspot and on the heals of that was Cyberlight. Steve did the design for the electronics and Scott wrote the operating system code.

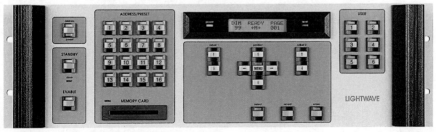

Universal Controller.

---

[2] Steve Tulk was one of the first engineers at Lightwave Research, the manufacturing wing of High End and Richard was one of the founders along with Lowell Fowler and Bob Schacherl.

[3] Lightwave Research's first fixture was the Color Pro in 1988. That was quickly followed by the Data Flash strobe and the Intellabeam moving mirror fixture in 1989. The IBeam 700HX really started to get High End noticed when Dire Straits took them on tour in 1991. The Trackspot was introduced after the IBeam.

My first project was the Trackspot special analog controller. That was one of these things that was about half finished and I walked in and they said, "Here, finish this." There was a little drawing on a napkin and some software. Then I did the Universal Controller and right after that the Cyberlight was on the boards. I did the boot code for the Cyberlight, which was the first implementation of bi-directional communications on fixtures.[4] I did the fixture side and Brian Jurek did the Link card.

RB: That was Status Cue then.

TG: Cyberlight and Status Cue both rolled out in 1994. I also did the software that ran the console. Steve did the electronics design, and I wrote the software to make it all work. There were two processors in there: a Motorola 68331 that did the lion share of all the key sensing and all of that, and there was an 8031 that did the encoders.

RB: Then you were handing it to the PC on a serial bus or via the Link card?

TG: It was on the Link card.

Cyberlight

An interesting thing about the Cyberlight is that from day one, there was a full bi-directional protocol that let you do everything that talkback allows you to do now, and more. If you wanted to download the contents of the flash ROM, you could do that on a byte wise form. You can read any byte in memory or write any byte. We were also talking about group addressing at that time.[5]

RB: When Cyberlight first came out, did

---

[4] Bi-directional communication on a moving light is a touchy subject. Vari-Lite holds highly contested patents that protect that functionality. That aside, Tom and Brian Jurek must be given credit for being the first to use the full duplex-ability of RS485. DMX (or LWR protocol) uses a shield and two conductors. We often think of it as a broadcasting protocol that does not listen for a response. Cyberlight interleaved bi-directional commands and responses between normal show control commands to send messages back to the controller. This is the basis of RDM (Remote Device Management)

[5] Group addressing made use of the way fixture addressing of Cyberlight fixtures was specified in LWR protocol. The intent was to send one command to a group of fixtures, for instance group 1 go to red. Normal LWR protocol required the "go to red" command to be sent to each fixture individually. Group addressing would have lowered data link bandwidth requirements.

it support both Lightwave protocol and DMX?

TG: The first protocol that was supported was Lightwave Research and that is probably why all the clever bi-directional stuff never saw the light of day, other than for software uploads, because all of that runs in LWR protocol. About halfway through the design we made the big shift to DMX.

RB: That made my life a lot easier because we had to deal with different drivers to read LWR.

TG: The deal was, you could do your own protocol but then you are stuck with the situation where if people didn't like your control desk or they didn't like your fixtures, you didn't make a sale, whereas if you did an industry standard protocol and they didn't like your fixtures, but they liked your desk, they could buy your desk, and vice versa. It made more sense from a marketing and sales point of view to go to a standard protocol.[6]

RB: And you guys were figuring that out far before Vari-Lite did. I guess the Series 300 Smart Repeaters had DMX on them just about that time too.

TG: This was '93/'94.

RB: So they already had the VL5 out by then. But the DMX implementation right at the beginning wasn't phenomenal. It was all 8-bit and nowhere near as good as it is now. As far as I've heard, the DMX code and the Series 200 code in the Smart Repeaters were two completely different animals. We complained about historicism on the VL5's under DMX;[7] a problem, I understand, solved much earlier by the Artisan and Series 200 protocol group.

TG: Isn't it curious that we're in an industry where communication is paramount and nobody communicates?

RB: I know – even when people are working in the same company. It's really rather frightening. Around the same time you were making the shift, Martin was making changes too. It was a lovely time for us because it made it so much easier when everybody talked the same language. Martin's first fixtures used DMX, but they changed the polarity. We used to have to have all these silly adapters around – not just 5-pin to 3-pin for your stuff, but the same with a polarity swap for the Martin gear.

---

[6] See Steve Terry's wish – Pearlman – page 64 and Cunningham – page 97

[7] The problem with a VL5's control system was that if you wanted to hit a spot on stage, you would get differing results if you came from one direction as opposed to from the other, even though the final output values were identical.

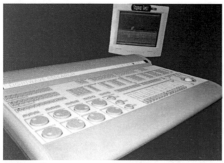

Status Cue.

You guys didn't do crossfades; you used the fixture's internal mSpeeds. The Status Cue originally didn't have a fade engine until you tried to market it more widely.

TG: The Status Cue was originally a Cyberlight controller, then it was generalized to be a DMX controller. That explains the layout of all the buttons and the number of wheels.

RB: With WYG 1 and 2 we didn't even try to build a state machine to deal with mSpeeds internally.[8] As time went on, more and more people started implementing internal fixture timing, or mSpeed as it became to be known. Mirror Speed – Motor Speed?

TG: I'm not quite sure which one is the correct one. Steve Tulk or Lary Cotten was the one who coined the term. The idea was that it was easier and quicker to do the calculations if you knew the start point and end point and how fast you wanted to get there. With a tracking algorithm you're constantly calculating and updating the motor data. In retrospect, you still have to do that every time a target changes or a mSpeed value changes. We've always thought that given the time, do we go back and implement a tracking algorithm? But it's interesting that in eight years now we've never really had a hole in time in when we could go back and implement a good tracking algorithm to put in all fixtures. I guess for expediency of time, we just stayed with mSpeed.

Currently, Studio Beam has a flat protocol that the Pig boys requested because, like you, all our modal channels drove them nuts. One of the things they asked us to drop was the mSpeed channel. So there is a protocol in Studio Beam that does not support mSpeed. However, I've never had the time to go back in put in the proper tracking algorithm.

RB: When you look at the mSpeed table you see the logarithmic scale that gives more weight to the lower speeds, but the very bottoms says "Fastest" and at the top it may say "Tracking". Most of us set it up so that is does

---

[8] The original WYSIWYG libraries had no idea of motor speed. If an attribute channel jumped from 10 degrees to 120 degrees, we would just draw the beam in its new position, ignoring the displacement. This was obviously a problem, especially with controllers that used mSpeed where there were no crossfades on the data line.

Tom, Scott Ingham and Brad Bierschenk (left to right).
Scott is responsible for a lot of electronics and embedded software that has come out of HES since 1992. Trackspot,Cyberlight (software), Studio Color 575, Studio Spot 575, x.Spot, the Catalyst orbital head and he started the DL-1 fixture. He also had a hand in the second Color Pro fixture: 'Mr. Motor'. Tom and Scott differed a bit on the philosophical side. Scott's view was that all control should be in the console. Tom was not timid when putting tricks into the fixtures.
Brad was with HES for a couple of years and worked with Scott on some of the aspects of x.Spot. Brad also worked on the recently released Color Merge, Color Command and Color Power products.

tracking and use console timing, but if it doesn't look smooth enough, we'll bring it down a notch or two to help smooth things out. Before the Hog's Effects Engine, that is the trick we would used to do. We would build a ballyhoo using four end points with hard step times between them, and then bring down the mSpeed to round out the corners. But if you're not doing that – what is the difference between Fastest and Tracking?

TG: None. It's doing exactly the same thing. We do cram some default speed in there but that's as close as we've come to implementing a true tracking algorithm. A proper tracking algorithm would have a history of the rate of change of the DMX values then make a guess as to what the operator actually

Studio Beam.

means with the next change in the DMX value. How much time has occurred since the last change and if the time is getting longer you can pretty well guess that we're slowing the movement down, or if it's ramping up we're getting faster.

RB: That would only be useful with clever profiles on the fades the console is outputting – like the Hog's Brake or Ramp profiles. If the console is just doing a linear crossfade, the samples in the 50th percentile will produce the same results as the ones in the 99th percentile, right?

TG: Yes.

RB: What you are saying is that you are basically over-sampling at every step along the way.

TG: Yes. In the published mSpeed table, at the very quickest you will see times of 0.15 seconds or some very, very quick times, and those may not be achievable by the motors in the fixtures. There is some range that is particular to each fixture and the processing in each fixture. The motor can't move that fast, so it will just move as fast as it can. Even if you dial in 0.15 seconds, it may take it half-a-second to get there, just because it doesn't have the required acceleration or velocity to do that move. So it says, "I give up, I'm just going to go as fast as I can". Writing a proper tracking algorithm is not trivial.

RB: So who does it?

TG: I'm not totally sure, but I think Vari-Lite does it and so does Martin. We just drove a stake in the sand and said here's how we're doing it and at some point in the future if demand becomes overwhelming or we get time, we'll do it. There are so many things to get done in the course of a day that we just haven't got around to it.

RB: The objective is to get them to move. And on that subject, nothing moves as quickly as the Intellabeam did.

TG: We get a lot of that. The mirror was smaller (it was almost Trackspot size) and there was a lot of processing power there and it was able to do that.

A lot of the ability to make very fast movements is based upon how quickly the main loop can make it around to service the motor given that you are processing each motor in a sequential fashion. If you can visit a motor two hundred times a second that sets your top speed or if you can process the motor a thousand times a second you can obviously go faster because you don't have to tell the motors to make quite as large a step. You can give it a lot of small incremental steps and get it to go faster.

RB: On the average stepper motor that we're all used to, how many steps would be in a revolution?

TG: Two hundred.

RB: And nearing the threshold of processing time, would you have to leave a motor and tell it to go ten steps? I clearly don't understand driving motors at this low level.

TG: You have to tell it to do each step individually; you can't tell it to go ten steps because it doesn't know that. It's going to go step by step by step and you have to walk it through each one.

RB: So it's just like you're hitting a button and it nudges it a step each time. So what happens in the worst-case scenario where all motors are moving, the code is un-optimized and the process is particularly poky today? What if cue timing suggest that on each go round that you need to go a number of ticks? Where does the actual aliasing come into play?

TG: I can only speak about our software. Each motor is serviced in a sequential fashion, and depending upon the electronics architecture, you may have to do the calculation for a motor and run it out, do the calculation for the next motor and run it out. Or, if your hardware is setup to handle four motors at a time, then you do the calculations for four motors and run them out. Every time you do an operation, it consumes clock cycles so if you can do things in parallel, you've increased your efficiency cycle.[9]

RB: So what's the average processor that's in a High End fixture?

TG: We like the Motorola stuff. You will see a lot of 68331's and 68332's.

RB: And those things are responsible for receiving DMX and servicing the motors?

---

[9] See Hunt on parallel processing techniques on page 236

TG: Yes, we do single processor implementations. It's the serial interrupt that's processing the DMX that consumes the lion share of the time. You have a packet coming every 44 ms in the worst case and you have to go out, get the data and then put it somewhere. So that might take 13 to 20 ms to do then you have the next slice of time left over to do something meaningful, then you get the next byte of data. So the serial interrupts is where a lot of time is spent.

RB: This spawned a big debate between CAST and FPS when Nils Thorjussen was trying to reduce the cost of WYSIWYG. With WYSIWYG Version 1 we had a board made by Pthalo Systems with a number or processors on it and 4 UARTs that nicely dumped 2048 bytes of DMX data into dual ported DMA[10] memory for us to go get at our leisure. We didn't have to worry about interrupts.

TG: Well, you had to move motors.

RB: Yes, true (in a way). We had to draw beams.

TG: Bits don't weigh anything.

RB: So Nils had Nick Archdale make an inexpensive DMX reception board that was interrupt based and we had to write the 86 instruction interrupt code. Although we saved a whack of cash on not having to buy the Pthalo card, we took about a 13% hit on the 166 MHz processor. The real headache for Rick Szijarto was that we were using Extended DOS so he had to handle the switching between Real Mode and Protected Mode. I believe the switching itself took a substantial amount of time. It wasn't pretty, but it made the product a lot cheaper to produce. It took a fair amount of work. Tom Thorne and Nick kept saying, "Don't worry – it's trivial". Yes, it's trivial to produce DMX, but to receive it reliably from different manufacture's transmitters is not.

TG: That's typical of managerial-type people. Oh, that's software. You'll have that done real quick!

RB: So… you did the face panel in Status Cue and Cyberlight, then from there you starting doing all this wacky code in these other fixtures.

TG: Technobeam was the next one, then Studio 250 (Spot and Wash), then Studio Beam, which was the last fixture I did.

RB: You didn't do the 575 series?

TG: No, Scott Ingham did those.

---

[10] Direct Memory Access

RB: Funny, it seems to the outside world that those things were so close in characteristics that you could use the same code. Seeing I've reversed engineered your code to build libraries, I know differently.

TG: Truth be known, a lot of the algorithms came out of Cyberlight, which Scott wrote, then I took his code and perverted it to run in Technobeam then further perverted it to run in Studio 250's and then again to run in Studio Beam. So you will probably see a

Studio 250

branch where Studio 575 goes one way and Technobeam goes the other way.

RB: This is where you and I started having fun. You started to conceive and write all these clever macros that make programming moving lights a lot easier, but made simulating them in WYSIWYG a lot more difficult.

TG: But you like a good challenge, don't you Robert!

RB: It was fun. We certainly learned a lot and you pushed us to change the way we did a great many things. If it wasn't for your clever stuff, we could have continued to use the WYG 1 library format. Pulsing iris, mSpeed tables and other things like that made us completely re-think the way we were going to model things and we needed a much more versatile library format.

A Technobeam will do so much more than a Trackspot did, but was it just the gain from the advancement of technology, or was it more market pull to make it easier to program the lights?

TG: If you were to actually look at the

Technobeam

code, you would see that in a way Cyberlight started down this path. When I started doing Technobeam, the request was made to consider the guys at the low-end of the chain; the guys that were using analog desks. Technobeam was (I know Richard Belliveau will roll over in his grave here, although he's not dead!) more for discos and these types of guys with less powerful control desks and we wanted to make it as easy on them to get a lot of different looks very easily.

The idea was to have one channel that you could slide back and forth very easily on an analog desk to get a mode, then use the channel right next to it to vary that mode.

RB: I would probably appreciate it a lot more if I actually did it on a slider desk. My problem was that I was always using a Hog.

TG: There was some debate as to what level we made these things functional. Do you make it functional for those guys who have really powerful digital desk or do you also make it very attractive and usable for the guys at the low-end of the market with an analog desk? The decision was made to make it attractive to a wide number of people rather than trying to exclude those that only had analog desks. Once again, it is one of those time things. Given sufficient time we would have probably done a set of protocols for strictly digital control. That is one thing that is still tossed around. At what point in the evolution of control systems do we say we don't care anymore about the small desk?

RB: The x.Spot could hardly be done on an analog desk – but then again – there is price differentiation there.[11]

I remember one of the first moving light shows I worked on at CBC. We were trying to control 8-bit Summa HTI's using vector positioning and mSpeed on a Strand Impact preset desk. It was all slider HTP stuff and a ridiculous method of controlling moving lights. We quickly moved to a Compulite Animator and life was much better after that.

TG: It is well known - the guys here on the Hog Farm requested that we stopped doing the internal macros.

RB: I was also in that camp pushing with them; trying to design a generic descriptive language to emulate all these things was very challenging. We're all better off for it now.

---

[11] The x.Spot uses 38 control channels.

So after Studio Beam, did you start on Handshake? This was really your pet project – you wanted to get into Palm software?

TG: I had acquired a number of Technobeams and there they were at the house and I have too many gadgets already. I didn't want a control desk sitting on the same desk with two computers and there wasn't any room. High End had wanted to do a hand-held application as far back as 1996. Lary Cotten had looked at using a Newton with the Apple port, which was already RS485.[12] There didn't seem to be as large an installed user base with the Newton to justify doing it. Then I was sitting around at the house and I thought "Wouldn't it be nice…" That's when I started to look at how to do it.

RB: And you thought of doing that rather than doing it on a PC directly?

TG: I wanted something that was right in my hand and I could take almost anywhere and use it because it would also be useful as a tool for technicians. That, and the fact that I really don't like Windows. I don't know how to add enough exclamation points and underlines on a piece of audiotape to tell you I don't like Windows. I'm an Amiga fan.

RB: I asked Tom Thorne if he liked Bill Gates and he said he was quite happy that every version of Hog I that went out had a version of MS DOS on it.

TG: The Palm Pilot thing seemed like a challenging project and I like a challenge to do something new and different on a platform that hadn't been used before in this fashion. I drew up the proposal and gave it to the guys at High End and it really didn't go anywhere until we did EC2.

RB: …when they got fed up of the water damage to the switches on the EC1's. The EC2 had no user interface.

TG: Right, and they needed some way to address it. Once again, setting start channels is the killer app in so many respects. So, how do you set the start channel on a fixture that has no buttons?

RB: And I was thrown deep into the water with that problem – literally – in a fountain at a casino I was programming. But that's exactly where you find these EC2's.

What was the development platform? Were you on a Windows machine developing code for the Palm?

TG: Yes. I used Metrowerks. In many ways I've very happy with what

---

[12] DMX uses RS485.

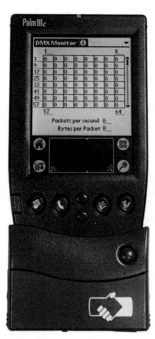

Handshake.

Metrowerks has done with their IDE.[13] I've looked at some of the other compilers and documentation and that just wasn't what it should have been. And because of my daytime job, I didn't have time at night-time to figure out all these little abstract details.

RB: So you did a lot of the code development on Handshake at home, not necessarily on 'company' time?

TG: . . . just to get it out on time. I was writing software for both the hand-held and the module so I would do it both the daytime and at night.

RB: That seems a little above the call of duty. Does High End give royalties out to employees?

TG: No, it's just the way I am.[14] It was a challenge and I like challenges and I was very keen on doing it. I'm single, no dependants, no plants, no pets. So I don't have all these other things to do, so this is what I do. I bit bang. I'm well motivated in that regard.

RB: How far into it did you get before you had to make that custom module that goes on the end?

TG: I was probably about four or five months into it before I had to have that. At some point you actually have to talk to the fixtures and the serial ports on the hand-held don't speak DMX compatible baud rates so you have to have some baud rate converter. At that point the handhelds didn't have enough horsepower to do the crossfading of 512 channels and do all the normal operating systems things that they would do. There was an immediate need to have that, but it took me about four months to get to the point that I actually needed it.

RB: So what comes out the bottom of a Palm?

TG: RS232 at PC standard baud rates. Not very similar to DMX.

---

[13] Integrated Development Environment – the editor, compiler and debugger built into one.

[14] See Cunningham on a whole different philosophy – page 94

RB: So what's inside your module?

TG: Two serial interfaces, one running at 115.2 K baud to talk to the hand-held and another at 250 K baud to talk to the fixtures. There are actually three oscillators in there, one to generate the PC baud rates, one that runs the micro controller at a system clock speed that will easily scale down to DMX baud rates, and the third is the 32.768 K Hz for the time of day clock. That's the standard watch crystal that's used all over the world.

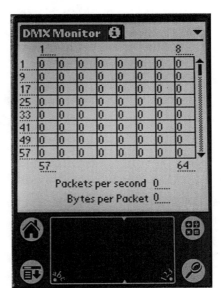

Handshake screen shot.

RB: I forgot that there was that in there. Clever little box. I remember when you first showed it to me. Now everybody and his brother are doing it. There is a bunch on iPac's too.

So you do all the crossfades in there?

TG: Yes, it can crossfade all 512 channels 44 times a second.

RB: You don't suggest a rate of 44 times a second do you?[15]

TG: It's user settable from 1 Hz to 44 Hz.

RB: Now did you have to convince 3Com or whoever was OEM that the cute little shell that attaches itself to the Palm that you were building a viable product?

TG: Palm made these available to any developer that wanted to use them as long as you were not using the case to do a modem. They didn't want you doing a modem that would compete with their modem. There is another

---

[15] Like I've said before, it's trivial to produce DMX, but it's quite another thing to receive it. When producing DMX, you choose the refresh rate and go along at your own pace. When you receive DMX, you have to receive the whole spectrum. The standard's tolerances are quite wide and many people can claim they are producing valid DMX, but it can be a radically different flavor to the manufacturer down the street. Being on the receiving end, you have to prepare for all possibilities. A general rule of thumb has been to never send at the top end, which is 44 Hz because many people could never receive it reliably.

company that used this same case that makes a nice digital acquisition system to measure voltage and current levels.

RB: And I've seen one that is a camera.

TG: Kodak did one.

RB: So this is just a tiny two layer board you stuff inside of this thing?

TG: It's four layers, but it's very thin. Palm specifies that thickness so it fits in the case properly. They specify the location of the connectors; the button and power jack so everything fits properly.

RB: What is the processor you used?

TG: A Motorola M-Core RISC processor running at 32 MHz. Metrowerks makes a tool to code it up as does Wind River.

RB: The Handshake has a very specific application, especially with the EC2's because an EC2 doesn't much work without one. But now it works with the whole product line. Can you go back as far as the Cyberlight and upload firmware to the fixture?

TG: It can't upload code to a Cyberlight at this point, but that is only software. There is no physical reason we can't because Cyberlight runs on RS485 at 250 K baud because that's what the LWR protocol ran on. That's why it was so easy for us to change Cyberlight to DMX because we didn't have to change anything electrical or electronic.

RB: So now everybody is using handhelds, be it Palms or iPacs, as DMX tools or RFU's. That's just evolution. I don't know if the war between Palm and Windows CE is going to be the same as Beta vs. VHS. I'm not sure if there is going to be a winner or a loser in this one. I would think it will depend on the development tools. That was always the failing of Macs (until very recently).

Horizon's iPac RFU took us through a two-week development cycle from conception to prototype. If anybody wants an RFU on an iPac, they just use 802.11b and Bob's your uncle. MA Lighting has really nice RFU for grandMA. Horizon has one, ETC has one, Strand has one.

We wanted to do a version of WYSIPAPER on Windows CE years ago, but CE had such a bad name for so long that we didn't think there was a market for it.

TG: That was an interesting choice of name Microsoft picked – Wince.

RB: I guess that's why they call it Pocket PC now.

TG: Yes. There is also XP Embedded now.

RB: Yes, and all the new consoles are running XP Embedded. It's my job to target the OS for our products. Talk about getting intimate with Windows!

It's a shame if you live in a world where you hate Windows. Since Windows 2000 I have been a lot less grumpy. Developing an Extended DOS application with a Windows based IDE with the Watcom compiler using Thinnet to network two Windows 3.11 machines (one of them a 486) was enough to drive me round the bend. The number of times we would have to re-boot during the day was unbelievable. Then debugging over a parallel port link. Talk about slow.

TG: Have we gotten to the bash Bill Gates portion of the interview?

RB: But didn't all your IDE's for these microprocessors work under Windows?

TG: They're DOS based. That's part of the situation that faces hardware developers these days; all of our tools are Windows based or DOS based. We've been using the Sierra stuff for some time now – you know the people that used to make the games. Since we've been using the 68331 and the 68332 and the 68340, these are all 68K things that compile under the same Sierra software. Of late we've been using Metrowerks stuff. I know Greenhill also makes some good embedded tools as does Wind River.

RB: For the uninitiated, on the 68K stuff, are you writing in C?

TG: Yes.

RB: So what's the balance between assembler and C code in the products? When you did the Links card, was it C based? Are the boot straps C?

TG: By and large we like to use C because it allows for very quick development relative to assembly language. Sometimes it comes to the point where you're just not getting the performance out of the C. Serial interrupts are a good case in point where you need good fast stuff. Anything we do that is not 8031 based, we'll typically write in C. There are C compilers for 8031 micro controllers; however, we remain dubious of the efficiency of the code written that way. In the 68K and higher world of powered processors, if we're getting the performance out of the C code that is acceptable to the project at hand, we'll stay with the C code. If the performance starts to lag, C is nice in that you can write the same algorithms in about fifteen or thirty different ways using different types of syntax. Sometimes you might use global variables versus local variables or drop back and start using pointers and whatnot. There are a number of different ways that you can accomplish the same general task.

You start to write it one way then the typical C compiler will translate C to assembly language then assemble the assembly language. So you can look at the output of the compiler at the assembler level and judge whether or not it looks efficient. Then you go and write your C a slightly different way and recompile to gauge the efficiency of the compiled output. Rather than first time you run into an efficiency problem dropping straight into assembly language, you can try some rewrites in C and typically reach some satisfactory solutions. The idea is that if you stay at the C level, the code is more portable and it's easier to maintain if somebody comes behind you and has to read your software.[16]

So the very low level start-up code, right after the processor comes out of reset, will be hand written assembly code that sets up all the various registers, then we drop into C and we stay there until we just don't get the efficiency of execution that we need.

RB: When in the development cycle of a product do you say, "We just can't do it with this chip, we need a faster one?" Then you have to bash it out with the powers that be in management or the guys who did the board layout.

TG: To date we really haven't had to do that. We've got very satisfactory performance out of the processors we chose at the start. We maybe went through a little bit of that when we started using the Motorola stuff. We would debate on how are we going to justify buying an eight or ten dollar processor when we could be buying a three or four dollar processor. That becomes easy to justify if it's only going to take you eight months to write the code instead of twelve months. There you can see the immediate cost savings. How much does it cost for a software developer? They cost a lot of money. Not only their salary, but the place they sit, the building they sit in, their insurance. You factor all those things in as well as time to market. It's sometimes very easy to justify buying a more powerful processor if you're only talking two times or two-and-a-half times the cost. Now if you're talking about using something that cost one hundred times the cost then you really have to bend over backwards to justify that one. By and large, the micro controllers we've chosen

---

[16] See Wayne Howell on working in C versus Assembler versus Machine Code page 335

have been up to the task.[17]

RB: How do you know when they're not? Does the light just crash or do you have an idle loop that you monitor to see how long the processor is just hanging out?

TG: Gas gauge. You put a gas gauge in the code.

RB: In Windows I can either watch the resource monitor or the task monitor or write a little text file showing interrupt times. How do you do it on an embedded system?

TG: There are variables in the code that track this and we just break execution and look at the value of the variable. We write the code and try to squeeze as fast a main loop time out of it as possible and make the motor code as efficient as possible. Once you have something that is usable, you put it into somebody's hands and ask them if it meets their requirements; do they have any problems with the way it is doing things? By and large, everybody has been happy with what we've done. There have been one or two occasions were we've had to go back in and make things faster. Typically it didn't take too much work - just squeeze out one or two more clock cycles.

RB: You can talk to any user and they will tell you stories about how any (and every) console has its crashes. Even Palm Pilot software crashes. I've had my quirks and my problems with front-end displays on your fixtures, but I don't think I've ever seen a light crash. With this sort of code, does it crash?

TG: It's easy to run into a situation where it gets hung up in some loop and just parks there too long. We use watchdog timers in all of our circuitry. It's either internal to the part we're using or we put something in an external circuit just for the odd chance that it does happen and you don't want it to go off on a tangent and execute in some unknown place. A lot of our products have fans and we control the fan speed, which means we're modulating that fan on some port and you don't want to park a fan in the off position and melt down a lamp. So we employ watchdog timers so if you see a crash the fixture will home. So, if it's homed unexpectedly, it's had a crash.

RB: Oh, so maybe I have seen fixture code crash, because I have certainly seen some 'unexplained' homing. I would have always, rightly or wrongly, contributed that to power or data issues.

---

[17] See Hunt on over-rated processors page 235 on how to bend under-rated processors to perform for you

High End Systems' C16.

Now your new fixture, the C16, will recalibrate itself every time colour wheel passes the optical sensor?

TG: Yes. It's not that we haven't wanted to do it in the past, it's just that we've never got around to it. We were aware of it and it just hasn't been an issue.

RB: Well, for an architectural fixture that will be on many, many hours a day without operator intervention, this makes a lot of sense. And knocking off this one that only has one parameter must have been an easy start. You may have more fun with x.Spot with 32 different sensors.

TG: x.Spot is unique in that you can tell specific things in it to home so you don't have to go through a complete homing process. That's another one of the things that we've always wanted to do, but we've finally taken the time and done it.

RB: It's a wonderful sound when you get a whole rig to home all at once.

TG: First time I heard a whole rig of Cyberlights home (I think it was in rehearsals just before ZZ Top went out) I thought it sounded like a flock of geese.

RB: From an operator's point of view it's very satisfying. It's just like changing your underwear. You feel you're once again on ground zero and if someone pisses you off again, you just call a tech.

The radio conversation is always the same. "Cyber 15's cyan flag is stuck." "Can you home it." "I've already homed it a couple times. It's not coming back. You better get out the lift." "<groan>".

What's this thing I now hear salesmen talk about – 3-phase stepper motors versus 2-phase stepper motors?

TG: Most of the stepper motors used in lights have two sets of windings and they are 90 degrees apart. Three phase motors have three windings that are 120 degrees apart, which does several things for you. It will get you more torque that will typically relate to more speed or more acceleration, and you also generally get smoother motion.

RB: Which of your products use them?

TG: Studio 250, Studio Beam, the later 575 series and x.Spots use them on pan and tilt.

RB: From a driver code position, is it any more complex or taxing?

TG: It's just a different way of doing things. You're basically driving a wire. You impress a voltage on a wire to induce a current which will give you torque which gives you acceleration and velocity. It's just the same with 3-phase stuff, it's just more wires. Well, actually you have one less wire because the ones we use are Y-wound, three wires going in that share a common centre tap.

RB: Now were you joking when you told me that you wrote code for pinball machines and slot machines?

TG: I was saying that's how I could spend my retirement! There will be life after High End. By that time I will be able to supercharge your toaster because by then there will be a micro controller in them.

RB: I was just in a grocery store and I saw 'pre-cooked bacon'. There's really not much time left.

TG: A lot of cars nowadays have 20-30-40 micro controllers in them all running on a serial data bus. The world is full of micro controllers that people never see and are totally unaware of.

RB: Strange if you write code for those. We write Windows code and I can tell you how many machines it's installed on. You're stuff sure has beaten us in the counting by a factor of 100 at this point, but think of those car and toaster guys' stuff.

I have first hand contact with my users, especially at trade shows and via e-mail. People call me up and ask for features or bug fixes or whatever. You probably do not have the same sort of experiences as GUI developers like myself or like the Pig boys do because, as with the consumers of toasters, many lighting techs don't pay a great deal of attention to the finer bits of code you develop for inside the fixtures.

TG: You'll get me in trouble now. This is a bone of contention that I have had with some. I don't particularly get the interface with the end user that I think

I should. Typically a lot of that is filtered back through salesmen or marketing people or service technicians. That is one reason why I'm always very happy to go to a trade show. I can then actually stand in front of somebody face to face, be it good or bad. Sometimes they pat you on the back and other times they kick you in the balls.

RB: I've done both to you.

TG: I think it is a very necessary thing that if you're developing software/ hardware for people to use; you definitely have to be aware of what they want. The sooner you're aware of that and the more feedback you get about that the better. That is something I try to point out to people higher up in the food chain. We could possibly make our products better and more efficient if we have more access to the end user. We've started an engineering feedback forum on our website so users can send us love mail or hate mail.

RB: Even if you don't respond to the e-mail, it's good to read it. I often find when talking to executives that a point can be made to them ten times, but if they hear it in the right context, they can make a major shift in policy on one user's comments.

To your tribute, I have generally had little problem with fixture code and I was much, much closer to it than the vast majority of users because of the library work we were doing. The typical user is much more worried about the front end. The fixtures are always assumed to do what they are supposed to do. (Mechanical problems on fixtures are a different topic.) Why do you think that is? Is it less lines of code, less user interface? I mean, generally, apart from the odd firmware update, you guys write pretty tight and robust code.

TG: I wish we had time to do a heck of a lot more testing. I wish we had the financial resources to bring in a lot more prototypes and allow for larger sample space for doing the testing. But I think statistically we do a fair job. Our products work out of the box. We've been responsive to fix problems quickly. In many respects, things are infinitely complex and you can only test a small subset of that infinite space. It's very easy to account for the fact that something just got missed. Unfortunately, on an initial release that may leave a bad taste in the mouth of a customer and you may have to fight to get them back again. We try to relay that to the ones higher up the food chain. If you give us more time, you get better products and everybody has a good taste in their mouth and ultimately you sell more products. There is the other side of things in that you have to start selling things to bring in money to write pay cheques. You try to hit a good balance. It would be nice to hold something for five years and then you get a nice rock solid product, but then you would never sell anything.

RB: That only happens if you work for NASA. Keep delaying the launch. Until the Russians try to put something in space before you, then you're damned. It doesn't matter if somebody dies – get it up there.

Let's talk about new protocols – RDM and how High End has really been involved in that for such a long time.

TG: We read the DMX512 1990 spec and it said RS485. To me RS485 is a multi-drop bi-directional, multi-transmitter, multi-receiver specification. Why on earth would you propose to use this if you didn't use it to its fullest? Everybody at High End shares this point of view.

When we started doing Cyberlight, we said we're doing DMX; here's the spec and it's bi-directional. Pins 4 and 5 were not well specified. There was no distinction that 2 and 3 are out and 4 and 5 are back and there are a large number of transceivers out there that are going in both directions. At that time, there was a large installed base of 3-wire cable and today there is an even larger base of 3-wire cable.

So now I sit in the ESTA Control Protocols Working Group and I'm on the RDM Task Group and we're working together to bash this thing out. ACN is something that is coming and we're trying to figure out how to make RDM and ACN work together. RDM is something we can use now. There are a lot of fixtures out there now that with nothing more than software upgrades could do RDM.[18]

RB: The pre-qualifier is having a transceiver versus just a receiver.

TG: And the ability to control the transceiver. They can't have hardwired the transmit enable pin; it must be under micro controller control. It may also be easy for them to rev. the board using the transceiver on board if they have to. RDM will allow ACN to bring fixture feedback and remote control rather than have someone climb on a rig. Some people say you may be putting me out of a job because that's the job I do. "I climb on rigs." My point of view is that I don't want people climbing on rigs. That's dangerous. It's time consuming. It's costly. There's no reason for them to be there. We can do this electronically. To all those people that feel their job is threatened, I apologize, but I would suggest they learn a new skill set.

---

[18] See Howell page 339 on his thoughts of RDM versus ACN

The abstract Device Description Language that ACN is proposing does cause some animosity between the RDM group and the ACN group because high volume products cannot afford the processors needed to deal with the amount of data they want to throw at them. There is a move afoot in the CPWG to deal with the issue of an RDM/ACN gateway. In some respects it's adversarial, but I don't see the need for that. I think that it should be a piece of co-existence and trying to figure out how to make this thing work together, because you will only make the industry better by doing it this way. That's a lesson we learned at High End Systems when we were doing LWR. If they like your fixture but they don't like your controller, then you don't have a sale. If you use a standard protocol, you'll sell some fixtures. It's the same thing with ACN and RDM. If you make it an either/or situation, you are going to lose sales. If you make it a happy coexistence of both situations, then everybody profits.

10 ERIC CORNWELL

Introduction

Richard Pilbrow first put me in touch with Eric, as he was fond of Virtual Light Lab. Since then, Eric and I always share a laugh or two at trade shows. As he explains here, he hasn't changed Virtual Light Lab in years, whereas we were coming out with different versions of software bi-annually. He's doesn't aspire to be a software giant. He likes the small stuff. Simple is better in his mind.

Eric's heart is in lighting design. He does his own Off-Broadway shows and assists on bigger shows. The first software project that really got him noticed was Express-Track, which he wrote when assisting Richard Nelson on *Into The Woods*. Today, with the power of computing, what they were doing then seems incredible. Express-Track shared exactly the same syntax as the Light Palette, the console they were using at the time, and a second operator worked in parallel with the main console operator, typing in, key-for-key, the same stuff. And this was all in an effort to satisfy the designer's desire for more information on the screen – more than the console offered natively.

His other big product is Virtual Light Lab. This is a very simple application that models a small black-box light lab. It has

a virtual lighting grid that allows you to place a limited number of fixtures in very specific locations and light a sphere.[1] It shows you how different colours of light will mix when they hit an object at different angles. It doesn't do shadows or textures or bump-mapping. You can't change the model or add specific manufacturer's lights. It's simple and he makes no apologies for that.

I remember a funny incident at USITT Toronto in 1999. Eric and I were sharing the stage showing students how you could visualize things on a computer. This was only a few years ago, but things like WYSIWYG were relatively unheard of, at least in the mass market. I knew Eric's thing was simple and WYSIWYG was a far larger piece of software by that time. We could draw anything; place humanoid models; hang any manufacture's lights (with proper photometrics) in any location; add any manufacturer's colour and projects shadows. It really looked pretty good – even way back then. Luckily, Eric went first and people were rightfully impressed with his creation.

While I was sitting, watching him demo on the big screen, my laptop was fired up and I was doodling around with my drawing. As a software developer, one of the most frightening things is demoing a product on a big screen in front of an audience. You always want to show the latest toys and you're always desperately worried that it might crash. Remember when Bill Gates was showing Windows 98 at Comdex '98? Somebody plugged in a USB scanner, which was supposed to be 'plug and play' and the whole thing crashed. I've been there and it's not fun.

For ages we were plagued with a bug in WYSIWYG where lights would randomly hit some objects, but completely ignore others. I thought I could get around it, but while we were there on stage, I noticed that my cyc was completely dark when my front lights hit it. I gasped. The last thing I wanted to do was make apologies. The crowd was big and this was my home town.

Then, out of the blue, it all came together in my head. When I built the library objects for WYSIWYG, surfaces were drawn using the left-hand-rule. The rule states that you draw all your faces, so that the vertices follow a clock-wise pattern. This makes rendering twice as fast because you never consider the inside surfaces when you build the list of objects that lights can shine on. My cyc was drawn by drawing a line and using the Extrude tool to give it height. The extruding code had a bug – it didn't follow the rule exactly as intended. Just seconds before Eric handed the VGA cable for the projector

---

[1] The non-demo version also allows you to project onto a cluster of geometric shapes or a pre-defined simplistic set as well.

on to me, I managed to rotate my cyc 180 degrees and voilà, front light on the cyc.

Eric had never seen a good demo of WYSIWYG. He admitted to me that he had no idea it could do all it did. Sheepishly, I never admitted my shortcomings.

Eric invited me to his Manhattan apartment to conduct this interview. I was most impressed when I saw a kit-built Theremin. He was impressed I knew what it was. In Led Zeppelin's *Whole Lotta Love*, Jimmy Page does a wonderful Theremin solo. I was also impressed with the do-hicky he had that you could talk to turn on and dim the lights. Something a little more advanced than the clapper.

Interview

RB: What have you been up to?

EC: My current project, six months after it was announced, is making its way out of the door. It's an interface between a cordless telephone and a control board.

RB: Yes, you did a short demo for me at a show?

EC: Right! So that's finally actually getting done. But it came from the realization that you actually make more money from software if you put it in a box than if you just put it on a disk. It's turned into a nightmare of box development, but it's been fun and educational. The concept for the code and the algorithm for equating twelve buttons on a keypad to a couple dozen console commands was quite a mental exercise. And once I'd done that, I basically had a software product, but if I had a way of distributing it, what would anybody pay for it? You actually needed a piece of hardware you could physically "plug into something" that makes it more valuable.

RB: And that's the problem we have with Horizon. Obviously it won't create DMX until you have hardware,[2] but for ages they said: "The software is free, the software is free." And I said, coming in as the product manger, that doesn't sell. Don't tell them the software is free. Tell them, here's our console, here's our device, here's "the box". "Oh, would you like to use the off-line editor?" You can download the off-line editor from our website. Don't ever use the word software and free in the same sentence.

We fought that forever with WYSIWYG. Back in '94, there weren't many

---

[2] During the time of this interview, we started work on Marquee, but Eric didn't know that.

significant high-end software applications in our market. There were your products and Lightwright and a couple of other CAD applications, but generally we were trying to sell to rental companies software; and we were trying to sell it for five or six thousand dollars and nobody liked that because it came on a floppy disk.

But what we did have was this thing that Sean Adkins of Pthalo Systems made - a DMX interface card. It was a full length ISA but card with a whole bunch of glue[3] on it. Then we did WYSIWYG v2 with the MIDI stuff on it and we actually reduced it down to a half slot ISA card with just a couple of UARTS and sold it for the same price. Customers were saying: "I want the big one".

EC: That's true.

RB: So you actually had to put this thing in a box before anyone would take it seriously?

EC: Yes, and I actually had to put it in a bigger box than it used to be, because I said to myself, if I'm paying $750 for something I want something fairly tangible . . . you know. Not a box that will fit in my pocket.

The subject of perceived value is interesting. And software has always had that problem. If you listed software that's been around since the early 90's, there's been a lot of it that's come and gone. I mean, Rosco used to have a whole line of software. However, that's another discussion - interesting things that somehow never made it. Maybe they were a little before their time, or ineffectively managed or marketed. I don't know.

RB: Software takes so much to support. You need a dedicated sales team with proper product managers, not just a catalogue sales company I think Rosco has it together now.

EC: Remember there was a time where Strand was selling software.

RB: The GSX line.[4]

EC: Yes, I don't know if they're still doing that, but it was a huge flop here.

RB: Yes, but I think they're much more successful with the way they're doing things now. They develop one line of software, tested and marketed in the big

---

[3] Glue is a term used to describe all the electronic bits that tie the main processor to the bus. Resistors, capacitors, chokes, buffers, etc.. The card looked very substantial.

[4] Released in 1993

550s and 520s, and then to make a cheaper version, they had to build a different box. It's exactly the same software!

EC: Which is great. It's the same thing ETC is doing with the Expression, Express and Insight line of consoles. Thank goodness it's all integrated now – you just buy the size of box you want. But there's just this fundamental limit for how much somebody is going to pay for a disk. Nobody has really succeeded marketing-wise (except maybe you guys with WYSIWYG) in selling a capability. People are willing to pay for capabilities. People are willing to pay for a wiggle light programmer on a daily basis and they don't even come with a disk. But, to pay for some software, which they can use for years and save however much time or enable them to do stuff they couldn't do before, nobody has been able to find a way of presenting that.

RB: Or…maintenance on it. People are quite happy investing money to keep their car going but it's so hard to try and sell a maintenance package for software in our industry. Huge companies that use CAD applications for the automotive and aerospace industry buy maintenance contracts and they don't think twice about it. Or technical support - not a problem. Big companies will pay for it. Why, in our industry, do people expect tech support for free? And they absolutely expect software updates for free.

EC: Well, it's hard to explain. It's weird. Obviously everybody knows what software is now. When the initial memory boards came out nobody knew what was going on. The idea of even separating the software from the hardware was unimaginable. But now you can buy a PC and you can buy a piece of software to put in it. It's influenced by so much consumer software out there that's so inexpensive and for the most part, pretty robust. It certainly has a lot more development dollars behind it than anybody in this industry can afford to invest. And that becomes the standard by which we're automatically compared.[5] Until you can bend peoples' minds around the idea that you're selling them a capability and not something that can be equated to a video game or even a word processor it's a tough sell. You have to educate the market.

RB: I had two theories on it. One is that we're all emotionally plagued by the notion that the show must go on. That's why people like ETC give free tech

---

[5] See Cunningham – page 92 about his philosophy on lowering manufacturing cost, citing examples of attempting to build your own CD player.

support 24/7 and we've just come to expect it - because the show must go on. And they expect the same with software. And the other thing is that I don't think we, as software developers in our industry, are mature enough to release a finished product. So we're constantly releasing a product that has bugs and a feature set. And as the bugs get fixed, the feature set grows. It's called 'feature-creep'. With big automotive software, they have a feature set that may have some bugs so they issue a patch, but they never add a feature. But they don't get excited about the new things because they know they can get that in a new market. We, on the other hand, just want to get the features out there, so we are constantly doing this dual elevator thing between patches of bugs and development of features. It's a horrible continuing cycle. And that's the reason we can't sell upgrades. We always seem to be giving software away.

Your software has been stable for ages.

EC: It has, and that's interesting-because we did one big upgrade from Version 1 to Version 2, which was coincidental with the Windows release (it was originally only on a MAC) in which we doubled the number of features and upped the price a little bit. That was a couple of years after the first release, around 1998. It was a while ago and my distributors had been bugging me: "We need to do a new release, we need to do a new release." People have to know the product is an evolving, living thing. They also have another product they are distributing that has had a new release recently. For a while people have been wondering if Virtual Light Lab is a dead-end product because we're still on the version we released five years ago.

What's new? Nothing – which to your other point is interesting. There is an expectation from the consumer software side of a release every year or every six months and we're driven to match that for unknown reasons. I've resisted it, stoically, because I look at my numbers and see that we're still selling as many every quarter as we were three years ago. Now I could spend a whole lot of time doing a new release, and we have a whole list of features that we want to put in a new version. But I say, what's that going to do? Is it going to increase software sales? No, the same people who are going to buy it next month are just going to be buying a better version.

When we did the upgrade to Version 2 there were increases in sales and part of that was certainly because it went to Windows, but ultimately the number of upgrades from Version 1 we sold is less than a third of the installed user base. They were paying twenty bucks for an upgrade, of which I was only getting a fraction. So how many hours am I going to spend making the next version of Virtual Light Lab? And what's the bottom line difference going to be between that and what it's doing now?

What I've elected to do is watch the numbers and when it starts taking a dive for two or three quarters in a row then we'll release a new version. This seems a weird thing to say and I wouldn't say it if I didn't have plenty of other projects to keep me busy! So much of what all of us write is driven either by personal desire to create the thing or personal need to use the thing. At this point I don't need to add features to Virtual Light Lab for myself, and there are other things that I feel I need to do.[6]

Historically, the initial version of Virtual Light Lab I made for myself. I can't sit there at my drafting table and try figure out what three colours to put in my cyc lights and really know how they're going to mix. You know, you can put one in front of each eye and do the whole nine yards and then I said let me hack around and see what I can do with the computer to do help mix colours. So the very first version of it was just about mixing three colours.

RB: On a flat plane?

EC: On the screen – a block of colour. Let's mix some colours. And it worked great. I got a little colour meter to scan gels.

RB: Did you ever work with Bill Warfel?[7]

EC: No. And I keep talking to Joe Tawil.[8] I say, you know Joe, I'd be happy to do a Mac version of GelFile. He says, yes, we should talk. Maybe one day it will happen, because his library is huge.

RB: I also spoke to him while at CAST because we were doing the same research. I didn't get anywhere.

EC: The colour manufacturer's should just publish RGB values for all their colours. There's a whole other discussion about accurate display of colour on monitors.

RB: Well, the dynamic range of the human eye is ultimately greater than that of the 24-bit colour resolution.[9]

---

[6] John McKernon writes Lightwright for himself – he needed it. See page 113 and page 115

[7] Bill built an application called GelFile that allowed you to select and mix colours and relate them to an IES chart. It had a great database of colour wavelengths and was quite accurate.

[8] President of GAM (Great American Market)

[9] 24-bit colour resolution means that you use one byte (0-255) to represent each of the (cont...)

EC: Which is fascinating. This actually ties into the history because I did this little colour mixing thing and was surprised that it worked as well as it did just mixing cyc colours on a block of light on the screen. I showed it to some people and they said "Can I get a copy of that, that's really cool." So one thing led to another and it became clear that with a little trickery and if you lock down a few parameters there are a whole lot of short cuts that can be made. However, you can't move the lights, you can't focus the lights and you can't change the model. If you accept those limitations there are a whole lot of short cuts you can do on the rendering. And I cobbled together pretty quickly the first version of it and it was a blast because it looked like a cool little light lab sitting there in your computer. It was sexy and fairly easy to do, frankly.

The first 90% is always easy and the rest is the next five years. My worry was that I knew what the limitations were and as I started really scanning a full library of colours and looking at it and saying, OK, here's R80 in the air in real life and here's R80 on the screen. It doesn't begin to look the same. And excuse me, Lee 119 and R80 coming up the same – this isn't right. But it's "right enough"…apparently. I don't know enough about the neurology of it and the perception end of it. My theory is it's about relative colour relationships, and the colour relationships you develop on screen are parallel to the colour relationships that you will have in real life (until you get to the extremes). In the normal framework of stage lighting the relationships hold true. To this day, I'm happily astonished that people use it to pick colours, go out and spend hundreds of dollars on gel, put their show up and are delighted on how it turns out.

RB: I went through the same argument with people about WYSIWYG. It's the critics that don't use WYSIWYG who say "Oh, it doesn't look realistic". But then there's the people who use it and say, "I know the light is on or off; I know that it's downstage, not up and I know that it's red and there's some sort of gobo in it." Then in the next move it does this and it does that. And that's a whole lot more information than we knew before and what we'd get

---

(...cont) intensities for red, green and blue inside of one pixel. People now talk of 32-bit colour resolution. Originally the extra byte was not used for all intensive purposes (it's difficult to divide 8 by 3), but 32 bit was used because the processors are 32-bit and it's much faster to move things around in blocks of 32. Today, Windows XP uses the extra byte and calls it the Alpha channel. It determines how transparent the bit is. 24-bit colour still gives over 16 million colours which is all the human eye can differentiate. The problem is that the human eye can perceive a much higher dynamic range (the range between lightest and darkest object in the image) than any monitor can display. This is half the fun of doing lighting on the stage – the tricks we can play with the eye and relative brightness.

with just numbers on the screen. You have to assume that the designers are still artists and they know that when they get to the stage, it's going to be art. But there's a technical factor in the mean time. And that's what Virtual Light Lab is too; it allows you to arrive with the right equipment.

EC: It's all a process and no one piece of software is going to do the whole process for you. I think one is much better served by having a whole bunch of little tools which are individually upgradeable or replaceable or ignorable and understand that each one of them has a purpose. And from the development point of view, it's a whole lot easier to develop something that has a special purpose with a clearly constrained set of features, and, in my mind, a clearly defined set of expectations.

Now here's an interesting story. One of my earlier software projects was working for Richard Nelson developing Express-Track software. That was in about '87 even though we released it in 1990. The initial version I did in 1987 for *Into The Woods*. I was one of the assistants on the show. Richard was very meticulous about keeping track sheets and this was long before off-line editors.

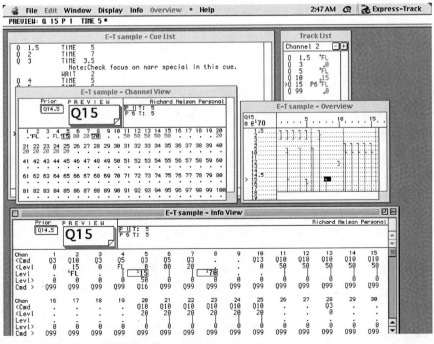

Express-Track (Now in colour!)

RB: Which console where you using?

EC: It was the first Light Palette II used on Broadway. Historically there would be an assistant whose sole job would be to keep the track sheets up to date. Richard wanted to go home at the end of the day with a pile of track sheets and his notes from the end of the day and walk back in the morning with a list of board notes, go to a cue, change its level, track it to another cue. This was the way he worked. It was my job to keep the track sheets. At the time, *Into The Woods* was the biggest show on Broadway. We had, probably, four hundred channels! It was a biggy. It was about groups and it was about jumping from here to there, and going to a cue and making changes and recording it somewhere else altogether. Well, the poor assistant there with some paper and a pile of erasers had no way of keeping up with this designer at the speed he was working.

I suggested we do it all on a computer. There must be some spreadsheet thing we could use. We could type levels in and copy rows and this that and the other. That quickly fell apart because what you obviously needed to do was write something that you could type into on a command line in the same way the operator was typing in. You would bring up a cue, make changes in it and ultimately record it as a different cue, so you didn't have to know that when you started. It quickly became a set of electronic track sheets with a command line interface that mimicked the Light Palette interface. Half of it was developing this command line and half of it was developing all these cool ways of displaying the information to make it more useful than just track sheets.

RB: Did you get the idea at this point that you should just be working for Strand and tell them how to format their print outs. All the stuff was there! The redundancy of data entry was just…

EC: Yes, it's true, but at that point we were still pushing the limits of what the poor PDP-11 in the Light Palette II could do to do the show in real time - which leads to a different concept of whether we should actually have different machines to do different things at different times. It's happening now with the wiggle light end of things. The board that's in the theatre to program the show is not necessarily the one that's in there to run the show – a long overdue concept. Even with conventional lights there are tools the designer needs when the show's in production, and there are tools that the third replacement electrician needs to maintain it – and he wasn't even there when the show was put together. They're not the same thing.

So we did all these cute little display things. For instance, such as looking at a part cue which has a little superscript with part numbers next to the level.

RB: Which computer were you using?

EC: It was a Macintosh SE/30 which was a tiny little box that had even more brains in it than the Light Palette. (Therein is one of the differences between consumer electronics and our world.) It had a 68030 processor, black and white nine inch monitor, GUI and all. Basically it was a second generation Macintosh computer, three years after the Mac was first released.[10]

RB: And you were writing this software in…?

EC: In BASIC. Future BASIC or one of those third party things. It was quite a nice little compiler. It gave you access to a good deal of the Toolbox routines. You were writing stuff that had dialog boxes and menus and multi window interfaces etc.

RB: So it wasn't a command line system?

EC: No, and writing a command line interface to go on top of this thing was a nuisance and so against the grain it was actually more difficult. If I had done the thing in DOS, it probably would have been easier.

Even on the little 9" black and white screen we were able to display a whole lot of information that the colour monitor on the Light Palette wouldn't give you. We could put more channels on the screen; we could show you what was going up and down in each part. That's something we did fifteen years ago, but I have yet to see it on any console.

I built a basic engine to display a matrix that said we're going to display rows of data, or chunks of rows actually. So a chunk might be in a normal display: the first row has channel numbers, the second row levels, the third row may be colour or part number. So I set up the a generic engine that could have up to eight rows and each of these rows could be displayed multiple times in each screen and you would have as many as you needed, and expanded and contracted as needed. If you picked something simple like two rows (channel and level) you could display a lot on the screen. However, you could pick something more complex with eight rows: channel, current level, prior cue number where that level was tracking from, next cue number where it's

---

[10] The 68030 was a 32-bit processor running at 16 MHz. The SE/30 also had a Motorola 68882 floating point unit and sold for just under $5000.

going to change, level it's changing to in that cue, etc.

This is the kind of information that - I can't speak for all designers - was really useful to Richard. We were sitting there in the middle of a multi-million dollar musical and making a change and wondering how far we want this to track. Where's it changing next? Where's it going? It's still just numbers on the screen, but it's the numbers you need. You don't have to go Page, Page, Page. You don't have to go Next, Next, Next; Last, Last, Last; Spreadsheet scroll or whatever - to have at your finger tips the answers that you need.

We put together about fifteen combinations of ways to display things. The other great trick on this thing was that the sequence in the stacks of things displayed is sorted by the value in the top row. So when the channel number is in the top row, it's displayed in channel number sequence. Pick another format that has level on the top row instead of channel number, and it's then sorted by level. Change the format around so Cue Number This Is Tracking From is in the top row, it's sorted historically by which channel has been at that level the longest vs. which one moved most recently. Or, reverse that order, and sort by the up-time for the part that the channel is moving in. There's all the stuff that's moving fast. And it's all the same engine. You just plug different stuff in and show and hide different rows.

RB: So, did this thing ever "come out of the woods"?

EC: Well it did and that starts an interesting 'marketing a product' story. We did this prototype for *Into The Woods* and it worked great. It was a hard sell to the producers to even pay any money to use it, and this is another story because their line was "Is this going to sell more tickets? Is this, in any sort of measurable way going to make the lighting on the show any better, or is this just going to make Richard's job easier?"

RB: It was the same argument we heard with WYSIWYG. Producers won't pay for it. The designers would have to pay for it out of their own pocket.

EC: It was a hard sell, but they finally came up with a few bucks and it was useful enough that Richard put together a company called Lucida with Eric Schultz and Tina Charney. Eric was actually the assistant electrician and board operator on *Into The Woods,* and Tina had assisted Richard on lots of projects over the years. So the three of them put together this little company to break off into architectural and display lighting and develop the software because they thought it was the next big thing and something that everybody needed and would pay money for. So the company, in its brief life, did two things:

developed Express-Track and did the lighting for the Reagan Presidential Library. The Reagan Presidential Library is still there and as I understand, well lit. But Express-Track is a distant memory!

I spent a year developing it into a real product, which is interesting because the 'real' one didn't do much more than the one we used on *Into The Woods*. However, it was more robust and there was a manual. I'm not sure I can find a version that still runs as I don't think it survived the operating system upgrades, in part due to our whole copy protection scheme – which is yet another discussion.[11]

I can' t speak for the marketing choices that were made because I didn't make them but obviously none of the partners had a background in it, which they'll be the first to admit. They talked to some folks, looked around at what was happening, and made some choices. First it was priced high, then it was priced low and then we made three different versions at different price points. We did everything we could think of and if twenty copies of it were sold, I'd be surprised.

RB: Who knows where to price software? You certainly can't price it on time and labour!

EC: What's weird about this business is that people will pay me as a lighting designer hundreds of dollars a day to come and sit in a theatre and talk on a headset. And people will pay me hundreds of dollars a day as a software person to come in and figure out why their motion control system is not working. But nobody will pay me hundreds of dollars a day to sit down and write software for lighting!

RB: And you'll spend many many more hours of your own emotional time doing it.

EC: The only people who do it, in large part, are the people who do it for their own personal satisfaction. If they make some money off it, great. If they make enough money to support it, even better. I've been fortunate enough to have a couple of products that have done that. Express-Track was not one of them, and gazillions of dollars went down the tube in this great exercise. I

[11]See more on copy protection on page 291. Eric eventually did find an unprotected copy of the software so he could provide some screenshots. He was happy to report that the Express-Track software, written almost 15 years ago, runs just fine on a current generation Mac despite the line having migrated to a completely different processor architecture (PPC) and underlying OS (Unix). Here, Apple displays an example of extremely well disciplined product evolution that lighting console users can only dream about.

mean we had beautiful packaging, a manual, we had labels for your keyboard.

RB: Couldn't you revive that now? You've written the parser which was the big thing. Now you're so much into this ASCII file format thing[12] - couldn't you just pull it in?

EC: Well, that was the next step we did. After it had been out there a year, we realized, as we did on *Into The Woods*, the problem was the mistakes in typing everything in. So I'm sitting there with my Mac next to the board operator who's typing stuff into the Light Palette and we're both on the headset listening to the same thing. I'd type stuff in and he'd type stuff in and at the end of the day, things were different. And, I would tend to think I'm right, but the bottom line is that what's in the board is right and I would need to get back to matching it. Then, during the morning work call, I would sit with someone who would know how to push the Next button on the console and we'd go through the entire show making sure the tracks matched what was in the board. Where they differed, if I knew the board was wrong, I would make a note. If it was just that something may have got missed and was off by 10% then I'd fix it in the track sheets. Well, this was a nuisance and we just wanted to read the disk. Part of the problem was that the Light Palette was 5¼ inch disks and the Mac was 3½".

RB: Weren't you thinking about serial communication at this point?

EC: Had I thought that far about it - and what's been done since then - the next stop would've been to put a plug on the back of the console's printer port and do a dump every day and parse that. I now have software that does that. When somebody comes to me and wants to do a show translation and they have an old Light Palette I disk, I can stick it in my Pro Palette and dump out of the printer port and parse it into an ASCII file and send it off to Expression Off-Line and generate an Express disk. It's great.

I believe when ETC sold the first Obsession to the Metropolitan Opera, who had had Light Palettes for years, part of the specification in that bid was, "Oh, and by the way, you're going to make our entire repertory run on this new board." And they got a student at the University of Wisconsin to write up a thing that sucked the data out of the printer port on the Light Palette and get

---

[12] The United States Institute for Theatre Technology has published a document that describes a standard way to represent conventional cues in a lighting desk. The objective is that you can write a show on one desk and load it on another. Many manufacturers say they can support it, but none very successfully. Eric makes a business out of filling the gaps.

it into Obsession format.

RB: This was before you were doing it?

EC: Thankfully ETC said, "Gad – we never want to do that again." So I redeveloped practically the same thing and expanded it and I am selling that as a service now.

RB: It's almost a product.

EC: Yes – people say, "Can we buy that?" And there's another interesting twist. The answer is always "No". It's too fragile. It's 10 different pieces of software and you need to use at least three of them most of the time to do a translation. It's a complete nightmare – it would take me years to put it together into one thing that somebody who wasn't terribly knowledgeable could go and take one disk and turn it into another disk.

RB: And they would do it… once! They only have to do it successfully once. It's not like changing the oil in your car.

EC: One of the biggest translation jobs I did was for the Royal Shakespeare Company. In London they had an Obsession II and in Stratford they had a Strand desk and shows were going back and forth between the two theatres constantly. Now I did that for them as a service, which was good for me because I could recover my investment in the time it took to develop the software. Selling it as a service, a capability, a "we need it now", an opera company called me up and they had a disk from two years earlier and they needed to put it in their new board and they're happy to spend 250 bucks to get it translated. If they're not happy to, that's because they can pay somebody to sit there and type it in from a printout less expensively - and that's fine with me. But, over the years, at $250 at a time it has more than paid for the equipment and time I have put into it. And it's helped pay for the things that haven't made a return. So it's interesting that as a service, rather than a product, with or without a box around it, the development process costs have been recovered.

RB: We considered that too with WYSIWYG at the beginning because we knew that it wasn't a consumer product. It was well beyond that. Originally we thought of just franchising the technology and selling the services at many different places throughout the world. By the time we released WYSIWYG 2, we needed to make it more of a consumer-based product. Then along came Version 3 where WYSICAD and WYSIPAPER were released and individuals bought it rather than companies. But now it's gained enough popularity that there are a number of people making a living out of buying a big WYSIWYG system, a big computer, a big projection screen, and having people come in to use it.

I think the reason why there is this tug-and-pull over making a product versus providing a service is just as you witnessed with Express-Track. Having one guy operate the program is quite easy, but to make it so that it's accessible, to make it so that it's documented...

When I was writing software, I could treat it in such a way that I could operate it for 24 hours straight without ever crashing it. But bring in one other person who just hits the wrong button at the wrong time - and bam! They just didn't know how to treat the software nicely, and you can't make a product out of that!

EC: With Express-Track the issue became getting the data in. Right about that time, Strand released Light Palette 90 which was fabulous because it had a 3½ inch disk. It was DOS formatted, it had a directory on it, and you could put the disk in a computer and read it. We tried to get Strand to give us the format of this thing so we could read the data from Light Palette 90 into Express-Track. We quickly went one more step than that and said that if we could write the disk, we could put it back in the board to become an off-line editor – not just electronic track sheets. Strand cooperated and we developed Switch-Track, a stand-alone utility that translated from Light Palette 90 disks to Express-Track format. Right about the same time ASCII cues was being developed so that got tied into it as well.

You then have the problem of the expectation of your customer. Express-Track had a number of features that suggested a direction, but didn't get you all the way there. Similar to what you said of the early critics of WYSIWYG – "Well, it's not photo-realistic." And you were saying, "It will do this, this and that" and they say, "Well, will it do this?" "Well... ah... no. But you can't do that on the board either." And they would go away saying, "What a piece of junk." Yet it has so much promise - but it falls short everywhere.

RB: You're preaching to the choir. "Yesterday you had NOTHING. Look what I'm giving you today!"

EC: So that was a very good lesson. It might have been one of the things that ended up sinking the product, but I've found myself in discussion with other people as I've developed other things and been very cautious about what the "perceived" feature set is going to be and how the thing is positioned. You have to make sure that you don't accidentally inflate expectations beyond what you're intending to deliver. This isn't even about hype – this is about accidental hype. It's about making this thing that I think is cool and somebody else thinks it does something different. Therefore it's not cool because it doesn't do what *they* thought it was going to do. It's a dangerous thing, and I haven't looked around enough to see if other products have suffered from the same problem.

RB: Believe me – it's an epidemic. Tell me about Virtual Light Lab.

EC: It's a particular tool that fits in a particular niche in the process that's early in the development of a design idea. It's basically used to select colour – but people want to do so much more. They say it's a great, simple interface. Well it's simple - because . . . it's simple. They ask if they can import their own models. Then I say, well then you're going to want to texture it and modify it in the application and so on. They you have a much more complex product on your hands.

One of the difficult things to do in designing an upgrade is not changing the fundamental character of the product by adding all these bells and whistles that: a) cloud the original purpose and b) suggest that it does things that it wasn't fundamentally designed to do or can't ever really do.[13] I have relented in some cases. People have wanted to see the beams of light. So now there's a little thing that draws angles. They wanted to know hard information about a light, like what's the beam angle and where is it actually hanging? But these things are accessories and I try to keep these features very specific and not suggest at all that they do more than they actually do. I think this approach has been successful so far.

RB: That's a very difficult discipline. I'm repeating myself when I say this but... I had a great relationship with the Flying Pig guys while they were developing the Hog II. They would never fall into the lazy man's code ethics. Some developers will put in any feature you want (if you're a customer). So if you hit this button, hold that one down, touch the back of the monitor just like this and scratch your belly – make it do this. Menu option 5-F2/3. Then you have your own special version Something-dot-something-rev-R software. When the Pig boys were doing their stuff I said it would be great if it could do this. They said, "Cool idea: if you can find a way to work it into our syntax structure without us having to build a special button or a triple-shift we'll do it

---

[13] Anne Valentino says a software product must have DNA and you can't violate that. See page 168

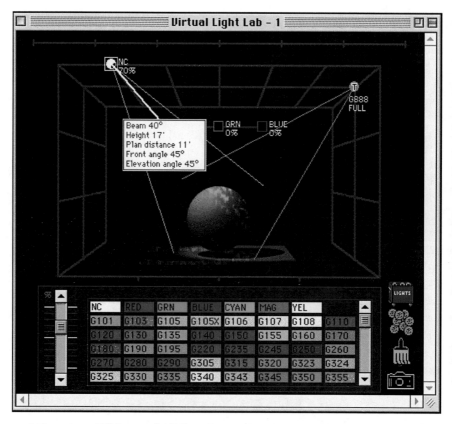

and if not – no. We're not building the product for Rob Bell, and him alone."[14]

EC: That's a good thing and that addresses the other thing that this industry has never had the resources or time or discipline to do - and that is employ people that are smart about user interface design. That's happening a little bit now, but it's always been the people out there trained as engineers or lighting designers or electricians who happen to know how to write software or happen to know how to solder circuits together who are the ones who have the time to 'donate' to develop products. But these are not necessarily the people that have a clear vision of what the interactions should be. They may well be board ops so they may know what works for them, but there are much bigger issues in human interface design.

---

[14] See Valentino – page 170 for a similar conversation and how you must manage the flood of requests you get from well-intentioned users.

RB: I agree, to a point. I think our industry is small and somewhat tolerant. That's why your products and my products and other people like us that design products enjoy success. It's because we do it; because we're there.[15] We know what is needed. And there are other products in our industry designed by people that haven't been in a theatre in two years. They've never put a c-wrench in their back pocket. People want to see the software work the way they're used to working. Sometimes to get the focus just right on a light we have to use some ND, some scrim, a pie-plate, shutters and a flag. It may not be pretty – but it does the job.

EC: As Roger Morgan is fond of asking salesmen: "When was the last time you were backstage when the worklights were off?" Off as in during an actual rehearsal or performance, not on as in during a lunch break. There are people who sell equipment into our industry and say, "Oh yes, I went to a show once – I went to a show last month." Hello... have you ever been in the basement?

RB: It's funny, the subliminal perception that the end users get. They don't know why, but they just know that the software they are using thinks more like them. It's not something we do on purpose – it's just something that falls out of it. It's like good parents equals good children.

EC: And part of product development is driven by our need for a tool. If I need a tool – I'll make it. I'm fortunate enough to have the expertise to do that. But it's also about - and I say this as I get older and looking back as much as looking forward - the fact that there's a hell of a lot of stuff I've learned along the way and I can then package some of that into a product.

Virtual Light Lab is about things that I find useful that I didn't know were useful ten years ago. This is something that can help someone understand what I didn't understand myself ten years ago. Rather than writing a book or making a video or teaching a course to ten people a year I said: "I could put this knowledge on a disk in a way that's dynamic and useful and disguised as a working product but is actually educational." Now, Virtual Light Lab is looked at as: "A great educational tool but I don't know whether or not the professionals would ever use it." Well excuse me – they do!

I'm sure WYSIWYG is looked at somewhat as an educational tool too because of things you put into it – things programmers needed to know. For instance, when using a moving yoke fixture, if you tilt it, is it going to go upstage

---

[15] See Thin Ice – page 13

or down. Well it depends on the pan orientation. Now here's a tool that helps you know something that you didn't even need to know you didn't know.

The same thing is true with Express-Track. It's so frustrating that there is all this stuff in a console that it won't tell you about, and that you *do* need to know. It would make you a better designer - or at least a less frustrated designer, if you had more ready access to that information.[16] Express-Track was really, in many ways, about Richard Nelson's way thinking about cues based on decades of writing them. He wanted to see on the screen what he couldn't get out of the console. So we made a product that really embodied, in a way, his mental picture of what the show would look like and connected that to the actual data of the show. So looking at an Express-Track display of one of his shows, you understood how Richard thinks about things. People would look at it and say, "Well, who needs that?" And then you would explain it to them and they would say, "Wow, I do need that. That's really cool."

RB: What was the first tracking desk? The Light Palette? The American one?

EC: Yes, probably.[17]

RB: The limiting issues, in the beginning, was the processing power, wasn't it? If you were in Cue 10 and you wanted to Goto Cue 183…

EC: No doubt. Not today. People had ways of overcoming that restriction though. For every X number of cues you could put in this invisible cue, a sort of preset cue or block cue. So if you wanted to go to Cue 250, the console could just go back to the nearest, what you might call, snapshot cue. The problem there is, whenever you track something through, you have to update all the snapshot cues. But the overhead on that is much less then the processing power of hitting the Back button ten times deep into the show.

But now processing power is cheap, memory is cheap, hard disk space is cheap. That's what's frustrating, knowing what capabilities could be available that don't exist. For example, a real audit trail of building a cue, where you've been and the ability to go back to a version you had five minutes ago or yesterday or last week. We have 10 gigabyte drives in the board. We could record a real-time snap shot every five seconds of what the board is putting out twenty-four hours a day for a twelve week production period and still have space left

---

[16] See page 370 for how Richard Lawrence equates lighting board operators to jet fighter pilots.

[17] Not quite. Richard Pilbrow commissioned Strand UK to build the Lightboard in 1976, four years before Light Palette was released in the States. See Cunningham page 81 when both the Light Palette and the Lightboard both arrived at the same convention in the US.

on the disk.[18] Yes, you need an interface to it...

RB: Hog III finally has an unlimited undo and I believe the grandMA already does to a certain extent. But undo is not what you are speaking of either because if you want to go back to yesterday at noon where I thought it looked beautiful on stage...

EC: Yes. I don't want to do thousands of keystrokes. I want to look at the screen and say OK, this is what the levels are now. I just want to peel away a layer and tell me what they were an hour ago. Then, you can say, that's what looked pretty there - or have some better way of refining it.

That's the sort of thing Express-Track did. We had this overview display that was like the precursor to the spreadsheet display on the Prestige (which actually might have existed at the time).[19] But it was in even broader strokes because it would draw a little vertical line for each channel without even displaying quantitative numbers. There were little things on it that showed if the line was moving up or down - or the line would disappear if the channel was off. So on a tiny nine-inch Macintosh display you could have an enormous amount of information with just these little threads of channels. We could display fifty cues deep and three hundred channels wide because each channel was just one row of pixels. There was a detail thing that you could go into with a cursor and show what was active, what cue number you were at, what channel was it, what level it was, and so on. But at a glance, you could see what chunks of things were moving, what was going on in the show. It was useful to Richard. And I find it useful.

RB: I can't believe you haven't been sought out by console manufactures and they haven't specified this stuff in their own desks.

EC: Well, they have a different set of priorities. I can spout out about it, but I don't have to run dimmers in real time or watch forty-eight submasters or provide twenty-four hours of tech support. All of those are things that effect how you design software. That said, I think it's inevitable that all these ideas will get integrated somehow.

---

[18] See page 373. Richard Lawrence, Philip Nye and I discuss how building and storing cues procedurally, rather than state by state would not only offer you more information on how you got to a certain point in the show, but would let you massage the look much more intelligently than just poking values into cells.

[19] Prestige was built by Colortran in 1984 and is yet another product designed by David Cunningham. See Cunningham – page 96. Express Track was built for *Into The Woods* in 1987.

I hope ACN[20] will open up the door to folk like you and me – there are hundreds of us out there - who know how to do lighting and how to write software. It will allow us to develop little tools to solve little problems; something for our own personal style of working; something for a specific project. If you're Disney, you go to ETC and say we need this and they'll develop it for you. If I'm me in my little off-Broadway show, forget it. And there's no reason to expect they would. But, if I'm willing to spend twenty hours working on it, give me a board equipped with an appropriate ACN protocol interface so that I can go and recreate my little Express Track things and make myself a display that shows cue numbers and where something's tracking from and where something's tracking to. You don't have to do that for me. I'll do that myself. Just give me access to the data.

ACN will allow a lazy manufacturer to build a console that has a one-way conversation with controlled devices, but ACN also provides the means for a forward-thinking manufacturer to allow a two-way conversation between a console and another computer. That way I could go plug something else into a console and say, "Tell me what you know". It's not just about a device plugging into a console and being told what to do. I want to plug into a console, request specific data, and generate my own damn displays of it.[21]

The software development tools that are out there are becoming more and more powerful. Look at Visual Basic. Horizon is written in VB, isn't it?

RB: The front end is written in Visual Basic and the fade engine is written in C++.

EC: Yes, I'm talking front-end stuff. I don't want to run dimmers in real-time. I just want to look at data in a fashion that's useful. That's the great thing. There are lots of software development tools out there and lots of smart people. The next generation of lighting designers will all be kids who are computer literate. In my generation, we were few and far between.

RB: In the mid eighties, you must have been the only guy in the theatre with a computer. The board wasn't a computer. It was a tool. Different thing.

EC: Well let me tell you what we went through to grease the wheels so that I, an Assistant Lighting Designer, could operate this piece of equipment in the

---

[20] Advanced Control Network – ESTA's proposed replacement for control protocols in the theatre, including automatic device discovery and patching.

[21] See page 356 on what ACN will and will not do for our industry.

theatre. Having a computer in the theatre was completely unknown at the time. I was told, in as many words, "That's a very nice piece of electronic equipment. We'll be happy to plug it in for you and provide a man to operate it." And I said, no, this is track sheets. I'm the assistant, I keep the track sheets.

RB: I was really nervous because I brought the first WYSIWYG onto Broadway with Richard Pilbrow doing *The Life*.[22] They let me operate that. The thing that blew me away was that after I left, during a dark day in the theatre, Richard and Dawn Chiang and the board operator came in, just the three of them, and were allowed to, with the permission of everybody involved, program all the preset focus positions. As long as they didn't turn on a light…

EC: That's amazing.

RB: It frightened the hell out of me back then because if that failed, in Local 1, the success of WYSIWYG would have been seriously hampered. It's the same reason John McKernon's stuff has been so successful – you have to be a friend of the union. Your software mustn't be threatening. Luckily IA sees WYSIWYG as a great tool and a great training tool for their junior members to play with to get their chops on some of the more complex desks.

EC: I ran into a situation last year where I got a call from a big international ballet company that was coming into town and had a disk on something-or-other and needed it translated to Obsession II for the theatre they were going into. I said OK, send me the disk. But then they never got back to me, and I was getting worried because I knew their schedule and time was running out. I finally discovered that the theatre, which is a major venue in the city, has new house rules that don't allow people to bring disks into the building. "Everything gets typed into the board here – thank you very much. We're happy to provide a man to type." And this was a place that, in the past, I have taken disks in; this was a new rule. It was brought in because someone took advantage of the situation where they had some broadcast event there and during lunch break they were taking the disk out to a truck and re-programming stuff and then coming back in and putting a new disk in the board, which is pushing it if you are supposedly going dark during lunch.

RB: I hope the rule does not apply to touring shows!

---

[22] Spring of 1997 at the Ethel Barrymore Theater.

EC: Yes, really! So it is all about personalities even more than precedents. It's all evolving as well because - bless their hearts - the old guard of house electricians and BA's[23] and everyone else is gradually being educated or replaced by young folks who understand that these are necessary tools.

RB: Have you read the book *Being Digital* by Nicholas Negroponte?[24]

EC: Yes, and I'm so upset that I left it on a plane and I never got to the last chapter.

RB: When working at CBC, the vice president of English Television almost made it a mandate of the corporation to understand Negroponte's take on the evolution of technology and how it relates to collective bargaining. It's all about the breakdown of the barriers between management and personnel. In the 50's, 60's and 70's you had a camera operator, he sat behind a camera. You had a lighting board operator and he sat behind a dimmer board. You had an editor and he sat behind a Steinbeck. You had a Tele-Cine operator covered in smelly chemicals. Everybody's job was classified by the gear they used. What Negreponte is saying is that everything can be digital. The audio mix can be digital, done on a PC. Even the tele-prompting can come right out of MS Word. So the guy who writes the script doesn't have to re-type it and put it on the little conveyor with the camera. Everything can be done with the PC. So all these barriers, these labour rules, are based on things that become difficult to enforce. If the tool of choice, even for the trade, is a PC, like it is now for audio and lighting and editing, it's exactly the same PC that sits on their manager's desk. It's tricky to say to management that they can't install certain software on their machines and edit sound bits for the evening news.

Those sort of rules, like you just said, are based on personalities and protections, I believe they will be very difficult to maintain. Especially as more and more PC savvy kids come into the profession. Infra-red ports - they don't even touch each other - voom - and here's the data.

EC: The problem arises when people abuse a situation and then everyone goes back to their defensive position. As with all scientific advances, there are good applications and there are bad applications. People can find ways to abuse WYSIWYG and they'll say "You're never bringing that into the theatre

---

[23] Business Agents – the ones that schedule the union staff.
[24] ISBN 0-679-76290-6

again". But if they're sensitive to everybody, as Steve Terry[25] says: "Technology will always win out in the end".

RB: That's very true. I've used that quote myself a number of times. "If you build it – they will come."

You mentioned that Express-Track's copy protection ended up being too much of a bother in the end.

EC: It was a pain in the butt for me as a programmer to implement and a pain to maintain because we were using hardware keys and things kept changing. We did build in 'trap-doors' so that if someone is stuck somewhere and forgot their key we could tell them what keys to hold down to get the program to run.

RB: Then they knew that. So then what?

EC: In the end, I advocated dropping it. It was costing us fifty bucks a copy for the hardware keys, it was a pain to implement and to this day, ten years later, I can't even get a copy of it to run anywhere because the key interface has changed and my own copy protection has defeated me. My argument was that if the point of copy protection is to increase sales by preventing people from using it without buying it, or prevent people who could buy it from using it for free, there's no evidence that it's doing anything for us, because if we take off copy protection what will happen is, yes people will pirate it. And I think in a way that's a good thing because we'll have more users. We built this thing to be used, not to sit on the shelf and wonder why nobody was buying it. At least that's my point of view, granted they all lost thousands and thousands of dollars developing this thing. I spent a year of time doing it for a dozen people! Now that's kind of sad. I would rather have a hundred people using it. The same dozen will still pay for it. There's no evidence that even in organizations that have paid for multiple copies would abuse it; we just made it more difficult to use. In the whole history of Express-Track, David Hersey is the only person who bought multiple copies. Nobody bought five copies of it because it was copy protected. They just used the one copy they had. Wouldn't it be better for five people to be using it at that place if they can't afford to buy five copies? But that didn't carry very far with the investors.

RB: I went through the same thing. The big debate was whether or not

---

[25] Steve was for many years a partner at Production Arts, then PRG and now at ETC. See his connection to DMX Pearlman – page 64 and Cunningham – page 97

WYSIPAPER should be free. I was always an advocate of it being free, however you have to buy the CAD package. In the same way as when you talked about site licensing, we had network dongles that allowed twenty-five people to use it at once. We had considered only allowing five or ten, but on discussing it, I asked what the physical limitations to the dongle were. The answer was twenty-five and I said – "Twenty-five it is then!"

EC: It comes back to the same thing – put software in a box, put an aluminium enclosure over it with a knob or two and people will buy five of them.

RB: Dongles provide you with a bit of that sense. Horizon now comes on a dongle – the whole damn thing. With DMX being distributed over Ethernet, who needs anything but a network connection? I was showing the dongle (or Horizon Universal Key) to Mike Falconer[26] and apologized because the first one we had did not have a ring so you could put it on your key chain. I though that was a real problem. He thought it was great. "They'll treat it with more respect." I guess people don't lose their wedding rings and they're about $4000 too.

EC: Which is a high cost per weight ratio. That's the problem with PDA's. You mean I can lose $500 that easily?

RB: The Hog II is way heavier than it needs to be.

At least the dongle is *something*. If we just did copy protection in the registry,[27] setting some arbitrary bits or whatever, there would be no perceived value because it's not tangible. Or, if we make it free, there's no value in something you give away.

EC: This is another interesting story and so it far has been successful. Years ago I wrote a little beam angle calculator on the Newton. Then the Newton died and I started becoming interested in writing Palm Pilot software. However, before jumping into this I thought about how I was going to sell it. I had just gone through a couple of years of marketing and selling Virtual Light Lab directly and I'm glad someone else is doing that for me now. Was I going to make it shareware or what? You can go out and buy the device, the computer the software runs on, for $150. I can't charge $300 for software to put on a

---

[26] Mike was at AC Lighting UK when they were selling WYSIWYG and was fundamental in the launch of our product and the Hog II. He just spent three years at A.C.T. Lighting (formerly AC US) and supports the grandMA. He has just started Doubleplusgood Media (www.doubleplusgoodmedia.com). A very good friend and an excellent resource.

$150 computer. Nobody will go for this. And it's polluted so much by it being such a consumer product and sold in such volume, and the software for it is sold in such volume, that companies can spend $50,000 developing software and sell the product for twenty bucks. I can't do that because our market is so small.

Because I like little tools for specific purposes, I write a whole bunch of little programs. That's in the spirit of the Palm Pilot as well. You want to do "a" thing. You turn it on and do your thing. You're not sitting there for hours working on some monolithic program. That's not what it's for. Why not write a bunch of little programs then sell them all together for $50 or $75. So maybe somebody only wants to use three or four of them, they have to buy the whole set. Effectively, you may only be paying five bucks apiece, and it becomes a more digestible equation.

So I went about it that way, breaking it up into little, single-purpose applications. Then, as I was finishing the development of it, I thought I could take it one step further and that was to organise the distribution of sales electronically. I asked myself if I wanted to make CD's, and do packaging, marketing, shipping and everything. Everything I thought about made the cost go up and put pressure on the price. Suddenly my $50 idea was now a $100 idea! And you can buy a Palm Pilot for less than $100 now, and it was just not working out at all.

So then I realized that if I did the distribution electronically - cut out the dealer level and production, packaging, everything - and market it directly off my web site, people could pay an honest value for it. So I now have a few Palm Pilot applications that range in price from $5 to $20. Most people buy them buy all of them and pay in the order of $50 to get the whole suite. Some people just buy the $5 DMX address calculator. There's also a colour names look-up table, a database with all the colour names and numbers. So you put into it 119. It will tell you Lee 119 is this, Rosco 119 is this and Gam 119 is this. You put in blue, and it lists everything that is blue. All these little things are appealing because they make your Palm Pilot useful for something you do in your job, not just for addresses and suchlike.

---

[27] Some software write hidden keys into the Windows registry, a massive database where all sorts of system variables are kept. Because of its sheer size, you can easily hide items by giving things very long and silly names that no one would ever search for. The problem with using this as copy protection is that if a legitimate customer upgrades his PC, you have to trust him when he asks for another key to unlock the software that he's not just installing it on his friends' PC too.

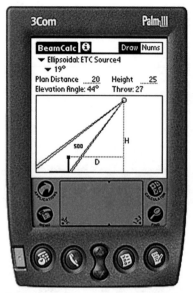

That leads to another topic of discussion: providing tools that make people feel good about their hardware purchase. It's something John McKernon hit on the head. Lightwright came out right at the time people were looking for excuses to buy their own computer and he gave them exactly the excuse they needed.[28] It was wonderful symbiosis. I wasn't imagining that I could do the same thing for the Palm Pilot, but it did work in that way. Oh, look, here's a cool thing, I can calculate what size is a 19-degree Source 4 going to be right here on my Palm Pilot. This is appealing. If I could do that for twenty bucks, wow.

RB: So, no copy protection?

EC: It's minimal. I distribute, archive and install all the software in demo versions. And the demo versions have limited functionality, or only run for a day. Then customers go on-line and buy a registration code to type in and make it real.

RB: You do the credit card transaction and all that?

EC: I don't do it myself; I have a link over to a big shareware sales handler. They do the processing, take their percentage and then they send me a cheque every month. At this point, development is done, the stuff is up there on the web site, and I don't do a thing. It's all so simple that there is no support. People send me ideas for new features, but that's the extent of any link with the hundreds of users out there.

It's nice. Now, if I put a little more effort into the marketing I would probably get a bigger cheque at the end of the month.[29]

RB: Point in case: I didn't know about it!

EC: There you go.

---

[28] In fact – that is how John decided to get his first computer. He wanted an excuse to buy one. See McKernon - page 113

RB: Put a quarter page ad in one of the magazines and you would get that many more hits. Or get someone to start talking about it on the LightNetwork.[30]

EC: I have to keep track of this sort of thing because there was a little sales spurt a month ago and I've been wondering what happened. It must have got into the right group and then there you go, every day there was a sale. Usually, there's a couple a week.

```
BeamCalc                    Nums  Draw
▼ Ellipsoidal: ETC Source4
  ▼ 19°
Plan distance    35    Height      25
Elevation angle: 29°    Throw: 40
                      Field    Beam
Angle:                18°      15°
Width at head:        12.6     10.5
Width at floor:       16.2     13.5

Lamp:   ▼ 575w HPL
Beam Candlepower:  250,560
Footcandles at head: 156              [i]
```

It's a little experiment. I'm delivering tiny little products at a tiny little price point and the Internet gives me a way to do that at basically no cost. It makes me think I should develop another dozen products. I could sell twice as many if I had twice as many.

The ability to use the net ties into the promise of ACN as an open networking standard and what ASCII cues did (not so terribly successfully) is open this all up to small time developers: people that have the expertise and the knowledge of business and the need to do something, to have a hope of recovering their investment and time.

RB: Do you know Paul Pelletier who works for Ericson Pro Audio (Martin) in Canada? He did the same thing with Delphi, calling it the LD Calculator. He gives it away for free. It's one application that has twelve tabs, all of them being individual tasks. You go to tab-Photometrics and type in your value and there you go. He has Ohms Law and it will do frequency and three phase power calculations for you.

EC: E-commerce gives you the ability to charge for these things. If there were a way to charge by the use it would even be better. Every time someone calculates a beam angle, I get a penny. That would be totally painless for them and…

---

[29] At the time of this interview, www.horizoncontrol.com did not exist. Since then, customers can purchase the Horizon control software using a credit card. We do have heavy dongle protection, so hardware needs to be shipped to new customers, but upgrades to existing customers can be done live on-line. With control systems and the growth of Ethernet based I/O products this is becoming more commonplace. Eric's stuff can be found at www.PocketLighting.com.

[30] A popular on-line discussion forum started by Nils Thorjussen and Arnold Seramie. See www.lightnetwork.com.

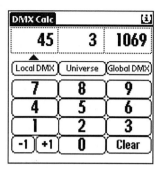

RB: We tried to do that with WYSIWYG when we came out with real rendering. We had the whole e-commerce model worked out on the dongle. You would charge up your dongle with five hundred renders or one hundred renders and as you completed the rendering, it would decrease the number. However, that didn't go over very well at all!

EC: Really!

RB: I wasn't so fond of the idea to begin with but the business people thought the industry was ready. There was a huge uproar from the user base. They figured that if they'd bought the software they should be able to use it, day or night, whenever they pleased. It's like saying to someone who bought a car, you can only drive 20 miles a day. We had to reverse out of the whole thing and recover from the political damage we had done.

EC: I wonder if you offered it as a service rather than something they could do on their own. Obviously turn-around is an issue. Would a customer be more comfortable after they had done the whole layout and set-up, giving CAST the file over the Internet and two days later I get these nice glossy prints from Federal Express. That, I'd pay $700 for. But I wouldn't pay if the software could do it for me locally.

RB: We tried a service of rendering moving image for people and delivering them the videotape, but pay-per-use software is just a non-starter. I think people believe that once they buy something, they should have the full use of it. Again, they understand that a car needs maintenance and they will pay for that, but software shouldn't break (so the theory goes).

EC: I'm annoyed every time I have to pay for a $30 ink cartridge to put in my $150 printer, even though I conceptually understand exactly what the deal is.

RB: Well at least there you're throwing something away.

EC: The fact that you're replacing the brains of your printer every time doesn't make you feel any better!

RB: People were not willing to put a quarter in and get an 8½ x11 out. Only the die-hard users who knew us intimately would accept it. People have to understand that to develop software takes a continued effort. When I left

CAST, there were five guys writing code, two guys writing libraries, one guy writing help, and myself. Bloody expensive! People continue to believe they should only have to pay admission once and see the show as often as they like, and get all the new benefits and features. That's the one that kills me. If they bought a known quantity and went away to never return, fair enough, but they all want it fixed, and to their standards.

Flying Pig has the same problem with Hog III. When I met them, they were building Hog II and they said they would never have to build another desk because they had touch screens and they would just put new buttons on whenever they needed them. I said I felt that it was a näive belief. They didn't think so at the time. Then they started to look at the numbers. There was only one guy developing the hardware and three doing software. Now for Hog III, the ratio is even greater. The problem is the hardware development is done once, but you still keep all the software guys around. When they were doing Version 2 of the Hog II software, they were thinking heavily of putting a dongle on it to sell new code, similar to what Strand did with their GSx. It would never fly; they couldn't market it. The only option they had was to throw out a gorgeous hardware design, the Hog II, and build a Hog III. Instead of eight faders, they're going to have ten; instead of three wheels, they're going to have four; you're not going to have an external trackball, you'll get an internal one; colour touch screens instead of black and white. And, you get a whole bunch of new software. That's the only way you can sell it. I don't know... I guess I just feel hard done by as a software developer.

EC: I wonder if the European market is different from, say, the American market, or the Pacific Rim. Do they all need something physical attached to their software?

RB: The interesting thing I found during the WYSIWYG life cycle is the attachment to the hardware. WYSIWYG 1 and WYSIWYG 2 were DOS applications. WYSIWYG 3, which had WYSIPAPER and WYSICAD bundled with it, were Windows applications and shared none of the code structure of the previous versions. We consciously decided to call it WYSIWYG 3 and charge full price to anybody who wanted to buy it. WYSIWYG 2 customers in North America were extremely upset because they were already in the WYSIWYG family when we brought out WYSIWYG 3 but it was *all new*. They knew it was all new, but they considered it should be sold at a discount. But the Europeans were quite happy to either stick with what they had, or pay up for the new stuff. If we had called it CAST CAD (as we thought we might have at one point) there would have been no debate. 'Oh, you did WYSIWYG, now you're doing CAST CAD, OK.' But we wanted to draw on the name, and we had to pay for that.

EC: It would be interesting to talk to John McKernon about when he did the change from ALD Pro to Lightwright and whether changing names made it easer for him. He may also tell you about when Gary Fails[31] got involved and also changed the pricing structure which turned out to be the right choice. He's now charging a higher price AND selling to more people. Who would have thought that?

RB: Maybe I was always wrong by giving away WYSIPAPER. We had always discussed charging $100 for it so we didn't de-value its worth.

EC: Then you could have given it away anyway and then they would really think they were getting a gift.

The other thing that works for me is the perception thing; the size of the company really does affect people's willingness to forgive. For my part, I'm always happy to pay for shareware stuff, but always annoyed when Microsoft's products break. It may be the same people writing the software for all I know. In a way I'm lucky to keep a low profile, because if I do a translation and the last ten cues get dropped, well if they tell me in time, I go back and help them out. But if they call me after the show opens, there's not a lot I can do about it. However, if I were ETC or Strand doing this translation, and ten cues got left out, there would be hell to pay.

It's the same everywhere. That's how Broadway has evolved. They have to charge $100 for tickets because the productions cost so much, and then they have to make the production what it is because they are charging $100 for tickets. Go to a workshop production of the same thing with no sets, lights or costumes and it may even be better. Look at *Chicago*[32]. There's never been such a success in years. On the other hand, you take something like *Phantom* or *The Lion King* or *Beauty and The Beast* or *Aida*, well OK – there's a lot

---

[31] Gary is president of City Theatrical and now sells Lightwright. See McKernon – page 114 regarding the change of name and change of distributor.

[32] The Broadway Musical Chicago is a story about two murderous wives on death row in the twenties and their struggle to get media attention. The production value of this particular production is not huge; there's basically only one set. Since this interview, the film version has been shot and released to wild accolades.

of production there and you pay for it.

Mandy Patinkin put together this concert of old Yiddish songs and I did the lighting design. We started it out downtown, Lower East Side in this old 19th Century Synagogue that was converted into a very funky arts center. We did it for several weeks down there with standing room only. It was a big smash hit – it was fabulous. So, we take it uptown to a large space - let's reach out and bring this material to a broader audience. We went through a whole process about doing production then ended up cutting all of that and ended up with a little black stage with a little light on it. It was not at all successful, but it was exactly the same show. Taking it from the Lower East Side where you have to walk five blocks through a grungy neighbourhood to get there and moving it up to 44th Street created totally different expectations.

RB: I went to see *Witches of Eastwick* in the West End. They originally produced it at Theatre Royal Drury Lane, and it wasn't filling the place. They moved it to the more intimate Prince of Wales Theatre and it not only filled the place – it got better reviews. But it was the same production. Actually – it lost some of the production gags because of the space, but it was much better received.

EC: Philosophically, I think this works in product design too. Simple products that are easy to understand, inexpensive, accessible and easier to forgive if they don't do everything in the world, are in a way more successful than big monolithic things.

Obsession software has gotten to the point where God bless the person who can find their way through all those menus and softkeys and do anything other than set levels. And they know it. It's a nightmare. It's a great example of a monolithic piece of software. It started as a small monolithic piece that really did correct a lot of problems and improve upon a lot of things in the Light Palette philosophy, but then because of perceptions or expectations ended up not being what it should have been.[33]

RB: Given your woes trying to do file translations, how do you feel about open architecture systems? We all know how DMX opened up our industry so any manufacturer's gear could be controlled by any manufacturer's control desk. ACN promises to give us more of that. On the flip side of things, I'm not sure, for example, if Vari-Lite would have succeeded in the 80's and early

---

[33] See Valentino – page 156 as she describes the Obsession as it went to market as being 'narrower and deeper' rather than 'flat and wide'.

90's if they didn't protect their protocols, and mechanicals for that matter. They were always assured that it was a trained, sworn-to-oath, technician working on their gear. The producer never knew if things went wrong, because the tech always had a spare up and running and the faulty gear under a tent.

EC: I think it's a combination of the two actually, at different levels. I think that console manufacturers should protect themselves from bad data getting into their systems. They can't take the Microsoft route and say re-install the software when the show crashes. But, to my mind, they would benefit themselves by providing an authorized way in and out of the system. That would enable legions of people like you and me and any high school kid that's taken a computer class, to add features that the manufacturers don't have the time or resources or desire to implement, support or document. If they get off the idea that they have to provide every bell and whistle that is going into the console, a sort of lowest common denominator feature-set that both satisfies the marketing people and the tech services people and the development people, then they're never going to keep up. The curve keeps climbing and there's no hope.

Open architecture is the answer because it's totally scalable and it leverages stunningly. Even the stuff that happens when lighting programmers exchange macros for doing better moving light programming - that's just the beginning of what could happen if there was a really good, common interface that all manufacturers could implement acting as a firewall for their hardware and their operating systems. Why shouldn't a Broadway show have a lighting assistant who is the programmer? Software programmer I mean – not a lighting programmer. Over a three-month production period their sole job would be to develop tools that the designer needs or the other assistants need to make the show better or do their jobs better. We can't have that position because the person who writes that code is in Scotland or Wisconsin or Texas.[34]

So the roundabout answer is, I understand the need for protection, but I certainly think there is a way to preserve that and open up the system and that would be to everybody's advantage.

RB: You asked earlier if Horizon is written in Visual Basic. The front end is written in VB, but the fade engine is written in C++ and is shipped as a DLL. We've been seriously toying around with the idea of making the user interface

---

[34] Strand, ETC and Vari-Lite respectively

a complete open software package and to give the code out, selling only the engine. Then, if someone wanted to, they could modify our front end to work with our engine, or completely rewrite, even on a Mac, a completely different user interface.[35]

EC: I had thoughts along those lines and it seems the product is the toolkit. We could develop a package as a toolset that someone could use to make their own console, which would use the DLL to run. Or, use the toolkit to write plug-ins for a standard desk so that if someone comes out with…whatever robotic fixture… Joe Schmoe can write a plug-in that goes into the Horizon toolkit to put a control for that fixture on the virtual face panel. Or somebody comes up with some cool 3D glove interface that they want to tie in for a particular application. Maybe it's a product; maybe it's a project.

In the mean time, I'm just going to noodle around with my little programs. It's fun!

---

[35] With all the development we've done on Marquee, the engine and the interface are now two completely different applications talking to each other (on the same machine or over a network or even the Internet) using Remote Procedure Calls. These RPC's would make it very easy for anybody to re-design a new front-end to Horizon. Since this interview, Eric has written a Hog to Horizon conversion utility using the older Telnet interface into Horizon's engine.

11 CHRIS TOULMIN

Introduction

Chris, first and foremost, is a lighting designer. He got caught up in the whole software thing because, for one thing, he likes computers, and secondly, he needed the tools. Much like myself, he hates to draw. Why try to do things yourself when a computer can do it much better than you can?

From heading up the lighting department at London's Royal Court Theatre, Chris was wooed by The White Light Group to head development of their Modelbox division. Modelbox was born out of the idea that The White Light Group wanted to provide CAD services to their customers and get out an equipment list from the back end to hand off to their hire division. It was a simple enough idea, given that CAD systems are used to producing a bill of materials at the end of the day.

As Chris unfortunately learned in the long run, it's difficult to mix development with services. You often find that development takes an awful lot of resources, that the services side pulls you in directions you dare not go if you are solely focused on a product. Striking a balance between these two disciplines can be better than the sum of the two parts, if you can manage it. As I stated in the prologue of this book, a product manager

that uses the product in the field to earn a living is able to serve his customers better by default.

Under Chris' supervision, Modelbox transposed itself from a services company to a software development house and back to a services company. Today White Light retains one employee to maintain their customers with CAD services. They hold the largest database of accurate 2D stage plans in the world and have a system of licensing the drawings to individuals on an annual basis. Their library of lighting fixture symbols has now been opened up to the public for free, but sadly, the development of AutoLight and LapLight has ceased.

As Chris points out, our paths crossed around the time I was leaving CBC and before CAST Lighting was formed. I was writing the suite of 'LX' products (CAD, DB and MOV) and wasn't sure how to take the ideas to market. As you will see, Modelbox was headed down the same route, but preceding me by a couple of years. Modelbox pursued a business in providing services, which precluded them from concentrating on their software development efforts. Chris is now doing freelance photography and I met him back at White Light to do this interview.

Interview

RB: I want to know a little about you and what you did before Modelbox.

CT: I left college early to get into the theatre, literally days before I was to sit some exams. I had wanted to become an air traffic controller. I loved planes, but didn't quite see myself as a pilot and I was really into air-band radios as a kid. I used to love listening to the aeroplanes going over and I thought: "That's it, that's what I want to do."

When I was fourteen, I became very friendly with a neighbour who was a drummer in a semi-professional band and they were doing the working mens' club circuit. I started off in the band as a bass player, but I was terrible, and was told to stop doing it. "But, what about if I flick the lights at the club?" These clubs would have a few different coloured Par 38's and simple stuff like that, and I got totally hooked into the whole concept of playing with lights.

So I built my own rig, screwing Par 38's into bits of wood and I was constantly electrocuting myself in clubs. It was absolutely dreadful, but I became totally besotted with it. I knew nothing of the theatre, I just knew I wanted to play with the lights. I didn't have any huge exposure to theatre when I was a kid. Then one of the guys in the band was going to a college that had a drama school and I signed up too (much against my parents' wishes).

RB: Were they keen on air traffic control?

CT: Yes, they saw that as a real solid occupation. But they have always been very supportive and decided they had to go with what I wanted to do. The problem was this drama class really was just that - a drama class. There was no technical aspect to it. So I had to do everything, including the dancing! However, I was always the one who volunteered to do the technical stuff and very quickly undertook it all.

Then an assistant electrician's job came up in Canterbury, which was completely the other end of the country from where I lived, but I moved there at the age of eighteen. It was a baptism of fire into the theatre world. I was enthusiastic, but didn't really know what I was doing. I suspect it was like that for many of us, although things have changed now.

RB: I remember how awful my first lighting gig was. I was very much into sound and had no idea about dimmers or anything like that. I could only relate to input channels on an audio desk. The guy asked us how many 'k' of lighting I needed. I didn't know what to say. I just said that I wanted at least forty-eight handles on the desk.

CT: What was extraordinary about this job was that there was so little money the chief electrician didn't even show up for the performances. So I went from being an amateur at the local theatre doing a bit of followspot work to suddenly having to operate all this kit in a professional theatre. I was virtually on the edge of a nervous breakdown because I could hardly cope with it. But you do. You get to grips with it, even if I did some absolutely dreadful shows. Eventually, I cracked it. But as soon as I had, I wanted to move on. I didn't want to stay for the money they were offering.

So I said to myself that if I intended to do this properly there was only one place to do it and that was London. So one day in 1980 I got on the train, went to London, booked myself into a very cheap hotel and phoned every stage door in the West End. My last call was to the Royal Court Theatre in Sloane Square and my interview with the chief electrician and the production manager was in the pub across the road. The chief electrician was also from the North of England, like me, so I was a kindred spirit from the beginning. And I could drink, so I got the job as dayman at the Royal Court.

The Royal Court was the home of new writing. We were doing a new play every six or seven weeks by new and well-known writers alike. It was a very high turnover of new work and the ethos of the theatre was very much that everybody in the theatre was involved in the work. So, even as a dayman, there was an involvement and it gave me an opportunity to actually design the lighting. To cut a long story short, within two years of walking in the theatre, I was running the lighting department. It gave me the opportunity to work alongside some fantastic designers, but also gave me ample opportunity to design.

The Royal Court was very much associated with white light; gel wasn't used. The whole approach was very 'Beckett'. That's what I was taught. All I wanted to do was something different from that, but I guess what it fundamentally did for me was teach me how to light. Then, when you're given your own head, you start using some colour. "Let me do it for you. Let me see what you think." Of course, it went down quite well.

RB: It's quite amazing to think that in 1982 the most exciting bit of technology was a piece of gel!

CT: The other exciting bit was that we were one of the first theatres to get the new Strand Galaxy console.[1]

RB: A bit of an overkill for a theatre of that size!

CT: Like a sledgehammer to crack a nut. But as I was already starting to play with computers and since I was the youngest (by some margin), I was probably the one most likely to understand what was going on with it. I had one of these Timex Sinclair computers.

RB: Me too.[2]

CT: I also had a Commodore 64. I used to spend hours writing in these lengthy programs that did almost nothing. I did this silly flight simulator that all you could do was come in and land. It was just a series of pixels. It's amazing how one could even stretch the imagination to say you were landing a plane!

RB: So even though the Galaxy was at the theatre, you were playing with these things at home?

CT: Yes, that's what was floating my boat at the time. I wouldn't say I had a

---

[1] See an extended discussion, mostly steered by Richard Lawrence of Strand, on the importance of the Galaxy on page 356

[2] See 'Four Yorkshire Men' – page 23

huge understanding; but computers just captivated me.

Even though in the theatre we were using a computerized lighting desk, there was no sign of computerization anywhere else. Everything was still done on typewriters. You could imagine the problems of running a lighting department without anything and then suddenly see the possibilities that computers could offer you.[3] But they weren't readily available. And since you found yourself in isolation, you would develop your own things. I even did the salaries for the lighting department on my own computer. I was right into it.

Toward the end of the eighties, I realized that I had been in one place too long; I'd become part of the furniture and it was time to move on. I was doing enough lighting outside of the Royal Court so it would be OK. I got married around that time and moved out of London. Initially, things went very well, because having the pedigree of lighting for the Royal Court immediately meant people would let me through the door and would want to use me. I got work with all the best companies; English National Opera; Opera North, the Royal National Theatre and lots of international tours.

RB: Obviously, at this point, drawing with stencils?

CT: Absolutely, and I hated it. I was a real 'two o'clock in the morning before it had to be handed in' merchant. I always put it off as long as possible. It is partly the struggle to conceptualize what you've never done and translating that into a plan. And the terrible, palm sweating experience of committing it to a plan.

RB: Wondering where the hell the director is and what his thoughts are.

CT: I remember Sir Peter Hall once saying to me: "It's all in the script dear boy; I don't think we need to talk beyond that." And I remember, I sat in rehearsals for days just to have that conversation with him. Similarly, you work with other people that won't give you any space to work.

RB: Richard Pilbrow talks in his book *Stage Lighting Design* about getting terribly frightened during the plotting session. He could handle rehearsals and drawing the plan and focusing the rig, but hated writing the first cue; the one where everybody is watching you. I sympathize with that. I think writing the first few cue is like writing the thesis for a doctorate. You wonder if you've

---

[3] Gordon Pearlman says that the American Conservatory Theater used the PDP-8 (the brain of the LS-8 lighting console) to inventory their scenery and run their box office. See page 58

got it in you, if all the work you've done up to now has been up to snuff. And you're naked, with everybody watching.

CT: It's waiting for the response. I was lucky, because I had the luxury when working at Modelbox that I could just pick and choose what design work I wanted to do. But certainly I remember that whole thing of looking for the feedback, looking for those nice noises coming from the dark. Then you think, "We're on." It's like catching a fish.

I liked writing cues, but hated drawing plans. But they are so necessary. Theatre has an approach to commitment that I've rarely seen anywhere else; particularly in a commercial sense: "Three years from today, on this particular day, at 7.30pm we are going to open this show and we will offer you this entertainment." They make those kinds of guarantees and they do stick to them. It's very rare that that doesn't happen. Whereas, when a building is being built, it usually opens two years after they said it would. I think it is a unique thing in the theatre that we actually have that approach. Everybody involved in the theatre invests in that concept and does whatever they have to do to deliver that product.[4] I think a lot of us move on from the theatre and take that same ethos into the world and you frequently find other people don't understand it.

RB: The show must go on.

CT: Absolutely. That's it.

RB: The nature of software development is so contrary to that because it's worse than buildings.

CT: The problem is that the goal posts get moved endlessly.

RB: Nick Archdale from Flying Pig said that software development is like a gas, in that it will fill the void it is given.

So after some freelance stuff in the late eighties, you met John Simpson of the White Light Group.

CT: Well, I had known him for years through my work in London. My agent was David Watson of Simpson-Fox and John is the Simpson in Simpson-Fox and Associates. After a downturn in the theatre business, David suggested I talk with John about White Light and Modelbox. So I met with John and he needed a lighting designer for a project they were building. He asked me if I

---

[4] See Mark Hunt – page 208 on how the show must go on.

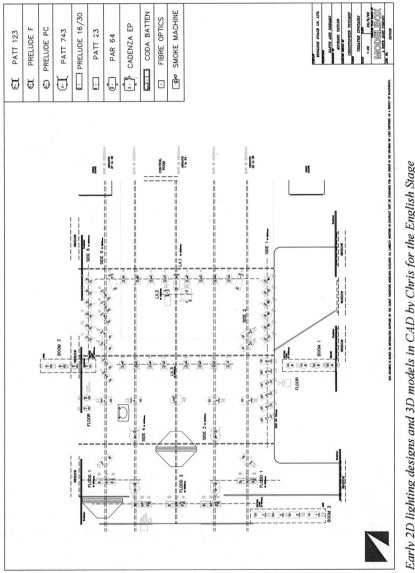

Early 2D lighting designs and 3D models in CAD by Chris for the English Stage Company's production of Rafts and Dreams – 1990

knew much about computers. So I lied and said I did, and he hired me.

RB: So Modelbox . . .

CT: It existed before me. What it was doing was CAD drawings for the theatre, but it was initially on a mainframe system on a landline to Cambridge. The main chap was Charles Morgan and he had an assistant named Ian Teague and they were working in a portable cabin in the yard of White Light. Then AutoCAD version 9 came out[5] about the same time the desktop PC's were getting popular and putting the two of them together was fast becoming an affordable solution. So they had already embarked on this AutoLight project and I was brought along as the lighting designer to give them the 'sensibilities'.

White Light also had a wish to tie this whole CAD thing in with their rental system. So, for instance, you could automatically create a pick list. It becomes a great service to the client. So you could come to White Light and and do your lighting design and afterwards print out the pick list. So that was the germ from which it started.

I walked into this incredibly steep learning curve. Modelbox had just invested in two Compaq 386/20's. These were the latest in desktop PC's. We also had two 21" Cambridge Technologies monitors. Half of the video adaptor for the monitor lived in the monitor where the other half was in the PC. So the two were inseparable. I dread to think how much the monitor weighed. It was a two-person lift. But this was absolutely state-of-the-art. I think we had one meg of RAM!

At that point they had already involved a company called CJG Consoles and they were a software writing company. I think that CJG actually worked for AutoDesk and had broken off, so AutoDesk had recommended them. AutoDesk had even sold us the computers. So with the purchase of the PC's and AutoCAD on the table and CJG being retained, the basis of the program had already been put together by the time I walked through the door.

RB: So who was steering the ship at this point, John?

CT: Yes, he was always the influence and the support behind it and it never would have been possible to do it without him. I'm not just talking about money. I'm talking about complete support and commitment to producing something.

---

[5] See reference to some brief history of AutoCAD in WYSIWYG seeds page 29. AutoCAD 9 was somewhat of a watershed release for many of us.

RB: And to clarify, the object was 2D plan drawings with symbols and attributes.

CT: Correct – to generate a plan and generate information for the hire system. The main player in the company was Ian Teague and his background was in set design. Therefore, the service that Modelbox was generally running was a database of theatres (mostly London ones) and they were taking touring shows and doing all the drawings for the sets and placing them inside the venues. What was fantastic about that is that you could knock out a twenty-venue tour in a morning, move your flying pieces and walk away with drawings the next day. So that was the value added service and the software was the development project.

So when I joined, it had attribute information attached to the 2D plans that would carry information like the gel and what gobo number it had - the very basic information. This information would shell out to a Foxpro database system for the paperwork aspect of it.

I think the paperwork was heavily driven to appeal to the American market. Although paperwork was an important thing on a West End show, certainly in my experience as a lighting designer and a chief electrician, the plan was everything.

RB: The British believe there should be one piece of paper and it should have all the information.[6]

CT: Funny story. When doing a show in Toronto, union rules stated that I had to have a Canadian assistant. I obviously sent the plan out in advance and when I walked through the door, the first thing he put in my hand was all this paperwork produced in Lightwright. I had never heard of it and I had never been confronted with so much paper and I found it totally intimidating. I said, "What's that?" He said, "Ah, well, this is the hookup, there's the dimmers…" I said, "You keep that. Where's my plan?"

So by the time we started working on AutoLight, we were certainly aware of the North American love of paper.

So sitting down at this program for the first time as a designer, I could see the pitfalls in it that didn't work for me. There were also things that for a chief electrician would not work in terms of the way the information was displayed. At that stage, the symbols were very much in their infancy, there weren't a lot

---

[6] See John McKernon on the fact that he is surprised that anybody in the UK uses Lightwright – page 113

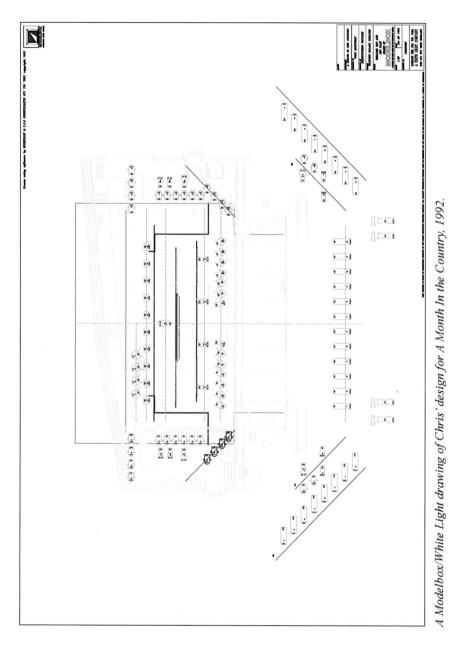

A Modelbox/White Light drawing of Chris' design for A Month In the Country, 1992.

of them, and they weren't fully loaded with information.

RB: Probably inconsistent.

CT: Very much so. So this became one of my first jobs, which was to draw up all the luminaires that we didn't have, which was a considerable number, and input all of the data for them. And with AutoCAD being very much in a world of DOS, it completely did my head in. I remember coming home at the end of the first month and saying to my wife, "I don't think I can do this. I'm going to have to bail out." Then, suddenly, it just clicked. I still favour being able to type in what I do, which was very much how AutoCAD worked back then. This is still to me a more comfortable way of driving it rather than through the Windows' mechanisms. It just becomes a generational thing. Once you've cracked dealing with that whole DOS thing, then all of those issues become second nature to you.

RB: I fought and lost the battle to put a command line in WYSIWYG. I now think that it's better not to try and mix the two.

CT: I like one, and I did get the hang of it. One of the things I found nerve racking was something that Modelbox still does and that is sessions with clients. A production manager could sit down with you and plan his tour. So while you were sitting there with him, you would be drawing all the while. I didn't like doing that.

As far as development goes, I could see things that we needed to do. For instance, projecting a beam out of the fixture. So we put the photometric data for the fixtures into the symbol. I think we always put in a rider that we used the manufacturer's photometric data. We didn't go out and independently verify it. We used to get derogatory comments about that. But, at the end of the day, having that data was a very useful tool. And certainly at the time when we were showing it to people at various trade exhibitions around the world, it was fairly gob smacking. We were doing something that, at that point, nobody else was doing. But, it was an expensive solution and in the long run, that would end up being the problem.

RB: By 1993, you had a production model. That's when I joined CBC and the lighting department there had already purchased AutoLight.

CT: Yes, and most of our clients were what you would call blue-chip clients, mostly because of the cost. Companies like the Canadian Broadcasting Corporation, The Royal Opera Company, the Sydney Opera House and Walt

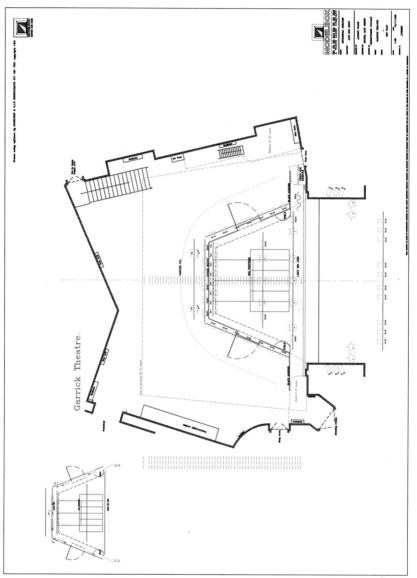

A 1995 drawing of the Live Bed Show produced at the Incidental Theatre..

Disney. There were very few small companies buying it. It was for the simple reason that the engine that was driving it was AutoCAD.

RB: The barrier to entry was $3000 to begin with. Add the cost of the PC and the plotter and you were talking about a $20,000 investment.

CT: For the big theatres, that was worthwhile. We were always trying to sell the added value. You're not just trying to sell a lighting package here. You're buying the most powerful lighting specific CAD package available.

RB: Unfortunately, by the time I got to CBC, I had written a fair amount of LXCAD in Lisp and we ceased using AutoLight. I never got to play with it. When AutoCAD 11 came out I started to re-write it all in C using ADS.[7]

CT: And, of course, AutoLight never made that leap. We came to an impasse and had to question whether we pushed on with this.

RB: I didn't have a wife at the time, but that's where I went home and thought I'm in over my head. Just compiling the 'Hello World' application in ADS was harrowing and their documentation at the time was almost non-existent.

CT: I think that's where we realized that we would have to go back and start everything again. And I think we had become very aware that the product's future was riding on this and there was a feeling that with the level of commitment and the money already spent measured against the return that we had, it didn't justify further development. I think CJD did do some C modifications to it and although I think some modules were adapted, it never really made the proper transition. It just wasn't viable anymore.

This brings me back to the problems of what I call blazing a trail. It's a very lonely place. It's quite exciting being at the front, and charging ahead, and going to trade shows and having everybody telling you how fantastic you are, but of course none of them are buying the damn thing.

RB: Damn straight. How many times did I hear from Broadway designers, "You're on to something here – this is amazing! I should use this on my next project." "Well, why don't you?" They never did. People get stuck using the tools they're familiar with. They are comfortable in the known quantity. They liked their Lightwright.

CT: That was something we certainly had to confront when we got to the States. There was an immediate excitement. I think the first show we ever

---

[7] AutoCAD Development System

took it to was USITT in Boston year. That was interesting for us, not only because USITT was very student/educationally orientated and we got very interesting feedback, but we knew we were certainly on to something, but we couldn't translate that into people wanting to buy it. Our biggest stumbling block was the sheer cost of setting the whole thing up.

RB: That was exactly what happened when I left CBC and left LXMOV behind and started on WYSIWYG. We couldn't charge somebody $3000 for a product that they couldn't use until they bought somebody else's $3000 product. So we were forced to start from scratch. And that was hard because it was DOS, but I wanted it to look like Windows because people were starting to use Windows. So we had to find a package that would do all the windowing, the menus, the dialog boxes, the OK, the Cancel, the Escape. That's what I spent the first four months coding up – the basic shell of the GUI, because we left AutoCAD behind. That's a downfall WYSIWYG still has – it's not AutoCAD.[8]

But, at the end of the day, you couldn't have expected AutoDesk to give it to us for free, because they did an awful lot of work on it.

CT: This is the problem with the entertainment industry – it's a niche market. Getting any manufacturer to come over, unless they are a part of that niche market, is so incredibly difficult. That's even true with the lamps we stick on our luminaires.

RB: So far, the HPL is the only proprietary lamp that our industry has.[9] All fixture manufacturers before the Source Four just took what was given.

CT: And in terms of AutoCAD and in terms of their global sales, we didn't really register on the radar, although they were interested in us because what we were doing was a bit different. And from their point of view, that was a big seller, even to the architects. "Look at the diversity of this product. Look what it's capable of doing."

RB: It's a similar story to Texas Instruments and Light and Sound Design regarding the Micro Mirror Device used on the Icon M. LSD supplies to practically every major tour rock band and they wooed TI executives by taking them back stage at U2 concerts and the like. But you're right; we are so small

---

[8] WYSIWYG can import and save DWG's – but some native information gets lost. See McKernon page 138

[9] See Cunningham page 99/100 on development and marketing of the HPL

compared to the automotive industry or anybody that maters, even if all their kids go to see U2.

CT: The other thing we realized in making quite a lot of visits to the American market, was that there was no getting around this paperwork thing. Most of the interest revolved around the paperwork. And of course, we were more than aware of Lightwright. We had even started seeing it more and more over here in the UK. There were LD's on West End shows that were using it. Some of that paperwork was starting to turn up in the offices of Modelbox as plans and information for tours.

So I think we bought our own copy of it and started playing with it. I can't remember this as gospel, but we may have even had conversations with John McKernon of Lightwright. It seemed like the logical thing to do to make these two things to talk to each other.

RB: John's problem was that he couldn't handle the handles.[10]

CT: For that reason, I expect we didn't get very far with it and we decided to do our own thing. So in the suite of programs, we added a product called LapLight to go with AutoLight, which again, was just a totally Foxpro based package. I guess it ended up doing an awful lot of Lightwright did. We said, "If that's what the electricians or designers in the States wanted, then let's put that in there for them". So it was conceived as a direct competitor. We even pitched the price the same.

RB: Foxpro could compile to an EXE?

CT: Yes.

RB: So you didn't have to sell licenses of Foxpro?

CT: No. This was what was really good about it.

RB: LXDB, which was part of LXCAD and LXMOV, was built with Foxpro for Windows, which was very neat, but I don't remember a scratch of that code now.

CT: LapLight became a useful package, but on a personal level, I never really took to it. I stepped back as we started to produce that and I very much let

---

[10] AutoCAD entities could have 'handles' attached to them when they are created. These were huge unique numbers ensuring that every object in the database could uniquely be identified. I used these handles to get information back and forth between LXCAD and LXDB so changes in one application would reflect properly in the other. Lightwright can now store these too.

Peter Byard deal with that. He was very enthused by it. Where I was very forceful with AutoLight and how that went, I took very much a backseat with LapLight. The thing I did like and what I insisted on, was that it did relate to AutoLight.

What it did do fantastically was a sort of reverse engineering. You could create the paperwork and it would create your plan. We knew we were banging our heads against the wall with AutoLight in terms of whom we were ever going to sell it to. It was only ever going to be these big companies and we were never going to hit into the domestic market. So we thought LapLight might be our solution. So we bundled it within our cost package with AutoSketch. So initially, it was creating lighting plans in AutoSketch for people.

RB: Hang on – this is the first time we've mentioned AutoSketch. You better explain that one.

CT: AutoDesk introduced AutoSketch as a very basic cheap package with obviously very little of the functionality that AutoCAD had but it could pump out a very basic lighting plot.

RB: It didn't use the core AutoCAD engine?

CT: Correct. But it could link to AutoLight as well. So it would talk in a more meaningful way to AutoLight. It had all the same symbols with all the attributes and it could produce a plan. It was very scary and certainly nothing you would ever trust completely. To be fair, the AutoSketch/LapLight combined package made a nice schematic of your rig to go with your paperwork, but it was no lighting plan. However, it was a nice solution. We were making those first steps in trying to make something much bigger.

This was also when we were realizing the potential of utilizing all the information that was sitting in the plan; the fact that with a luminaire you had its patch information, and what gobo was in it, what gel and of course the beam data. Our most basic wish for it initially was what if this became a mimic for what was on stage. I guess it was the, 'do something once', which I think is the whole point of CAD - do it once then translate it into as many places as you can.

I think that's true of anything we do on computers or multi-media or anything. Once you've taken a photograph with a digital camera, there are a million other things you can do with it from that one act of taking that shot. Looking back into the early days, we were thinking of doing the same thing with that information. Take the information and drive it to as many places as you possibly can. One of which was a good plan on the screen. Now what if that was sat next to the lighting desk and had a real time communication with a luminaire? You either generate it form the plan end, or once it already exists, you can update the plan from that. That is when we started to talk to manufacturers like Strand and Arri. We talked to Flying Pig, who were the only company that I would say were enthusiastic. They could see where it was going.

The problem was that an overwhelming load of it was AutoCAD. Even if we did find a way of integrating it in those days, you were talking about somebody adding a PC and $15,000 to the cost of a console. There was no way around the cost of AutoCAD, apart from bespoke writing, which was way beyond where we were.

There was a lot of talking done in those days, an awful lot of talking - from exhibitions onwards and from manufacturers to people using the product. That's primarily what went on!

RB: So just about the time you were talking to Strand and FPS, I was simultaneously doing the same?[11]

CT: Absolutely. And of course, our paths had crossed at that stage. We were dealing with your friend Mr. Plotkin at CBC, who was one of our most vocal users, and I also remember you contacting me about coming over and working with us. I think it was the time when you were looking away from CBC. I guess you were already working on your own product at this point.

RB: A lot of the code I wrote existed before I joined CBC, but around this time LXMOV would have been completed there and I quit CBC to find employment elsewhere.

CT: I guess you were looking at broadening your horizons further and we were a natural potential partner because we were working towards the same end. We had met at a trade show somewhere so we had that conversation. I was certainly more than aware of who you were. I remember going and having a conversation with John Simpson and saying that I think we should do this.

What that did was open up a whole can of worms for us. We obviously had the commitment to the programmers; we were contracted with them. We could see possibilities with some of the ideas you were throwing at us, but at the time, I think, we were right in the middle of the pain threshold with the software.

---

[11] See introduction to Tom Thorne – page 181

I think we were already at that stage where we were giving up. Commercially, we were still pushing it out and we were still supporting our customers, but I think we were already moving on and starting to feel that this wasn't going anywhere. So we just decided that we couldn't afford to take anybody else on at that point or do anything else that was different. Needless to say John and I had cause to regret this course of action on more than one occasion. So, WYSIWYG popped up and the rest is history I suppose.

RB: Not quite. Modelbox shifted gears and went specifically into some pretty cool services.

CT: It never stopped doing all those things. It never stopped providing its CAD services to the theatre industry. That was still the money earner. What was coming on-line throughout that process was this exploration of 3D and we touched on that even in AutoLight. So initially, a luminaire could project a beam out and it would show you it in a plan view. It would show you the hot spot and the falloff. You could actually have a whole lighting bar and activate all the lights on the bar and it would throw all their beams on the stage. Then

Early complex 3D Studio model taking advantage of textures.

drawing a line through all those beams in AutoCAD, it could generate a graph of the photometric readings right through that line. We were getting into fairly interesting territory there. Certainly interesting to TV people for instance, because in those days, those light levels really mattered, much more than they do today.

Then we thought it would be much more useful if it were 3D. So then you end up throwing out the 3D cones. Then you take it a step further, which is the beam interruption; what happens when it hits that 3D object on the stage? Then you find that you've flogged that one about as far as you can in a 2D/3D CAD package, because there is only one place to go beyond there, and that is visualization. The real deal is rendering.

So we played with all the toys including the animation program that AutoDesk came out with that wasn't very good - the one that made 'flicks'. Remember that? We loved doing those. The scary thing is that in 1990, 1991, that excited people - soft-shaded 3D CAD models with fly-around camera that would show you what the set would look like for industrials.

RB: I remember television commercials in that era. Pharmaceutical companies

A more complex rendering in 3D Studio using volumetrics.

wanted the computer generated look – the CG look. But it was too expensive at the time. They would have artists physically paint 2D animations to look like VCG. The demand was huge.

CT: It was sexy. Look at Disney's first foray with Tron. That was unbelievable. But now you look at it . . . it was trail blazing at the time.

Then the toy that turned up at our door because of our relationship with AutoDesk was 3D Studio.

RB: We're not at 3D Studio Max yet. This was still DOS 3D Studio.

CT: Oh yes, very much so - the old four windows DOS thing. But it was fantastic. Peter and I took to this like ducks to water. We got very very excited, but immediately ran into its limitations; particularly in the lighting front - what it couldn't do lighting-wise and how unrealistic the lighting was.

RB: That was one of the big problems I had with LXMOV. AutoCAD only supported two-hundred-and-fifty-six colours. If you wanted to fade a red light, you got about three shades then black.

CT: I have a feeling that the early versions of 3D Studio were much the same. Mind you, it was probably a limitation of the graphics cards available at the time. You were still having to use dithered stuff.

I think one of the things that went on our wish list right away was volumetric lighting. We always wanted that. I used to spend hours recreating fake volumetric lighting. Creating opacity maps and applying them to 3D cones to make it look like I had a volumetric light that would fade off to transparent as it hit the stage.

The other thing you couldn't do in the early version, which is now commonplace in virtually all the packages, was that they never got to the concept of gobos.

RB: Well, you had four light sources, the ambient light, point lights, spotlights and the sun. "What's your problem?"

CT: Absolutely. So we would scan in a gobo and make a 3D object of it and stick it as close to the front of the light as you possibly could. I used to spend a great deal of time on that, just messing about trying to get it to sit in just the right place.

RB: Then wait for it to render.

CT: Which took some time. But immediately, we were getting everybody excited again because we were creating looks for their shows and things that were really turning them on. The other thing we obviously saw because of its animation capabilities was, "What if that talked to moving lights?" By this point, we had got beyond Vari-Lite and there were a lot more manufacturers out there. There were lighting desks like the Whole Hog and you had possibilities. There were all these other things going on. We were trying to talk AutoDesk into taking this on board. Then in the mid nineties, I remember having discussions with Jere Harris of the Production Resource Group and he was very interested.

RB: At that point he wasn't purchasing everybody. Production Arts was still Production Arts. I know, because they were one of the first to buy into WYSIWYG around that time.

CT: Yes. In 1996 I went over to do a demonstration in New York with the DOS version of 3D Studio. It still hadn't made its move to Windows. What we were trying to convey to everybody, as we were the sort of evangelists for what CAD could do, was that you could create a real-world model, port it into this animation product, and simulate things. Now from PRG's point of view, we were not just talking about lighting, we were talking about complex scene changes.

During this time, we got quite busy just doing visualizations for people. We grew from just three people to about ten. We had grown to the point where the IT needs had become so high with the render farms and all of that that we needed the people to support it. We were nursing this thing. We used to have to sit with it 24 hours a day.

Lawrence O'Connor and Steve Wentworth were full time CAD guys and I moved over to be Chief Exec of the company. Our main focus became 3D models, computer visualization and video editing; you know – mostly TV stuff. Development really took a back seat, although we were having discussions with people like Stage Technologies, who have gone on to develop their own custom systems.[12]

But in those days we saw all of this stuff that those systems were capable of doing. As you've seen, the doors to the manufacturers were just not open to that kind of integration. Everything it was doing was there. All that XYZ data . . . that's all it was. You just needed to find a good way to pipeline that information from one thing to the other, so you could pre-program a show or

---

[12] Philip Nye talks about control and the unique things Stage Technologies does on page 363

similarly, you could have a real time mimic of what was going on on the stage.

Now these are all things that have come to pass, which I'm pleased about, but also hugely irritated with. You see visualizations of stage sets in magazines now and think there were people doing that ten years ago. In many ways it was more exciting then than it is now. It's all become so commonplace and in some ways less interesting.

In the mean time, Modelbox continues and thrives!

Pictures of Brighton West Pier on facing page courtesy Louise Stickland.

12 WAYNE HOWELL

Introduction

Wayne is a bit of a rebel in the industry. He has a 'let's just get on with it', attitude that tends to frighten some of the more purist intellectuals who would rather see things done in a more conventional fashion. That is not to say that Wayne's products are in any way shoddy. He just manages to get things done in an efficient fashion while many others will drag things out and get bogged with the details.

My first contact with Wayne was in January of 1995. CAST Lighting was lighting the Juno Awards, the Canadian equivalent to the Grammies, and we had a huge Vari*Lite rig. The event was taking place in an arena and we had a large rig of VL5's above the audience, which I wanted to animate with the Lamp Tramp, his first real solo project. I saw it six months earlier when Pink Floyd came through town, but I quickly found out that such specialized equipment was way out of our price range.

The problem, as Wayne explains, was that Lamp Tramp was a *project* to begin with - not a *product*. He is a guy that solves people's problems by building black boxes. When you have a job that needs that special thing that you can't purchase from your average vendor, Wayne can build it for you. He will then, quite likely, turn your project into a product.

My next experience with Wayne was when we were spec'ing a new WYG/ DMX interface box. During WYSIWYG 1 and WYSIWYG 2 days, we used custom-built ISA cards that went into your PC. Laptops were really not all that prevalent, but by 1997, we had to abandon the ISA cards and come up with alternate solutions more suitable for portable use. AC Lighting, WYSIWYG's distributors at the time, commissioned Artistic Licence to build two models - the Vision 500 and the Vision 2000.

The Vision 500 was largely based on Wayne's parallel port DMX-Dongle II that he was already building. The Vision 2000 was a different beast. It was to accept four streams of DMX and output one of MIDI and communicate with the PC via Ethernet. This had never been done before. CAST was to develop the TCP protocol and Wayne was to build the box.

Only now do I understand why Wayne pushed us so hard for a written spec. I didn't understand what could be so complicated. In my mind it was simple: 5-pin in and Cat 5 out. I was well aware of the complexities of the protocol and the fact that receiving DMX from (potentially) four separate sources, at four separate clock rates, was a nightmare, but I figured that we would sort it out as we went along. It had to be done. When you read about his harrowing experience with Pink Floyd, you will have an appreciation for just how you can get burned by agreeing, in principle, what a product should be, without writing it down. I guess we all get a little wiser as we get a little older.

I went to visit Wayne at Artistic Licence in London and we walked across the street, in typical British style, to have a pint. We were joined by Tracey Patterson, Wayne's wife and co-worker, and their dog, Monty.

Interview

WH: The pub came before the office. We were working in a real dodgy location not far from Hanger Lane, close to Avolites, and Tracey came down to look for somewhere to move the office to. Tracey and I had recently just bought a flat in this area and she came back and said "I've found the perfect office. It's twenty steps away from the pub and I've checked the beer and it's fine." That's how we ended up with our office.

RB: Congratulations on your newest product – Colour-Tramp – I think it's quite amazing. I tell everyone about it.

WH: This is an evolution of the Lamp-Tramp system. It is much more sophisticated but the big difference is that it controls colour rather than just intensity. The product has been very well received in the architectural world as has won us some big contracts.

We've just completed two major installations at Broadgate in the City of London. The first one is a lit floor in a public plaza. There are some 650 LED colour changers in the ground. The entire thing is controlled by Colour-Tramp using a combination of Art-Net and RDM[1].

RB: One of the first 'real' installations of RDM – out before the ratification of the standard.

WH: That's true. We've used the V1.0 document that is out for public comment. It has been a great opportunity to check that RDM does actually do what it says on the can.

RB: And does it?

WH: Yes – big time. The Broadgate installation is the World's first and largest RDM install and it works brilliantly. All the LED fixtures have sensors that tell Colour-Tramp their temperature, voltage and whether there is any moisture inside. RDM also allows Colour-Tramp to remotely address all the lamps and even upload new firmware.

LEDs in the ground at Broadgate in the City of London.

---

[1] Remote Device Management – a method of using the single balanced pair in DMX lines to do bi-directional communication.

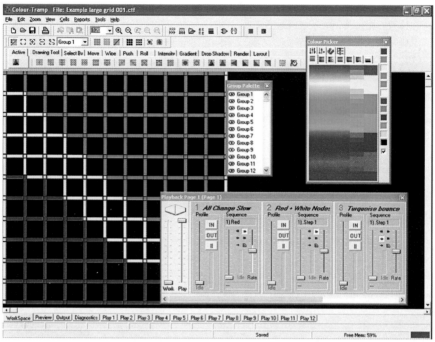

The Colour-Tramp control and monitoring system is a combination of a lighting board and a paint program.

RB: So Colour-Tramp is more than just a lighting controller?

WH: Very much. Our concept was to integrate lighting control, installation management and building management into one package. For example, Colour-Tramp can email you a report on all of the sensors and whether any maintenance is needed. It's this kind of integration that matters to the end client. In an installation of this type, you could easily spend more on monitoring and maintenance over its life, than the original capital cost of the equipment.

RB: Is that what wins you the contract?

WH: To a large extent yes. But I think most important is the fact that we will take on the entire project from concept design, through manufacturing and installation to commissioning, staff training and maintenance. We like to provide the total solution.

RB: That takes us to the beginning and how I often think of you and your company. It's both about the products and the projects.

It was the summer of 1995, Nils Thorjussen got us passes to Pink Floyd's Division Bell tour as they came through Toronto. It was quite a night, and one that quite literally changed my perspective on lighting. We got to sit with all the board operators for the show and I spent most of my time with Gareth Williams who operated the Whole Hog I and Lamp Tramp. That was the first time I ever saw your stuff in action.

WH: I was a bit younger then, but I have to say that the whole project took several years off my life. It was one of those projects that started out fairly simply where we were commissioned by Brilliant Stages to do some basic motor control effects on the tour, and also a controller to allow them to control a two-dimensional array of lights. At the time they didn't really have a feel for the functionality they needed out of any of this. In actual fact, we were at the other end of a verbal specification via an intermediary.

Unfortunately we produced what we were verbally told to produce. There was this classic day of turning up at Brilliant Stages with the prototype motor control boxes and motor control software and lighting control software and attaching it to these massive great big periactoids that were going out on the Floyd tour. After a morning of getting everything configured I was a bit chuffed because it all worked exactly as had been requested.

RB: ...as in a telephone conversation.

WH: ... in a telephone conversation. Then Tony, who was the General Manager there, came down and started asking "How do you do this?". "Well, it doesn't do that." "Then how do you do this?". "It doesn't do that." "How do you synchronize the movement of all the periactoids together?" "Well... they don't

– they just go to position." Then Tony says "Ah... best I go and get the boss." So Charlie Kail came down and I go through the demonstration and he starts asking exactly the same questions that Tony had asked. By this point I was beginning to realize that something had been lost in the translation and what I thought was rather excellent was not what they wanted at all.

To cut a very long story short, they

Wayne at Pink Floyd's Division Bell rehearsals.

fired the guy who had been dealing with all of the technical management for the tour, and bearing in mind that there were two weeks to go before the equipment is due to go into containers to go out to rehearsals, they asked me if I would take on the whole job. I said, "All bets are off, no guarantees of anything, but we'll give it our best shot." We went away and re-designed everything.

We were still configuring and testing as we were loading into containers. We then flew out to San Bernardino in California for what were notionally meant to be the rehearsals.

RB: Did you have to change hardware?

WH: Yes. There were fifteen periactoids, eight with banks of triangles on them and there were four spinners, which were multi-axis machines that came up out of the stage at a frightening rate. We built all the hardware to do the motor control information to interface to AC inverters and so on and the control system for that. Within the lighting control systems was this thing we wrote called Lamp-Tramp, which had no specification for it apart from, "We'd kind of like to have hieroglyphics come up maybe 'Hey Teacher'."

RB: Was the concept Marc Brickman's or Mark Fisher's?[2]

WH: It was difficult for me to tell the division, however, there was an amusing

The Pariactoids that were controlled by Lamp-Tramp and Mission-Control that became famous for spelling 'Hey Teacher'.

---

[2] Brickman was the lighting designer on the show where Fisher did the stage design.

moment. Tracey came out to the rehearsals - at the time she was not working full-time for Artistic Licence - because I needed some help as things were getting seriously out of hand. In the distance across the hanger I saw her talking to Marc Brickman, and of course she didn't know who the hell he was. Now forgive me if I'm misquoting, but it went something like this: Brickman said to her, "You know I designed all of this," and Tracey said, "Funnily enough, I thought we did that bit." It's one of those things that can only happen to if you don't know who you're talking to.

In some ways it does answer your question. The thing I find funny is the interaction between the technical engineering lighting designer and the artistic lighting designer. I actually much prefer being in the situation where I get a wish list and you try to figure out how much of that wish list you can implement and how many ideas we've got that we can feed back into that to give them the tools to work with it. Lamp-Tramp, I think, was a classic example of that because we expanded it significantly after the Floyd tour and it went out with the Rolling Stones.

RB: Voodoo Lounge. Another memorable pass for me, thanks to Nils.

Wayne and wife-to-be Tracey Patterson.

The Rolling Stones Voodoo Lounge tour was the second high profile job for Lamp-Tramp.

WH: I don't think anybody had ever tried the concept of mixing a lighting desk with a paint package before. It's one of those things that once you start thinking in terms of working with a two dimensional grid of lights, you can suddenly steal quite a lot of ideas from a simple program like Paint Brush. It becomes quite obvious when you think about it – there's no reason you can't map text. Then the whole thing snowballed from there and you discover there are other applications for it. We sold quite a lot of systems into Japan where they used them for a whole range of applications from controlling advertising on buildings to concert tours, etc.

Fooling around inside the set pieces that pop out of the Division Bell floor via Mission-Control.

For the Floyd tour, I never did see the written spec. I'm reliably informed that it was two inches thick, but as we'd never seen it in the first place, and it was two weeks before rehearsals, it was rather irrelevant. It was a case of let's get as close to what they were describing as possible. It was painful in the extreme, but we got there and we didn't have any equipment failures on it during the whole tour. It actually pleased us so much that there was only one Lamp-Tramp system and one Mission-Control[3] system on that tour and there was a backup Hog. That made my day. I consider that to be such a compliment.

By the time the tour had finished, we had a MIDI interfacing system going on so that it could be triggered from the Hog. The Hog's MIDI macro output functions went in specifically at our request so we could slave the things together.

RB: What did you do before Floyd? What were your beginnings?

WH: In the same way as many of us, I got into a bit of lighting in school, a bit of am-dram stuff, and did the lighting at the local community centre. I went to college to do nuclear physics.

RB: At Birmingham University?

WH: Yes. I got involved with the whole student union gig there.

RB: Did you see Light and Sound Design there?

WH: Yes. There was a group there called Stage Staff who did all of the gigs at the students' union and in the end we ended up being temporary road crew for LSD. Take into account that LSD had really grown up from their local area by this time, but there were people there who had gone to local universities and we all knew who was who.

That's when I really started getting into lighting and some lighting design and worked as a board operator. It was at the time when there were shows coming in, that would now have their own LD, but in those days didn't. They basically had whatever house lights were available. So you actually got to run lights on acts, such as UB40 and the like, that you would never get a chance to do now.

I did live sound for a bit too, and then I got offered a job with a company that unfortunately went bust just before I took up the job. They were making one of the first automated pan and tilt moving head things. They had some technical problems when they were out on a Billy Joel tour. They started getting motor failures on the pan and tilt drives.

RB: What year would this be?

---

[3] Mission-Control was the name of the motor control system Wayne built.

WH: '84. So I never got to take up the job with them. There were two people running that company called Nick and Rowena Lynch. They had one employee (Steve Warren) and I was to become the forth employee. In any case it, all went pear shaped for the company and Nick and Rowena were taken up by Avolites, theoretically to start designing Avolites' first moving light. Shortly after that Steve Warren was offered a job there as a wireman and a couple weeks later I got a phone call from Steve saying they needed another wireman, and did I want to join them?

I went up for my interview and was interviewed by Paul Ollett who was sitting on the floor surrounded by what was to become the QM500, the first one about to go out on Michael Jackson tour.[4] So I got the job and started as a wireman. Because it was a small, but very fast growing company, I went from wireman, to production manager, and to service manager, in a very short time-frame. I did service for three years and spent my time flying around the world just before shows went up. It was the early days of memory desks in the rock and roll industry so we were pleased when it worked when it left the factory. Nobody had really started worrying about formal quality control and we were learning as we went. I don't think there was anybody at Avolites at that time who had had formal training for what they did. We all just learned things as we went along.

I worked as board operator for Avolites for a while on things like the Eurovision Song Contest. Then the time came where someone came to me and asked if I could write software.

RB: Did you finish the physics degree?

WH: Yes.

RB: Was there a computer element to that in the early '80's?

WH: Minimal.

RB: So that definitely was not your training for writing code.

WH: I have always been a bit of a tinkerer. I had an interest in electronics and I would take things apart and try to make them better.

RB: But in the mid '80's, you didn't own a PC because they were only just

---

[4] Released in 1983, the QM500 is a classic a big-ass rock board that could compete with the audio console as a chick magnet. It had memory, but its most endearing feature was the very rapid response time on the flash buttons. That, in conjunction with analog outputs to analog Avo dimmers made operators feel very connected with the performance.

coming in. How did you know you could write software?

WH: I didn't. I just figured that it couldn't be that complicated. I've looked at source listing for some stuff and if you logically went through it; it kind of made sense.

I remember saying 'yes' on the Friday and Saturday morning going out to the bookshop and buying a couple of books and spending the whole weekend reading them, then going in on the Monday and starting working as the second programmer at Avolites.

RB: At that time, what hardware were they using?

WH: It was all 6809 based. I first got into doing hardware design on the QM500. Again, we were all learning on the job. I taught myself how to design circuit boards with tape and a scalpel and I taught myself about basic electronics. As projects came up, I just taught myself. It was the same for writing code. It was quite funny actually. To compile the operating systems for one of the desks was the start of the concept of a long lunch at the pub for me because you would set it compiling at midday, there would be no point in coming back from the pub until three in the afternoon because it would still be compiling.

RB: What machine were you compiling on?

WH: It was an Apple IIe and a 6809 processor in it so it was a native compiler, which was why we were using it.[5]

RB: Which language were you using, if any?

WH: All assembler, with a bit of machine code here and there because there were actually bugs in the assembler that you had to work around.[6]

---

[5] Mark Hunt has exactly the same story at LSD when building the Icon. See Hunt – page 212

[6] There may be a little confusion here between assembly language and machine code. Most people who know a little about writing code think of high-level languages like C, C++, Fortran or Pascal. If you write in these languages, you use a compiler to create an object file, then a linker to create machine code. The problem is, you are often at the mercy of the guy who wrote the compiler. He has to take a very high level language and optimize it as he sees best, not seeing the bigger picture of your application. If you really want to optimize your code, specific to your application, it is better to use assembly language. Assembly is a much lower level language and is specific to the chip you are writing for. It may include a statement like PUSH, POP, INC, DEC and MOVE (see the watermark on the cover of this book). Once you've written your application or subroutine, you push it through an assembler and it creates machine code. This is literally 0's and 1's, but you can actually look at it Hex. Wayne had to edit the true Hex values to get some stuff right. Today processors are so fast and so cheap and compilers have gotten (cont...)

I look back to then and the design cycle was weeks to get a circuit board out because you were doing it all with a scalpel and weeks to get a software release out because you could only realistically be doing one compile a day. Compare that to today where knocking a circuit board out, that includes a PIC[7] processor card, can be done in a day.

RB: And you compile eight to twelve times an hour.

WH: There isn't time for a tea break between compiles these days!

I went on doing this at Avolites for a while. I did most of the design for the Rolacue[8], and quite a lot of the circuit board design for the production version of the QM500. Also I did odds and ends on dimmers.

Finally the company went through the classic small company growth phase and pain phase and then Ian Walley, who owned it privately at that time, sold it to a holding company. I had been there about five years when it all starting to change politically, at which point I decided to start up my own company and see what I could do.

Initially the concept was to establish a design/consultantancy operation. I nicked a couple of jobs from Avolites as I left - they were jobs they frankly didn't want very much - like the service contract for the Hippodrome[9] and things of that sort, which kept me going for the first year as I gradually built up the business. After about five years we started to make the transition from what was effectively a one-man-band freelance designer into one with a product range.

RB: I must say for a guy with your design philosophy, Artistic Licence is a wonderful name.

WH: I take the company name quite seriously! Lateral thinking is the most important part of design.

RB: When did it actually start?

(...cont) so much better that it is unlikely that today's applications have to resort to assembly language. Higher-level languages also allow you to seamlessly port code from one machine to another just by changing your compiler, where it is impossible if you wrote in chip specific assembly language. See Grimes' thoughts C vs. Assembler on page 259

[7] PICmicro is the brand name of the micro controller family of chips made by the company Microchip. Priority Interrupt Controller or PIC processors are used everywhere, including in your dishwasher. They are commonly used to read button presses on face panels and in moving lights to drive motors.

[8] Nifty board that had a large cylinder that you could write all your band's songs on with a china-marker and roll it around to change your patch and the like. Today we commonly refer this action as changing 'pages' on your desk thanks to the Whole Hog.

[9] Huge night club in London.

WH: Around 1987. The first couple years involved a lot of design work. I still did freelance design for Avolites and I also did quite a lot of production work for companies that were doing interactive A/V projects - the kind of situation where you couldn't buy a box off the shelf. You actually had to sit down and write a program.

Then we started playing around and getting into products. I think the first ever product we made was a protocol converter. This is where you learn about trying to sell things internationally, and all that that involves.

Lamp-Tramp became the first mainstream product. It was based on a PC program called Light-CAD, which I wrote in the first year after leaving Avolites. As it turns out, it was before its time. It was an off-line editor, which at the time nobody was doing, and it worked with Avo, Celco and Jands boards. It was painful in the extreme to use in that everyone was using non-standard disk formats and memory cards and so a whole load of interfacing had to be done.[10] We sold some of these, but it turned out that it was one of those products that everyone wanted until you tell them it's actually going to cost them money. Then suddenly it's, "We didn't expect to pay for it."

RB: Was it a pure software product?

WH: It was software with an optional card reader so you could plug in those Celco memory cards into a PC. We used the core of that software for Lamp Tramp.

I think the first successful product was Micro-Scope, the DMX tester. That's what turned us from a services company into a product company. I took on a guy as a business consultant, when I first designed it. He was worried that we were taking too big a risk by manufacturing twenty-five of these in the first batch. However, the first twenty-five sold in the first two weeks. We had never seen anything like this before.

RB: Was the DMXter out by then?[11]

WH: The DMXter was out, but in all honesty I had never seen one.

RB: You don't see them on this side of the pond much.

WH: I have to say that in Europe we do seem to have taken over the test side

---

[10] Eric Cornwell makes a good living out of converting show files between consoles, sometimes using the USITT ASCII Cue Format, and sometimes not as he explains it – it's never a simple task. See Cornwell – page 280

[11] The Lil' DMXter by [Bob] Goddard Design was the American standard DMX tool for years.

of the market, although Bob is still very much leading the market on the American side of the pond. With these products, it tends to be who got there first. On the European side we got a good foothold very early on so that's the one that took us into being a product company and gave us the learning opportunity.

RB: What processor was involved?

WH: When it was released, it was a PIC1742, and it's now a 17C44.

RB: And you wrote all the code in there?

WH: Yes.

RB: You did the circuit board and all?

WH: And the case design, silk screen, the manual and the flyers – at that time I was the only designer at Artistic.

There have now been numerous versions of the product: Micro-Scope, Micro-Scope 2, 2A, 3 and 3A. One of the things I'm proud about is that we can still upgrade the very first unit to the latest software. That has been a big thing for me with design; you make it as future-proof as you can and you make it as re-usable as you can.

It's worked for us with all of the custom projects we've done over the years as well. As time has gone on, we've built up a pretty massive inventory of circuit board designs and software building blocks. That has allowed us to say "yes, we can do that job" because we know it's one of those, or that's the basic design but we need to relay the circuit board to do this. You fundamentally know you have the knowledge in the bank. You can look at what is a really complex job and break it down into things you've already invented or problems you've already fixed in the past. I suppose that's one of the reasons that most people probably perceive us as a manufacturing company. However, we are still about 50:50 between projects and manufacturing. The dividing line between the two is very loose in that custom projects

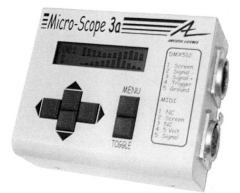

Version 3a of the popular test tool Microscope.

generate new products and feed back in to future products. It's worked out well from that point of view.

I don't do all of the design any more, which is a major step forward. I still do concept design and focus R&D and so forth.

RB: Do you write any code now?

WH: I do. There are certain products like Grand-Master Flash![12] that have gone through five or six years of evolution without biting the bullet and just saying we're going to rewrite it. You can't really hand that code over to someone.

We now share the workload on new products. I like to work with people that can do both hardware and software design because I've never really understood how you can do one, but not the other. People who do software without hardware design tend to lack the understanding on how it all links together - and the short cuts you can take to improve it by doing things in just a slightly different way.[13] It does make for an interesting life. I would hate to do circuit board design as a full time job, but on the other hand, if you're doing one every couple of months then it's good to make sure that you can still do it.

RB: So what product came first – Grand-Master Flash! or the DMX-Dongle? Was the DMX device a great product that needed software or was it the case of software needing an output device?

WH: The DMX-Dongle was one of those products I did without any market research. I just thought it would be really cool given that PC's were becoming more powerful. At the time, we had no idea about how powerful they were going to get. I just thought the Dongle would be a really funky product so it's just one of those things

The DMX Dongle sends and receives DMX using a PC's parallel port – this product OEM'ed as WYSIWYG's Vision 500.

---

[12] PC based lighting control software.

[13] See Hunt – page 240 for the same thoughts.

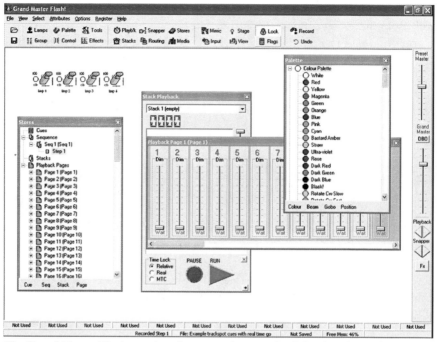

The Grand Master Flash user interface – another popular PC only solution for lighting control.

that I did. Happily, the thing sold brilliantly. Interestingly the key market was as a piece of test equipment.

We were looking for a way of doing a PC based lighting desk. We already had Lamp-Tramp in the bag, but Lamp-Tramp required a hardware co-processing board to do all of its calculations and we wanted to do something that was completely PC based. The Dongle just had a simple processor in there to keep the DMX refresh rate going. It didn't have the processing power to do calculations.

Funnily enough, it was about the same time that Borland launched Delphi. Although I'd been programming C for some years, I had never done any Windows stuff. DOS was still the platform that we were all using. We all started to use Windows, but we hadn't really considered it a viable platform to run real-time applications on, or develop real-time applications on. Then Borland came out with Delphi, which was a real turning point in being able to do visual programming with some real power under the hood.

I put together a Win 3.1 application called Grand-Master, which was very very simple by today's standards. It was a two-scene preset lighting desk with memories and sequences and a few fiddly bits here and there. We started selling it as an option for the Dongle and it started going really well. We ran with that for about two years then the power of PC processing was really starting to come through and we saw that you could run some serious lighting on a PC based platform. That's when the Grand-Master Flash! program started and was the concept that it was a moving light control program that could also control conventional lights as opposed to the other way around. Horizon went the other route where they were controlling dimmer channels and they then added moving lights.

Add to that the fact that you had another generation of lighting designers coming through that were used to PCs and were used to some form of Windows, over a period of a few years, we saw the question, "Why would I use a PC to control lights when I could have a lighting desk?" change to, "Why would you use a lighting desk when you could use a PC?" That shows the kind of sea change that the industry is going through! Interesting times!

Take the PLASA show in 2002. There wasn't anyone I had to convince that the PC was a viable platform for running a lighting show. It's probably the first PLASA show where I didn't hear the comment: "Oh, I wouldn't want to use Windows to run my show," or that kind of thing.

RB: So Grand-Master Flash! is still a very serious part of the product line.

WH: It still is and we keep underestimating it. One of the things I find is that we have so many products in the line now, and if you include all of the variations and themes and OEM modules, I think we have in excess of 150 products, it tends to mean you lose focus on things.

About six months ago, I was having a beer with a guy who regularly uses Grand-Master Flash! for conference work. He said to me, "You know, it really is an excellent product – you should push it much harder than you do." It's good to have that kind of feedback because you tend to forget about things and you look at it and you say, "Gee, it is pretty good; it does do what it's meant to do." It's got a pretty well-defined market place. It sells heavily into conference work, because it means freelance LDs and lighting techs can bring their own lighting desk along on their portable. It sells well into museum control and that kind of thing.

It's still core of the range, but at the end of the day it's a product that sells

The Net-Link box, one in a line of Art-Net compliant protocol converters.

hardware and we're much more a hardware company that we are a software company. That was the concept behind making the drivers for the Dongle available free of charge, so that anybody else that wanted to develop software for it could do that. That worked. I think we've got about seven or eight different companies involved in writing software for the DMX-Dongle and we've extended that sort of concept with Art-Net and keeping all of that in the public domain, so that if people want to work with it they can. If, at the end of the day, we can still sell boxes, we can still buy beer (and eat)!

RB: It's a unique approach because so many people have spent an awful lot of time protecting protocols. You are very much a rebel in the sense that when you see a pie, and you know you're not going to have all of it, you're content to just have a reasonable portion in return for your efforts.

WH: I think that's important. We kicked off with our first Ethernet design, which was the link up with you and the WYSIWYG interfaces. We used the Vision 2000[14] as the springboard to develop our own hardware platform. We have a perception of what customers wanted in terms of Ethernet/DMX distribution products. We really wanted to wait around until the whole ACN thing happened because I am a great fan of standards.[15] I like everything being able to talk to each other. It's the engineer in me. I like it to be symmetrical and for everything to plug together and just work.

It was clear that ACN wasn't going to happen any time soon (and I'm not sure that has changed much). It was also clear that we weren't a big enough company to 'Do a Strand' or 'Do an ETC' in terms of imposing something on the market. So in the end, we said let's just do something really simple that does the job and will work for the products that we want to design and then publish it.

---

[14] CAST Lighting worked with AC Lighting and Artistic Licence to build the Vision 2000 – a rack mount device that received four streams of DMX and outputted one stream of MIDI and talked to a WYSIWYG PC via TCP/IP.

[15] ACN is Advanced Control Network – ESTA's proposed replacement for control protocols in the theatre, including automatic device discovery and patching.

We figured there would be other small companies out there that may pick up on the Art-Net protocol. If we were right it would probably generate more box sales for us.

We had no idea that we were lighting a major fire in the industry. We were suddenly being approached by major players who wanted to get involved with Art-Net. ADB was the first. Then followed a string of other companies: MA Lighting, High End Systems, Whole Hog and so on.[16]

Many people have asked me if I'm worried about that now I've published this thing, I'd end up with competitors using all our hard work and the software and intellectual property that we have given away for free. No. The bottom line is that we've helped to generate a whole new market within our industry, or at least accelerate one that was going to happen anyway. I don't want to take over the world. I'm not stupid enough to think that I can possibly have 100% of the market. I would just like a percentage of it, and that seems to be working.

RB: The Vision 2000 was built in dire need. We desperately needed a device to get DMX into a laptop. Our ISA DMX cards were looking very tired and useless on portables. I really wanted to do a USB solution, but Nils Thorjussen argued that until he could buy a USB mouse at Comp-USA there would be no point. He was right. We couldn't rush the market. Many of our serious users were using Windows NT, which didn't even support USB. That was the real issue.

WH: I would agree. Although this is one of those dangerous statements to make, I'm still not convinced that USB will be around that long as a mainstream interface for PC. Everyone is moving so heavily in the Ethernet and Wi-Fi direction and the new standard for power over Ethernet is now out. Ethernet has hugely more bandwidth than USB and you already have the volume there with the chipsets costing peanuts. It's not at rock bottom yet. So I would have thought that over the next year you will see PCs with multiple powered Ethernet outlets. The USB connector, if it's still there, is going to be perceived as the keyboard or mouse connector as the PS/2 is today.

That said – I wonder if I'll be eating my words by the time I read this in print! I could be wrong on that, but that's the way I see it going and that's why

---

[16] AC Lighting Ltd, ACT Lighting , ADB, Avab Transtechnik, Avolites, Barco, Cameleon, Doug Fleenor Design, ELC Lighting, Electronics Diversified, Enttec, Flying Pig Systems, Goddard Design Co, High End Systems, Horizon Control Inc., IES, i-Light Group, Jands Electronics Pty, LewLight, MA Lighting, Martin Professional, Medialon, Mediamation, SandNet, Touchlight Systems Ltd and Zero 88

we jumped over the USB technology because I just see it being an interim hardware platform like those 100 MB floppy disks drives that were around. I think that certainly within our industry, and hopefully in the computer industry generally, we will go towards the multiple powered Ethernet ports, like hubs built into the PC.

We went down a number of dead alleys when developing Art-Net, primarily because we couldn't find a processor that could handle a TCP/IP stack. Then a number of different processors were coming out that had TCP/IP stacks built in with Ethernet hardware or a compiler that had it. We played around with those then spent quite a lot of money proving they couldn't really process in real time.

Then we started looking at it in more detail and we went through the barrier of realizing that the TCP/IP stack isn't witchcraft after all. Add to that the realization that 95% of the stack isn't needed for the kind of work we were doing, so we decided to write our own. It was an expensive development project but we've written our own software to run on our PIC 17 micro at 32 MHz and we can handle two universes of full bandwidth DMX into it, port that off on Ethernet and we've still got 40% idle time on the processor. Once you get into hand coding this to run on your own processor, you suddenly find that you can run it on stuff that you otherwise wouldn't have thought possible.

RB: The thing is, every single building being built today is riddled with Cat 5 cable.

WH: It's nice that you can go into a building for an exhibition, go into the control room, put in a temporary hub, steal some patch lines, and you have your lighting control network ready to go. You haven't run a single cable. That's a huge benefit.

RB: Look at ADSL technology. The only reason it was developed was because we've had some much copper buried in the ground for so long.

WH: And the IEEE has got projects running at the moment, like the one referred to as the First Mile. That's working on a way to get reasonably high speed Ethernet from that bit of copper inside your house to that box down the road. They're making good progress on that. It's amazing what can be achieved when you're faced with a market potential of homes that have a crappy bit of wire running to them. I'm a great fan of using technology that's available and looking upon it as tools rather than get bound up about what they were originally intended for.

Yes, we've had a few companies shoot at us about the way we've dealt with the IP addressing in the Art-Net protocol. Whilst we haven't done anything illegal, we've probably introduced a couple of curved balls in terms of how IP addressing was intended to be done. At the end of the day we've achieved our goal, producing a system where the end-user doesn't even have to know what an IP address is or what it's for! It's about making it easy for the customer; making sure that they don't have the aggravation. You're meant to have that aggravation in the R&D department. The punter is not meant to have to worry about it. [17]

RB: I don't know if we broke laws or bent them with the Vision 2000, but we only wanted one dial on the front. First time round on the network you may have got an innocuous warning from Windows that there was an IP address conflict, but riding on the header packets from some other devices allowed us to find out a great deal about the LAN's subnet. It's not as if we were melting anything.

WH: We were all learning on that box. It may not have been elegant, but it worked.

RB: I was surprised to hear Tom Thorne's predictions that everything is going toward PC based control, especially being as it came from the director of a company that makes undeniably gorgeous hardware.

WH: I don't think that's true. I would love it if it did. Ignoring the fact that many lighting consoles actually have PCs in them; if you were to compare a laptop to a lighting console, there are always going to be applications where frankly you will want a lighting console.

You are not going to do the Stones tour with Grand-Master Flash!, with all due respect to your product. And I suspect that neither of us would try to sell that concept into there. It's just not going to work. Maybe as a special effects controller synced into the main desk - there are great applications.

For touring stuff, I think there will always be a console. That may be a PC with a very expensive keyboard, which is arguably what most production

---

[17] Wayne's implementation of TCP is a little unpopular with some purists because he bends the rules a bit. Art-Net would not behave itself properly if it were not on a dedicated LAN (i.e. if it were hooked to the Internet) as it uses a reserved subnet. This generally does not concern the average user and they are quite happy to build their little lighting LAN in their building, as long as they get the flexibility of configurable DMX distribution.

lighting consoles of today are anyway. I still think PC based control is a niche. Its volume will increase. Having that new generation of lighting designers who are perfectly Windows (or Linux) literate and think it is perfectly normal to do things on a PC, I think that will certainly have an affect.

I see the PC percentage of the market going up and I can see it taking over completely for installation work. I think the touring market and to a large extent the theatrical market will stay with the full-on console.

RB: What I call furniture.

WH: Absolutely – the lighting furniture. And there are good reasons - it's not just the ego of the operator. There are good reasons for having a large board when you've got multiple instant access to parameters and things like that. We're going through a phase of technological developments like the ACN and RDM and we don't know where the cards are going to fall. These things will make a huge difference in the way things are done. It's difficult to call, but I don't think the lighting board is dead yet.

I try to be up front with my customers. I don't try to sell them a solution that is not right for them. I like to have happy customers who are likely to come back to me in the future because they feel they've received good advice, rather than a short term return and a long term pissed-off customer. Long term pissed-off customers are dangerous to business health!

RB: It's good to stay friends with as many people as possible in this small industry. It's not like we don't all see each other at least three times a year.

WH: As they say: don't tread on people on the way up because you may need them on the way down.

RB: You've said you often used a project to make a product. You get done with the project and think, "If I just write a manual for that, I'll have a product."

WH: I would love to be able to say that it is much more sophisticated than that!

It's often said to me that for the size of the company we've got, we do a huge amount of trade shows. It's true. Our marketing budget is of the same order of magnitude as our R&D budget. One of the reasons we do that is not from a selling/marketing point of view, but from the point of view of getting feedback from the end user.

There's a perfect example when we were at the SIEL trade show in Paris a couple of years ago and we had just brought out the Micro-Scope 2a, which was the first version that had a moving light library built into it. We had hard-coded all the moving light libraries, so it was turning into a major task for us to keep these up-to-date and issuing new PROMs and things like that. So I got talking to this guy at the show and he said to me that it would be great to have a PC application that allowed him to edit the lamp library and then just download it to Micro-Scope. I explained that we would have to change the whole design and things like that. Then, in the bar, that evening after the show, talking again we got to thinking about the MIDI port on the product and with a bit of clever electronics in a bit of cable we could link into an RS232 port, and maybe we could do it. Now you can edit, change configurations and defaults and download it to the device. In the latest version, you can even customize the menu structure to get rid of functions you never use. Now, on about 50% of the Micro-Scope sales we also sell the programming

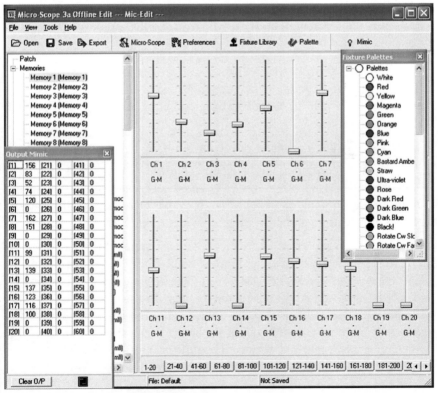

The Microscope fixture editing software.

software. All of that had come from one off-the-cuff comment from a customer at a trade show.

That's the kind of thing I like - the feedback from end users. Because end-users don't tend to be polite about crap things, they tend to say what they think because they haven't been intimately involved in the project so they don't realize that if they say they don't like it, they're actually being quite insulting. They just say, "No, I don't like it." It's where you get those ideas to go from. That's why we do so many trades shows and that's why we talk to lots of freelancers and we make sure we listen to the e-mails that come in and we keep the suggestions list and why we've set up a web discussion forum and things like that. At the end of the day, even if someone comes up with an idea you just can't do, it doesn't matter. It can be used in the next design idea.

I think that some of the bigger companies in the industry have lost this connection.[18]

RB: I think there was a trend for a while when software developers didn't even show up at shows.

WH: A huge mistake.

RB: It's funny, you can be told something three or four times by the same person, but until you hear it ten times by ten different people or one time from the right customer…

WH: It certainly has a different effect doesn't it?

RB: I think it's very important that people like you sit in the booth.

A lot of people may criticize Art-Net as a protocol because it may circumvent the process that's going on in ACN, but it's a product that actually happens while we're all sitting around waiting. It is something that is usable.

WH: That's my view on it. I know that there are certain higher echelons at ESTA that perceive what we've done with Art-Net as an attempt to derail ACN. What we've done is get DMX-over-Ethernet equipment to market. It's all firmware up-loadable. If ACN comes out and it's usable, all we have to do write the software and put it on the website and everyone can upgrade. It's not an attempt to de-rail ACN at all. I'd be the happiest guy in the world if ACN were ready tomorrow, because I could stop developing Art-Net, which is taking significant resources of the company, and we could just get on and

---

[18] See Grimes on his frustration of not having enough access to end users on page 263

follow the standard. Unfortunately, I think ACN is probably trying to be too many things to too many people. I think technical standards have to understand marketing as well as engineering, and historically too many technical standards have been written by engineers.

Had they come out with something called ACN that was a simple as Art-Net or Strand Show-Net (which are very dumb protocols at the end of the day, but they do a job) there would have then been a migration path to a more intelligent object orientated protocol for the future. But at least ACN would have by now been in use and doing something useful and you could have built from that. MIDI did that and it worked.

RB: It makes me think of all the wasted work that went into the two opposing systems of HDTV, the digital and the analog. So often the fault of this entire lag of achieving standardizations is the Americans. It's in the States where the battle between the marketing people and engineering is so prevalent. The US economy is just so big and has so much momentum. Often the technically right thing is not done for marketing reasons that have greater weight.

WH: I'm not so sure you're right. The big problem is that we get too many engineers in one place and they are trying to design something by committee, and it can be a huge problem. However, it can also work well.

If you contrast the RDM development program against ACN, RDM has been running for less than a year now and we've put the first document out to public comment.[19] ACN has turned into a somewhat bureaucratic committee nightmare. They are trying to solve the entire world's problems with one protocol when what the industry needs is for them to get something to market. It doesn't matter whether or not it's perfect. It really does not matter. Just 'good enough' would be fine. If there are major flaws in it, fine – just build on it. If ACN does solve all of the world's problems, but it's another twenty years before being released, then it hasn't succeeded.

RB: I don't think there is a more highly debated topic in our industry.

WH: That's why you see other groups starting to think about lighting data over Ethernet using a more object-oriented way – getting away from 512 channels in a packet. People can't wait anymore.

---

[19] In the summer of 2003, ESTA's Control Protocol Working Group voted in favour of sending both RDM and ACN for public comment. A demonstration of both protocols was done at LDI 2003. Our Marquee console was in the booth outputting ACN and Wayne's Colour-Tramp software was talking RDM.

Art-Net is not all that complex. The first definition of Art-Net had about five packets because all we wanted to do was move DMX data (and lots of it) over the same wire. It had a few other bells and whistles. Now we've added bi-directional control for RDM. But it's still not breaking the core concept that, at it's simplest, you can move lots of DMX data down the same wire, which is what people want.

What we're trying to do here is get away from moving over to multi-cores with DMX cable which is a ludicrous concept. DMX was supposed to save us from multi-cores, not re-invent them.

RB: I worked on the U2 Pop Mart Tour. Nils, who was marketing WYSIWYG at the time, was trying really hard with Willie Williams to get WYG on the tour and also the Hog. This was the whole time when there was a lot of talk about the Callahan patents, the Vari-Lite patents, Vari-Lite suing High End and so on. LSD has made a business of getting around patents – which is what the concept of patents is about – making people think intelligently about how to solve a problem in more than one way. We so often think of patents as being a hindrance to the industry as they stop people doing work. What they are supposed to do is promote thinking. LSD has done the thinking and turned it to their advantage, executing it in broad daylight, even if you think it's in a somewhat dirty way. LSD went straight to U2 management and said, "Look, you want to control a moving head with DMX – that violates patents so on and so forth." Williams wanted to use the Studio Color and the Studio Color can only be controlled via DMX. The Whole Hog only outputs DMX. U2 could start their tour using the two together, but there is no guarantee that they would finish the tour if a pending law suite sited them. The only people that could control the Studio Colors completely clean of all patents was LSD. LSD had their UGLI boxes – the Universal Guest Luminaire Interface boxes.

WH: I didn't know what it stood for.

RB: But, did you know that every one of the 212 Studio Colors on the U2 Pop Mart Tour was addressed at DMX address 1? And they had 212 five-pin cables leave front of house and go out to every single fixture with a terminator at the end of it.

WH: Scary. The silly things you have to do to earn a buck.

Harping back to the standards thing - I think IBM had an incredibly progressive view when they designed the PC.

RB: The ISA bus.

WH: Yes. They released all of their information so that other people could play and feed on the whole gig. There are some people who say that that was a stupid call because look what happened to IBM. You've ended up with the likes of Dell and Compaq ruling the industry. I don't know if that's true because I compare it to what Apple did.

RB: Apple still only has three percent of the market.

WH: Absolutely. Look where IBM are now. OK, they don't have the PC market any more as a significant percentage, but they have re-invented themselves as a company that is a serious player within the market. Arguably, all of that development, and more importantly, all of the learning about the market, has allowed them to do that. They may have won the game. As with all of these things, they made mistakes along the way, and I'm not suggesting for a moment that the reason they published all of that information about the PC was an altruistic act, but none-the-less, it worked. In one way or another it worked.

It's the same kind of concept with Art-Net. I'm not pretending that it was a totally altruistic act, I just thought it could work. I also like the idea of things being open. That is one of the reasons I have huge issues with some of the patent things that are going on in our industry. Some of the Vari-Lite patents I find scary. You can't really justify patenting bi-directional communications with a moving light. Given a lighting desk and a moving light, a school boy studying electronics would be able to tell you that it is obvious that you want data flowing in both directions.

We're facing the same problem with a major US company. We started using LED colour changing technology way before this company even existed. To us, it was so blindingly obvious that it didn't even occur to us to try to patent it. If it had occurred to us, we wouldn't have bothered because we would have assumed that we would have been laughed out of the patent office!

RB: That's because you don't live in the States.

WH: That is, in many ways, true. I think the patent system we have in the world at the moment is fundamentally flawed, because it doesn't allow for the concept of multiple inventors inventing a concept coincidently in a given time frame.

RB: This is being debated right now in Canada regarding Alexander Graham

Bell. He had the $200 to apply for the patent when Meucci, the Italian, only acquired much weaker protection.

WH: There was actually a third guy in France who apparently came up with it three months before that and was still refining it before he patented it.

In this day and age, the concept of first to the post is a laughable. It's embarrassing. It forces designers into worrying about who is first to the patent office rather than perfecting the design. I think there needs to be a concept where you can differentiate between fundamentally conceiving a design and executing application of the design.

RB: In the early days, many venture capitalists and legal types suggested I patent the concept of WYSIWYG. Concepts can't even really be patented in Canada - only products can. Patenting software is really such a waste of time - there are so many loop holes and the only thing a patent does is give you the right to *start* the fight. Also, the geographical protection you acquire is useless given the international nature of our industry. If you want to make a decent living, you have to sell world wide. The best defence is do it first; do it fast and do it well. Then back it up with exceedingly good support.

WH: I'm sure that over the next five to ten years we are going to see a significant move towards reforming the current patent system - particularly if you add into the equation the copyright problems that come with emerging economies. The whole concept of intellectual property, patents, trademarks and copyrights need to be addressed globally.

I suppose on the flip side of that is what you said earlier. Patents aren't meant to be a protection racket. Patents are meant to be there to engender advancement of design. You are meant to find ways around the patent, because the concept is that that way we will advance mankind's technology. And sometimes it works, but unfortunately most patents are used as a blunt instrument, wielded by the company with the largest lawyer budget![20]

We've recently come up with a new modulation technique, BAM (Bit Amplitude Modulation) for which we rather pleasantly won a product award at PLASA. There were numerous technical reasons why we were looking to replace Pulse Width Modulation, and there were also commercial reasons as well, because we wanted to find as many ways as we could to move away from anything that was covered by another's intellectual property. In the

---

[20] Valentino – page 176 re: VL, Morpheus and LSD and their respect for each other – also Hunt – page 217

process of doing that, we struck upon this new modulation concept. To the best of my knowledge, it's a new technique that nobody else has done before. It's got a bunch of technical and a bunch of economic benefits and if the patent problems didn't exist, then perhaps we wouldn't have made the discovery.

What did we do? Rush out and patent it? No we published it on our web site so anyone who wants to use it can do so. I prefer to compete on product features and quality in the market place rather than use blunt patent instruments! Maybe patents can be a positive thing but all in all, I find patents hugely fucking irritating!

13

WHERE WE'RE GOING – WITH RICHARD LAWRENCE AND PHILIP NYE

Introduction

I asked two long-time friends to help take a look into the future. Richard Lawrence is the Strand Lighting code guru and is responsible for the 300 and 500 series of consoles, Strand's ShowNet and also some of their dimmers. Philip Nye has his own company called Engineering Arts and is known for his work on the DHA Light Curtain, the City Theatrical AutoYoke and most recently ADB's moving head fixture. Both Richard and Philip have been instrumental in the development of ACN, the industry's proposed new communications protocol. Recently I've joined the ACN task group to give my opinion on the development of ACN's Device Description Language and more generalised technical marketing opinions.

Richard Lawrence (left) and Philip Nye (right) with the author.

There is a lot of buzz around ACN and although it won't radically change the face of the industry, as Richard suggests in this interview, a lot of people are placing great hope in it. Some think it will open a lot of doors in places we never expected. For example, Eric Cornwell hopes he'll be able to hook into the show control database and get more information out in ways never before possible. This conversation is not particularly about ACN nor control in general, but those are topics we are close to. It is difficult to talk about the future of lighting software and not touch heavily on control. As much weight as possible is given to general purpose software, but in this ever shrinking world of instant access to data, the lines between control, database management, devices and the protocols that hook them all together becomes blurred.

A common thread in this conversation is the method of dealing with this data; in particular, 'too much data'. If you get right down to it, that is what we use computer for – data processing. Putting a show on stage requires a lot of zeros and ones to be moved around quickly. I'm not suggesting that mounting a musical is more complex than launching a space shuttle or balancing the books for a small country, but it is an exercise in managing data. The better we can do that, the easier our jobs become and the more we can accomplish in a day.

Interview

RB: I wanted to talk about the future, but I've been warned that you, Richard, will not let me get away without mentioning the Strand Galaxy console and its importance in the evolution of control.

RL: Well, if you're plotting history, you need to mention the Galaxy,[1] because one way of answering the question of where are we going to, is, we need to get back to where Galaxy was. There are still people out there who say that nothing is as good as the Galaxy IV (Nova) for controlling lights. Now, a lot of that is nostalgia and a bit of the rose tinted glasses thing. But it does actually deal with what I believe is the biggest problem at the moment and that is too much information. We are all fighting with getting too much information into this lump of hardware in too short a time by people that are too stressed and under too much time pressure. Everything comes down to that. I'm not too aware of any other industries that have that problem. A lot of other industries

---

[1] Strand Galaxy series was released in 1980; the Galaxy IV (Galaxy Nova) in the early 1990s. This product never made it to the US. It really builds upon what they did with Lightboard. See page 17

have the 'output' problem: we have this 'input' problem. We have both problems, but inputting the data is more complex.

One of the things that Galaxy was good at, was dealing with big channel counts. It had 600 odd channels when the thing first came out. It dealt with multiple users and it all just worked (apparently, if you believe the rhetoric). Whereas now, desks are focused on the individual doing one thing at a time. Therefore, everybody has to make that one person work better. At the moment, we're all geared up to make he or she as efficient as possible. That is one way of going. The other way is to get more people involved or make that person multitask better. Current desks don't really do that.

RB: But your desk has rave reviews of being able to do that now.

RL: They do if you've got things networked together. That's where the topic of networking will come into this discussion. Yes, we've all done multiple desks linked together and that's a big future, because now all three of us can be working on the same show together with the same central data. That's brilliant and that is why today the designers are getting involved. But whether they go as far as typing in channels and . . .

RB: That becomes a political thing; not a technological thing.

RL: Yes, it might be the union over on your side of the pond and more of a philosophical culture thing over here. It will happen and more and more networking helps that. That is just making more people doing the same thing in parallel.

The thing that Galaxy did was to allow the person to multitask on the one desk. Desks are getting better in that respect; multiple playbacks are an example of that. Hardly any desk has moved away from one channel controller. If you look at the Whole Hog, it has one programmer, full stop. They don't even differentiate between Output and Blind, so you can't even do blind touchups and live things separately; you've only got the one programmer. Whereas, ETC desks and Strand desks at least have Blind and Output separate. But on the Galaxy, you could have as many as four separate channel controllers and you could be twiddling four different things as well as your subs and your playbacks and this, that and the other.

It would be nice to get back to that, now that we have much higher channel counts and many, many moving lights with twenty odd attributes each.

PN: And use underlying technologies like networking.

RB: When you are talking about networking, do you mean distributed processing?

RL: No, that's different.

RB: Some people truly believe that is where we really have to go. Vari-Lite originally knew that the processor they had in the Artisan would not be near powerful enough so they did all the fade processing out in the heads. Then Flying Pig, who thought the world would never outgrow 2000 channels of control, thought their i960 processor would suffice.[2] Now they're believers in true distributed processing; the Hog III is built around it. I'm in a different camp. Processing power today is so cheap and so so fast. For example, we (Horizon Control) now have a job that fades 7000 channels independently quite happily on a 1.2 GHz off-the-shelf PC.

RL: The way Galaxy worked was also driven by the way the hardware was designed. They only had little dinky processors that could only do little things. That's why they had one processor per channel controller and each of those talked back to a central thing that didn't have to do that much. Whereas now, we do it all on the one processor, which is good and in my mind, a much more economical way of doing it - but it also focuses on the fact that everything must be done sequentially because writing multitasking, multithreaded code is harder than writing single process code.

PN: Software for those kinds of applications is derived from single user/single threaded operating systems. The tendency now is to put these things on Windows XP or Linux or something. That means that if you want another channel controller, you just open another window with one in it.

RB: Similar to what Mark Hunt does with the LSD UGLI boxes.[3]

PN: Yes, you just run another process of the same thing.

RL: People are now quite realistically putting Windows on a lighting desk. You could probably consider it five years ago, but you could not have even

---

[2] The Hog I advertised that it could fade 6000 channels of DMX and it used a 386 processor. See Thorne page 196. When building the Hog II, 2000 channels became the norm for large shows and fitted quite well into the market place. They were forced to expand the capabilities of the Hog II to control 3500 channels, but admitted that was really pushing the limits of the i960. They currently believe the Hog III's distributed processing output nodes and their complex multi-user architecture future proofs them as any one system can have as many processors as needed.

[3] See Hunt page 231 on how the Icon Desk's Universal Guest Luminaire Interface boxes are basically 68000 processors running many basic lamp code processes simultaneously in different shells.

entertained it ten years ago.

RB: Even if it wasn't a Broadway success story, five years ago Horizon was viewed as the first serious lighting controller using Windows. In the beginning, using that operating system had been a detriment. It is now moving so quickly that I think that running under Windows is not only acceptable, but it's actually an asset. The fact that people can run Media Player on their lighting desk, rather than on their laptop sitting beside it, is what people want.

RL: Everything is becoming software. We still have this hang up of having a hardware console because people like the feel of it, but it is also the fastest way of getting the information in. Now if you wanted to use your information on a big West End show's heavy plotting session, there would have been no way you could have just done it with a PC keyboard.

RB: That's why when I did a West End show on Horizon we built these wings with palette buttons and wheels so I could get to things more quickly.

The fundamental problem I see with using Windows in a theatre is exactly what makes it so good when you are in an office. Instead of having many control surfaces for inputting data, you basically simplify it by having one – the mouse. When you are working on a document, you interact with it – on the screen. And that is OK. The mouse is a very good extension of your arm *if* you can see the cursor. When you are in the theatre you should be looking at the stage. It's distracting to take your eyes from the dark stage, to a bright screen, get your bearings, then back to the stage again. That's why operators like consoles like the Artisan or the Icon Desk where there are many many buttons that they can feel but not have to look at them.

RL: Then you have very good operators on other desks that are touch typists.

PN: They want to do it all from a numeric keypad with a few extra buttons.

RB: That requires an awful lot of setup, building groups and palettes and so forth. Then you also have to be very good at remembering numbers.

RL: So you expand it a bit from the average QWERTY keyboard to a dedicated lighting keyboard and that's why we still have desks. You still have 'the numbers problem'. Until somebody solves that problem, things will only get better incrementally. It won't get sea-change better. Whoever comes up with that solution first . . .

RB: Before we solve the problems of the future, what faults do you find in the current methodology of the numbers problem? Many people believe what Light Palette did with the Execute button was a huge step forward to solving that problem.[4] If that's what Light Palette did, how did Galaxy deal with it?

RL: It was completely different.

You have to understand the cultural differences between America and the UK. In America you've got a lighting designer who wants to do everything, talking to an idiot, as he perceives, on the desk and as such he calls out all keystrokes. "You Mr. Idiot, go 1@5. I've got a video monitor so I can see what you're doing because I don't trust you. So once you've gone 1@5 I will read that command back, make sure you've typed it in correctly then I'll say Execute. I'm now giving you permission to hit the big enter key."

RB: Anne Valentino calls it the 'Human Macro'.

PN: Very good voice recognition.

RL: Maybe that's a good way of working, who knows? It's arguable both ways.

RB: Anne said that worked well when it was all intensity channels and it didn't get more complicated than that, but with moving lights with many attributes and rig management, it falls down.[5] "Group 5, Position 8, Colour 2" etc. doesn't work very well if you don't have every single palette set up. And it always falls down because you want to adjust every cue just a bit. You can't keep saying, "Left a bit. No, too much, back it off." As a designer, you also can't keep track in your head what each light is doing in the dark - the marking cues and all of that. You have to give up a little control.

RL: What you will find is that lighting designers in America know the console quite well, where in Europe, you tend to have a board operator that is doing a job and a lighting designer doing a job and the two jobs are actually different. The lighting designer will say things like, "I want that light up," or "I want that light red".

PN: "I want the red wash please," and, "Can you get a special on that guy up stage there?"

RL: Yes. So the board operator has to know far more.

RB: That's how Gil Densham and I worked when we did TV together. He

---

[4] See Valentino page 152 on the 'beauty' of Light Palette syntax.

[5] See Valentino page160-161

didn't care how I patched the rig or what my palettes were. He would sit in the truck and say, "Let's do this number in blue with white stars and see what that looks like. Oh, I like that. Soften that one over there a bit and give me a warm special on the back of his head." He has a good eye for that sort of stuff.

RL: The good thing about that, is that it offloads work from the designer. The bad thing about it is, if you've got a crappy board operator, the designer is hugely inconvenienced. In America, or the command line way of working, the worst thing that can happen to a designer with a complete idiot board operator is that he may just be slow, but at least they can catch his mistakes.

PN: The designer says they want it in blue with a star break-up and the board operator says, "Sorry, I can't do that." The designer then says, "I put the blue lights up there and star gobos were in them."

RL: The Galaxy was a board for the board operator. To get a channel up, you don't go 1 @5 <enter>. You just go 1 @5. The board operator doesn't need to confirm what he's doing. He's got to know what he's doing.

RB: That's how the ETC Express line works. The problem is the channel grid keeps bopping around on you. If you are working in the 200's and you start typing 201, it scrolls to channel 2, then channel 20 then back to where you were working. In any case, I feel the argument for a syntax that does not use the Enter key falls apart a bit when you count the keystrokes. 1 @5 <enter> is the same number of presses as 1 @50. I like the fact I can check myself before it goes to the stage. The last thing I want is a director asking why the light keeps going out before it goes to the right level.

RL: The other thing that Galaxy had was remote control surfaces for the designer. They were far more accustom to actually playing with the lights. There wasn't the rule that the LD shouldn't touch anything. Again, that has led to a difference in the way of working. The frustrating thing I find about the command line method of working is that you've got two people, but you're not getting two peoples' worth of brainpower working for you. It comes back to the numbers game. You've got hundreds and hundreds of control channels and we've got to find a better method of managing them.

PN: It's not just the shear number of handles you have to control, but moving lights bring in new dynamics. The only dynamic used to be whether or not the light was getting brighter or dimmer. Now there's all this moving around, changing focus, changing colour and doing it all at different speeds.

RB: So, the problems we're facing managing all this data, can they be solved by re-thinking syntax or inventing a new language, or is it going to be things like new hardware, faster processors, networking or true voice recognition?

RL: I think it will be more philosophical developments. More computers and more networking is helping, because what it is actually doing is allowing more people to work on the show at the same time. Desks have done that in the past, but not to the extent that you get now because they were constrained to a huge great lump of wood and metalwork. They couldn't just pick up their laptop and go into the stalls and look at it from there.

Networking is helping do things like that. Software is getting better. Windowed graphical user interfaces helps you display the information better. We're changing all of that and that is getting better, but we're not changing the input in any way.

PN: The use of a keyboard and a mouse is going to have a place, because as Richard said, people want to use their laptops. Despite the fact that you want a big control surface with lots of lights and buttons on it, there is a pull the other way because people want to work on their laptops and carry them around with them. I think that an awful lot can be done, given that control surface of a trackpad and keyboard, to improve the controllability of the lights.

One of the things I've seen on this is the work Richard Bleassdale has done with his show control work – it's phenomenally powerful user interface stuff, particularly for the power user. You just click on a number and start dragging and the number racks up and down. There are no buttons that you have to fish for beside it that have to appear with arrows or whatever.

Some of the things that Kunst Machina did were very powerful along those lines.

RB: They could never market their ideas. They were too far ahead of their time. I've had a number of meetings with them and I always walked away not knowing what it was all about. Can you sum it up?

PN: They were doing things like representing everything in three dimensions through and through. Every light had a three-dimensional space associated with it. For things like moving lights, they said you should be able to draw a gesture on the screen and it should be able to do it. They would get all the crossing points of a bunch of lights to follow a path through space.

RB: The other thing was that it wasn't cue based.

PN: No, and all their calculations were inherently three-dimensional Cartesian calculations. So, if you moved a light from here to here, it actually moved through a three-dimensional traverse between; it didn't just have end points in 3D.

RB: Editing that becomes a real issue. Building a concept from beginning to end as a unit may be simple enough, but easily fine tuning that later is what makes a good product a great product.

PN: They were taking the control view that comes from using graphics packages where if you want to edit a path, you've got a handle on it and you pull them around on the screen and watch the lights change as you're doing it.

Stage Technologies is doing that with their 3D tracking software where *The Witches of Eastwick* fly out over the auditorium. They have a 3D spline curve on their screen and you can change the handles and it's just like changing a bezier or spline curve in Adobe Illustrator and the witches all move in that new path.

RB: I have a hard time with that method. I fully see its merits on the trade-show-floor example where you have two lights that you are demonstrating and they are going to show a set procedure. But in a show situation where you may have three hundred moving lights, and there are multiple things happening at the same time - well, at the end of the day, you have to have cues. We're talking about live theatre, not SMPTE synced multi-media presentations. I think the tradeshow demo where two lights follow a bezier falls down when you start to layer things up and ultimately let stage-management call the show.

RL: And, how do you represent that information back when you are looking in Blind.

PN: The example of the bezier was one way of viewing it. They also did time-lines like MIDI scores and such. They had an idea of a comprehensive database that was based on dynamic behaviors rather than static end-points. Then they would pile on more and more ways of viewing that database of information.

A lot of people saw what they were doing and they thought it was WYSIWYG-style visualization. They had to say, "No, look, the lights are doing it. I pull this spline here and move it and the lights that are following that path now have a bump that appears in the circle." It was all dynamically linked back into the database and the playback was linked there too.

RB: Again, I think the complicated bit is going back deep into that database and editing a single idea, once it's all been layered up. How do you find it and how do you isolate it for playback. It can be done, but I don't think they had the relational database management all worked out. Representing a cue as a movement from point A to point B is much easier to handle, even if you use a funny path to get there. The Jands Vista desk doesn't store endpoints. It's timeline knows where the light is the whole time. Let's watch to see how they manage it.

RL: You made a point of whether or not the world was headed towards more distributed type systems. I don't think so. I think what Flying Pig is doing with Hog III is all wrong. I think they are actually making a rod for their own back. It sounds attractive to have things distributed and in some ways it seems a sensible thing to do. However, the trouble is, all that information still has to come back to the single place where the guy is sitting there, typing in all the cues.

PN: My view of distributed processing is different to that. There are two things. Firstly, the network is always the bottleneck and there will always be bandwidth problems. If you go to a faster network, then all of a sudden everybody has millions of lights rather than thousands of lights.[6] Distributed processing allows you to do processor intensive things other places, which means you don't have to have huge network traffic. The other reason is that you've got processors out there anyway. In something like a moving light, in order to get from A to B, it's got to ramp up to speed doing all kinds of stepper-motor calculations then ramp down at the other end. Then maybe the endpoint changes once it's halfway there so then it has to re-calculate on the fly.[7] It's tracking a moving target. That processor knows all of the parameters that it has to work with, so that's the best place to do all the calculations connected with how that motor moves.

---

[6] Pixeon was a company that manufactured tubes of LEDs, each one having many many sources. Controlling that via an array of channels can quite literally get you into millions of lights quickly. Currently these sorts of devices are controlled bit-wise using algorithmic solutions rather than pure cue-to-cue execution. It is also becoming much more popular to just feed these arrays with video signals and process the images with graphics programs. Wayne Howell's Colour-Tramp lies in the middle ground. see page 328. I think looking at controlling millions of sources over a network will be an interesting one to watch.

[7] See Grimes page 251 on servicing motors.

With moving lights, tracking the DMX ramp is a pain because you could do much smoother things than that; you could do much better moves.[8]

RB: That is what Vari-Lite always did and not many people will tell you that there is a smoother looking light.

PN: The argument for distributed processing is to put the processing where it is appropriate. It is appropriate that the motor control processing should be close to the motors and maybe do a little bit more work than they are doing at the moment. I'm not saying that it should have all the cues stored in it for the entire show.

RL: We must differentiate the difference. A dimmer is a distributed lighting fader because at the moment we speak to it using an 8-bit number and it dims the light smoothly, probably interpolating it using a 10-bit algorithm much smoother than 256 steps. To reduce the bandwidth, we use a higher-level command. That's were ACN is going to help us by reducing the entire thing down into one single command. What I don't think is sensible is when you start distributing the information because you get a great big communications problem. That is a difficult software problem.

RB: When you had to save a show to disk on the Artisan, it used to take an hour to get all the cues down from the lights.

PN: It was also impossible to ask the system where the light is in Cue 50. The light knew, but the desk didn't.

RB: The light wouldn't necessarily know where it was. Not if it didn't have a cue 50. It would only record the cues in which intensity was greater than 0%, so Cue 50 may not mean a thing to it. You also couldn't rely on the fact that Cue 49 was before Cue 50 – they may not be related at all.

PN: I think it was just a bad implementation rather than a failure of distributed processing per se, because it was a bad thinking through of what information you need in what places. You do need to know where that light is in Cue 50 and you need to get that information within a second (or tens of hundreds of milliseconds). You don't need to know that in milliseconds (or instantly), but equally, you don't want to have to wait minutes for it. I never understood why things were so slow on the Vari-Lite network, even though they were using

---

[8] See Grimes page 248 on how HES has got away with not doing proper tracking of DMX. Also see Hunt page 222. Mark actually drives the motors from the main processor. He can do that because he is *not* working on a network.

fairly crude networking technology. It should have been faster.

RL: There are pros and cons for distributed processing. We used to have an outboard i960 to do off-board fades because we didn't think the 386 was going to be beefy enough. Then the 486 came out and that had more than enough power for the job.[9] To my mind, the biggest problem is writing the software to get the complexity down. Distributed systems are more complex. There is a trade off. For an infinite amount of money, you may get the lowest bandwidth, but at the end of the day you've got to write the code and debug it and this is not an industry that pays a lot of money for control systems. Software costs have to be kept down because that is now the biggest cost factor in most of these products.

PN: A desk should be a database and there should be a number of things that tap into that database. One would be the control surfaces and the user interface; another would be a playback and there are other devices such as moving lights.

RB: So how will this work with ACN, where the technicians just plug all things together then apply power and everything just introduces itself to everything else? Is it easy to figure out who's in control? At different times, different people can be in control. Somebody has to say, "I'm going to store the cue data."

PN: That is something that ACN itself will not answer. ACN is neutral to that. It will be up to the people writing the software in the desks. If you have three Strand desks and you poke them all into an ACN network, then each of those desks will go out and say they've found five hundred lights. They might also say they've found two other desks, but it will be up to them to sort it out. ACN doesn't provide a mechanism to say, "You take on the conventionals and I'll take on the moving lights and he does the backup." That is higher-level stuff.

RL: ACN is purely about getting the data from A to B in a way that both A and B understand the data.

PN: It's really optimized to get data from controllers to control and the status back. It's not really even optimized for shifting data back and forth between controllers. If you want that, the desk manufactures should be putting SQL technology into desks. There is much more generic technology available for

---

[9] See Thorne page 194 on decision to use a single 386 vs. distributed processing in Hog I and page 186 on trouble with multiple processors on the DLD.

those sorts of things.[10]

RL: I don't think ACN will fundamentally solve the bigger problems we are facing, like 'the numbers game' and getting the data into the consoles faster. It doesn't touch any of that. I think people believe it will do. What it will do, for the first time ever, is make two-way communications much more possible. You will be able to communicate with the light and you will get information back. What you get back is debatable and arguable, but at least you will get something back. The dimmer will finally say that the lamp has blown, which you can do now using proprietary communications on integrated systems, but you can't plug an ETC Sensor into a Strand console and have the Sensor tell you that it's going into Over-Temp or something like that. ACN gives you the potential that that can happen. ACN only gives us what we can do now, proprietarily, but more open.

PN: The other thing it does is remove a whole lot of bottlenecks that the DMX way of thinking forces us into; like the ability to send high-level commands such as, "Here's where I want you to be in five minutes time." ACN allows those.

RL: But so does DMX.

PN: Only if you impose a high-level command structure on top of it.

RL: It makes it more obvious that you can do that. You could do the same with DMX. You could say that byte offset three is go to such and such a position, and byte offset four is how long it takes to get there.

PN: DMX is very bad for that.

RL: It's only because you don't get feedback.

PN: It's not just not getting feedback. It's because there is no standardization of it. ACN is doing that – it will standardize those things.

RL: No, the DDL[11] is doing that.

PN: Fair enough, I was talking of ACN as a whole, not just the communications protocol.

RL: I don't think ACN, per se, will solve any of the big problems we're

---

[10] See how this comment would sadden Eric Cornwell on page 288 and his dream of how ACN might have allowed him to display cue data in his own environment.

[11] The Device Description Language is a subset of the ACN suite of products that fully describes the capabilities of a device and the best method in which to control it.

facing. I think what it will do is allow us to have those same problems across different people's bits of kit and it will be faster and using cheaper technology rather than one of those black boxes doing all the translation all the time.

I'm really very concerned about what ACN is really going to give us, if anything. I look at it and wonder, if I don't want to talk to anybody else's kit, ACN gives me absolutely nothing.

PN: Oh, but you do want to talk to other people's kit.

RL: I don't want to be misunderstood. I always think there will be pressure for us to do ACN, but in a world where you've got Strand consoles, and Strand dimmers, you wouldn't have to and ACN gives me no benefit. It would be the same if High End bought a dimming company. They would then have dimmers, moving lights and a console. ACN wouldn't give them anything. It only gives us the ability to talk to other people's kit.[12] It doesn't sort out the problem of getting information from the system. ACN is very important, but it's not a magic bullet. Come 2010 (or whenever it finally happens), we're not all of a sudden going to be in a world of new lighting because of ACN.

PN: I originally got into all of this because years ago I wanted to build a moving light and I was shocked to find that there wasn't anybody out there that made a console that could control it - and I didn't want to design a console.[13] That is really what got me sucked into all of this in the first place.

RL: To me the DDL is the most important bit of ACN, because that is the standardization element.

RB: All of the other work that has happened in the task group, as far as the layman is concerned is that, "It's an RJ45, right? I plug it into an Ethernet hub and route it the way I want. If I shout 'Hello' here, it comes out 'Hello' over there." It damn well should. I think you are right that it is more the DDL that will makes people's lives a little easier.

---

[12] See Grimes page 266 on why he thought DMX standardization *increased* everybody's sales. This, in my opinion, is a widely accepted view.

[13] Philip's Digital Light Curtain and Digital Beamlight had strange methods of control. For instance, you could re-adjust the absolute upper and lower limits of the tilt motors and the full limits of the channel control would re-map to suit. This allowed you to put exclusion zones in for the light that could not be broken by the control and it also gave you maximum resolution for the given zone in which you decided to work. Some may say this is unnecessary and can easily be handled by the control desk, but it gives you insight in to Philip's thinking that all things should be possible in a control environment, whether it's the device or the controller that gives you the flexibility.

RL: It's making it easier for a couple of reasons. One is that there will finally be a way of standardizing the description of what the light or the dimmer can do. Secondly, because it is a good description, we can then start to give it commands like, "Go to 5% over 10 seconds." That will change the way consoles are written. If you are currently writing a console that does everything state, by state, by state, every 25ms, you then have to have something that says that thing is going to happen in six seconds. Now forget about it. Then that bit happens in ten seconds. Then forget about that. Then there are questions on how to represent that to the user. It gets very messy. Cues are not just a start and an end. Anything can happen at any time. And just like we were saying about Kunst Machina, it becomes difficult to present it to the user.

RB: One of the things I loved the Hog II for, was that it finally gave us independent timing for every single channel on a DMX desk, rather than limiting us to eight parts per cue.

RL: Theatre desks time the cue, not the channel. A lot of moving light desks have been born out of timing the light and banging it all together in a cue.

PN: In that way, a cue is a set of things that start at the same time.

RB: Even if their task is to wait a few seconds before they start to do anything at all.

It all becomes more interesting if you know the capabilities of the light and more so its limitations. That's what I wanted to evolve WYSIWYG into – a control system that could limit your possibilities before you would have to figure out whether or not the rig was capable of it. Since WYG was so aware, not only of the characteristics of the light and we knew their orientation within the venue, it could do amazing things for you in a control environment. If you had a bunch of VL5's pointed upstage and you asked them to go out to the audience in 0.5 of a second, it would tell you the best it could do is to do it in 1.5 seconds. It would also tell you not to try to use the Cyberlights in the wings to hit the mirror ball out in the house – they just can't reach it.

RL: Something like WYSIWYG is powerful because it captures more information and you would think that if you had a control desk, you could then use that information far more sensibly. One can only assume that ETC has access to that information, they have the potential to do a real kick-ass control.

PN: The whole way lighting desks work is still very conservative and bound up in the fact of that the people who are doing it are people that are moving incrementally on from something else. It all goes back to two-scene preset desks.[14]

RL: There is no compelling alternative.

RB: Since we've moved away from saltwater dimmers, we've been stuck with sliders and keys. When will we evolve beyond that?

PN: That's why I come back to Kunst Machina, who took a complete outsider's view. That is, perhaps, why they've failed. They weren't bound up with a historical perspective of what a cue was and that you had to use cross-fades and this sort of stuff. They took the Windows operating system, with a screen and a mouse; and yes they could add on extra control surfaces, but their objective was to control a load of dynamic stuff with it. It was cutting lose from any sort of history, and when talking to people in lighting they just met completely blank look. It was also a time in the industry where an awful lot of people were not very computer literate.

RL: I think that more people now, who are running computers, are aware they are running software. But if you move so far away, you almost end up solving the wrong problem.

PN: You might have a significantly better system, but it might require such a huge learning curve, so anybody who already has industry background is not going to receive it well. The bright student who would get to grips with it in no time thinks, "Wow, this is fantastic", but he is not going to be the person who has the opportunity to use it on a big Broadway show.

RL: Again, the quality of the control desk is one issue, but (and I go back to this), it's the sheer quantity of data we have to get into and out of the desk.

RB: Getting data out has never been an issue.

RL: Oh, I disagree. If you go through a five hundred cue show with moving lights, on a DOS text based system, that is very difficult. WYSIWYG solved that problem. That was a good output solver. That is a problem that many people have in many different industries – how to get information out of a system. Look at a jet fighter. It's all about getting a lot of information out of the system and into the person. It doesn't have to do a lot of getting out of him

---

[14] See Valentino – page 152 on how all consoles are either emulations of piano boards or manual preset desks.

and into the system. WYSIWYG is brilliant for that. Now window based GUI's will give us a lot of that. Desks will finally be able to do simple things like give you pictures of the moving lights. So then we end up with even more information to put into the system. A criticism of WYSIWYG is that it is too difficult to setup, because you are capturing so much information and you've got to get it in. Luckily, you only do that once.

RB: When the electricians go and change things the problem is that your data gets out of sync with the real world. This *is* where ACN may be able to help us.

PN: DDL's aim sets out to do some of that for you, but a light understands what it does, but it doesn't understand where you've hung it . . . yet.

RB: The x.Spot does have a sensor in it to say whether it is up or down.

PN: But it won't say whether it's five degrees off the piss.

RB: But it easily could.

PN: You could put a GPS transceiver in each corner of it. We laugh now and we'll probably laugh for the next five years, but five years after that, maybe it will make sense. Then you name all your lights by their latitude and longitude.

RL: Imagine calling the numbers out for that.

RB: Quite. But imagine how easy it would be to do your downstage centre focus.

RL: How's that?

RB: Well, if every light knew what its capabilities were, how bright it would be at certain positions of the set (because it was aware of the set), how big or small it could be, and where datum was - it would be easy for them all to hit spike marks.

RL: You're misunderstanding me. How would they know, grammatically, where downstage centre was?

RB: Ah, yes. This is where I wanted to take WYSIWYG. If you have all the information on the lights *and* the stage *and* the cue structure, you could do wonderful things. Imagine you are about to touch up a cue. You could tell the desk, "What I want now is the stage to go blue, and I want sharp, red streaks to be coming from that direction." It could come back with, "Right, these are the lights that are currently not being used, and I know I'm safe for the next five cues. I have gobos. They could be sharpened up and turned red. They're over there. Let's turn them on and focus them over here." It could then present you with a number of ideas. I had all this thought out. The set elements would coach the lights on how they wanted to be treated. We all know the proper way to light a podium. That could be built into everything.

It may sound radical, but so did spell checkers and grammar checkers years ago. People still write the documents; the computers don't write things by themselves. These are just tools to steer us in the right directions. Writing routines in MS Access is a wonderful example of where this can go. You can write a very complex relational database application and hardly touch the keyboard. Everything is presented to you in limited lists and you just choose the right option at the right time. I'm no Access wiz, but I can get quite far just by poking around. Moving light rigs are not used to their full potential at the moment and I wonder what things might transpire.

RL: It's a matter of capturing the right data at the right time and then getting it back.

Rob Halliday has been on to me about this idea for some time now. Let's say you have this one bar with six lights on it and you like the look on the stage and the lights are doing whatever the hell they are doing. How is it best to think of those lights? Is it six individual lights - or is it the two end ones are doing something together followed by the middle four? Or is it the bar? Or is it just a bit of the first three bars and the first three bars are working all together?[15]

PN: What does it matter?

RL: It matters because if you then want to change something.

PN: If you want to go back to that look. But I want it in green rather than blue.

RL: Or you want to understand the look on stage, which is built up of dozens and dozens of lights, how do I know what to change. Why, for instance, is that area over there a little brighter? It is for a special reason and that is why you can't change it. That is a lot of information. To do a lot of these high-level things, you need a lot more information going in, or you have computer systems that can intelligently interpret the information. At the moment we don't; lighting desks don't tend to interpret what is going on. If you type in '1 thru 5 @ 10' it stores every channel at 10%, but it loses the fact that you've typed in '1 thru 5', for example.

---

[15] See Valentino page 175 for more discussion on this issue.

RB: This is one of the things I've always been on about too. Rather than have a memory structure that is a bunch of pigeon holes with data in them, the command line would be sent out at run time. The easiest way I describe this is what I call 'group palettes'. The cue is recorded like this: 'Group 5; Colour 2; Position 12.' We are all very familiar with updating colour palette 2 and position palette 12, but we are not familiar with the fact the group could change. If this was implemented, you could take a very small studio set-up of a rock show and load it into a huge stadium size rig and all the intention and look would be preserved, even if the kit is not the same.

RL: It is capturing what it is you meant when you put it in.

PN: That is very like the way that CAD has evolved. AutoCAD is the old way where you've got a database of vertices and the relationships between them. That represents solids in space. A very static database. If you look at something like Solid Works or Inventor, you've got the 'build tree' down the side of the screen that describes how you've built the model.

RB: It's procedural modeling.

PN: Right, and even if there are a hundred steps in your model, you can go right back up to the beginning and say, "At that point, two steps in from the start, I made a hole through here at 10mm. If I make it 20mm, that will ripple down and all the shelling and fillets and so on are affected by that hole and their location around it and so on."

RB: Think *Back to the Future* where if you go back in time and change things you see the effects in the future when relationships are altered.

RL: I would love to do that sort of thing, but I secretly keep thinking that there is another way of making this huge array of numbers slightly more manageable. That's why groups are so good. Instead of saying, "1 & 3 & 7 & 9 & 14" you can say, "Group 12". So now you remember one number, not hundreds. There is a direct reduction in numbers that goes towards solving the numbers problem. I'm not sure if procedural cues give us everything we're wanting. On one hand, it does give you the history, but the problem of having just the history is a bit like just recording all the keystrokes. That still doesn't necessarily convey the meaning.

PN: I think you would have to be more sophisticated than representing more than just keystrokes. When you are building up an object in CAD, you still need a lot of thought: how are you going to set out, what shapes have you got, what order do you put them together, and what is the most efficient way of building it? Having completed that thought process, you then have a very powerful model, because you can go back and change early steps, and the effects ripple through. You ask, "What happens if I fillet this corner 10mm rather than 12?"

RL: But if you look at the end product, you can't tell that each of the individual parts were at one point separate from each other. It's a way of looking at the problem, but I'm not sure if it actually would help lighting per se. You either put more information in, or you more intelligently get more information out. At the moment we don't tend to do either very well.

RB: The audience is demanding from us more and more information and more dynamics (as un-artistic as that sounds.)

PN: People are still struggling with moving lights and they're not getting the full capabilities out of them. In a big rig of moving lights, there are just so many things that could be done and aren't being because the controls just aren't there. Not the back-end of the controller that people are using, but the paradigm that people are used to working in.

RL: Most lighting desks can make lights do anything, because they all have fade engines. What they can't do is express that easily so a human can comprehend how to achieve what they want.

PN: Humans probably can't comprehend what they want anyway. I mean, until you give them the right paradigm, they don't actually have a way of thinking about the way lights move. You can think about one or two lights, but when you have a whole rig of them, you very soon get to the point where all you can say is, "OK, I want a whole block of them to do this at the same time." or "I want them to do this alternately," or "Focus them all to one point and follow that point around."

There is a bit of a chicken and egg thing going on. Until there is a more full and rich model for people to think in terms of, it's not possible to either make the control desk to do it, or to have people get what they want.

RL: And, you have to do all of that in half-an-hour on the night before. It doesn't happen all the time like that, but it does happen quite a lot. I don't think that you could ever come up with a solution that takes quite a lot of keystrokes to get to be perceived as a good solution. A guy who designs financial software doesn't do it with somebody blaring in his ear going, "Right – you've only got five minutes to do this! This is costing us real money!" More likely, he goes off into a quiet office somewhere and he thinks about it.

RB: We are unique in that way. On the other hand, I'm sure every industry has special challenges. I often wonder what it was like designing the Apollo moon landing systems and the troubles they faced. They were under some real pressure. At least in lighting, people rarely get hurt.

Whatever happens, the designers and technicians will learn to use the tools provided to them. They quickly master them and do things with their craft we, as product designers, couldn't imagine. It's like a craftsman building a Stradivarius violin; he may be able to play the instrument, but he'll never be a virtuoso. We just have to learn what we can from the users and try to build things people like to work with. At some point you've got to drop one set of tools and pick up a different set. And you will - because they're better.

INDEX

ENTERTAINMENT TECHNOLOGY PRESS

FREE SUBSCRIPTION SERVICE

Keeping Up To Date with

LET THERE BE LIGHT
Entertainment Lighting Software
Pioneers in Conversation

Entertainment Technology titles are continually up-dated, and all major changes and additions are listed in date order in the relevant dedicated area of the publisher's website. Simply go to the front page of www.etnow.com and click on the BOOKS button. From there you can locate the title and be connected through to the latest information and services related to the publication.

The author of the title welcomes comments and suggestions about the book and can be contacted by email at: rob@shocklighting.com

Titles Published by Entertainment Technology Press

ABC of Theatre Jargon *Francis Reid* **£9.95**
This glossary of theatrical terminology explains the common words and phrases that are used in normal conversation between actors, directors, designers, technicians and managers.

Aluminium Structures in the Entertainment Industry *Peter Hind* **£24.95**
Aluminium Structures in the Entertainment Industry aims to educate the reader in all aspects of the design and safe usage of temporary and permanent aluminium structures specific to the entertainment industry – such as roof structures, PA towers, temporary staging, etc.

Basics - A Beginner's Guide to Stage Lighting *Peter Coleman* **£9.95**
This title does what it says: it introduces newcomers to the world of stage lighting. It will not teach the reader the art of lighting design, but will teach beginners much about the 'nuts and bolts' of stage lighting.

The Exeter Theatre Fire *David Anderson* **£24.95**
This title is a fascinating insight into the events that led up to the disaster at the Theatre Royal, Exeter, on the night of September 5th 1887. The book details what went wrong, and the lessons that were learned from the event.

Health and Safety Aspects in the Live Music Industry *Chris Kemp, Iain Hill* **£30.00**
This title includes chapters on various safety aspects of live event production and is written by specialists in their particular areas of expertise.

Hearing the Light *Francis Reid* **£24.95**
This highly enjoyable memoir delves deeply into the theatricality of the industry. The author's almost fanatical interest in opera, his formative period as lighting designer at Glyndebourne and his experiences as a theatre administrator, writer and teacher make for a broad and unique background.

Focus on Lighting Technology *Richard Cadena* **£17.95**
This concise work unravels the mechanics behind modern performance lighting and appeals to designers and technicians alike. Packed with clear, easy-to-read diagrams, the book provides excellent explanations behind the technology of performance lighting.

An Introduction to Rigging in the Entertainment Industry *Chris Higgs* **£24.95**
This book is a practical guide to rigging techniques and practices and also thoroughly covers safety issues and discusses the implications of working within recommended guidelines and regulations.

Lighting for Roméo and Juliette *John Offord* **£26.95**
John Offord describes the making of the production from the lighting designer's viewpoint - taking the story through from the point where director Jürgen Flimm made his decision not to use scenery or sets and simply employ the expertise of Patrick Woodroffe.

Lighting Systems for TV Studios *Nick Mobsby* **£35.00**
Lighting Systems for TV Studios is the first book written specifically on the subject and is set to become the 'standard' resource work for the sector as it covers all elements of system design – rigging, ventilation, electrical as well as the more obvious controls, dimmers and luminaires.

Lighting Techniques for Theatre-in-the-Round *Jackie Staines,* **£24.95**
Lighting Techniques for Theatre-in-the-Round is a unique reference source for those working

on lighting design for theatre-in-the-round for the first time. It is the first title to be published specifically on the subject, it also provides some anecdotes and ideas for more challenging shows, and attempts to blow away some of the myths surrounding lighting in this format.

Lighting the Stage *Francis Reid* **£14.95**
Lighting the Stage discusses the human relationships involved in lighting design – both between people, and between these people and technology. The book is written from a highly personal viewpoint and its 'thinking aloud' approach is one that Francis Reid has used in his writings over the past 30 years.

Practical Guide to Health and Safety in the Entertainment Industry
Marco van Beek **£14.95**
This book is designed to provide a practical approach to Health and Safety within the Live Entertainment and Event industry. It gives industry-pertinent examples, and seeks to break down the myths surrounding Health and Safety.

Production Management *Joe Aveline* **£17.95**
Joe Aveline's book is an in-depth guide to the role of the Production Manager, and includes real-life practical examples and 'Aveline's Fables' – anecdotes of his experiences with real messages behind them.

Rigging for Entertainment: Regulations and Practice *Chris Higgs* **£19.95**
Continuing where he left off with his highly successful *An Introduction to Rigging in the Entertainment Industry*, Chris Higgs' new book covers the regulations and use of equipment in greater detail.

Sixty Years of Light Work *Fred Bentham* **£26.95**
This title is an autobiography of one of the great names behind the development of modern stage lighting equipment and techniques.

Sound for the Stage *Patrick Finelli* **£24.95**
Patrick Finelli's thorough manual covering all aspects of live and recorded sound for performance is a complete training course for anyone interested in working in the field of stage sound, and is a must for any student of sound.

Stage Lighting for Theatre Designers *Nigel Morgan* **£17.95**
An updated second edition of this popular book for students of theatre design outlining all the techniques of stage lighting design.

Technical Marketing Techniques *David Brooks, Andy Collier, Steve Norman* **£24.95**
Technical Marketing is a novel concept, recently defined and elaborated by the authors of this book, with business-to-business companies competing in fast developing technical product sectors.

Theatre Engineering and Stage Machinery *Toshiro Ogawa* **£30.00**
Theatre Engineering and Stage Machinery is a unique reference work covering every aspect of theatrical machinery and stage technology in global terms.

Theatre Lighting in the Age of Gas *Terence Rees* **£24.95**
Entertainment Technology Press is delighted to be republishing this valuable historic work previously produced by the Society for Theatre Research in 1978. *Theatre Lighting in the Age of Gas* investigates the technological and artistic achievements of theatre lighting engineers from the 1700s to the late Victorian period.

Walt Disney Concert Hall *Patricia MacKay & Richard Pilbrow* **£28.95**
Spanning the 16-year history of the design and construction of the Walt Disney Concert
Hall, this book provides a fresh and detailed, behind the scenes story of the design and
technology from a variety of viewpoints. This is the first book to reveal the "process" of the
design of a concert hall.

Model National Standard Conditions *ABTT/DSA/LGLA* **£20.00**
These *Model National Standard Conditions* covers operational matters and complement *The
Technical Standards for Places of Entertainment*, which describes the physical requirements
for building and maintaining entertainment premises.

Technical Standards for Places of Entertainment *ABTT/DSA* **£30.00**
Technical Standards for Places of Entertainment details the necessary physical standards
required for entertainment venues.